MATHS
IN ACTION

Mathematics in Action Group

Members of the Mathematics in Action Group associated with this book:
D. Brown, J. L. Hodge, R. D. Howat, J. Hunter, E. C. K. Mullan, K. Nisbet, A.G. Robertson

STUDENTS' BOOK **4B**

Text © Mathematics in Action Group 1995

The right of Mathematics in Action Group to be identified as author of this work has been
asserted by him in accordance with the Copyright, Designs and Patents Act 1988.

First published in 1987 by Blackie & Son Ltd :
New edition published in 1995 by:
Thomas Nelson and Sons Ltd

Reprinted in 2001 by:
Nelson Thornes Ltd
Delta Place
27 Bath Road
CHELTENHAM
GL53 7TH
United Kingdom

02 03 04 05 / 15 14 13 12 11 10 9

A catalogue record for this book is available from the British Library

ISBN 0-17-431438-8

Cover photograph courtesy of Rutherford Appleton Laboratory
Typeset by Tech-Set, Gateshead, Tyne & Wear

Printed and bound in China

CONTENTS

INTRODUCTION

Maths in Action—New Edition provides a course in mathematics that covers the Mathematics 5-14 National Guidelines, Standard Grade and Higher Grade in Scotland, the Northern Ireland Curriculum and the National Curriculum (1995 Order) in England and Wales.

The new edition builds on experience gained in the classroom with the original series, and particular attention has been paid to providing a differentiated course at every stage. Book 4B provides a course for Standard Grade at Credit level and for NIC/NC mainly at levels 6–8 and further material, while Book 4A aims at General level and levels 5–8. Each chapter starts with a Looking Back exercise, which can be used for revision and to assess readiness for the topic, and ends with a Check-up exercise giving a further element of revision and assessment. Investigative work features prominently in each chapter in the many puzzles, projects, challenges, brainstormers and investigations. Answers to every question (except puzzles, challenges, brainstormers, investigations and 'Topics to Explore') are to be found at the end of this book.

Each *Students' Book* is supported by a *Teacher's Resource Book* and, in the case of Books 1 and 2, by revised books of *Extra Questions* and *Further Questions*.

The *Teacher's Resource Book* contains Standard Grade, Northern Ireland Curriculum and National Curriculum references for every chapter, photocopiable worksheets, notes and suggestions for further activities, and the answers to the puzzles, challenges, brainstormers, investigations and 'Topics to Explore' in the *Students' Book*. In addition, there are grids which may be photocopied and used to record and assess students' progress.

THE GRADIENT AND EQUATION OF A STRAIGHT LINE

1

LOOKING BACK

(i)   (ii)   (iii)

1 Ski slopes are colour-coded in order of difficulty: blue for gentle slopes, red for medium, black for steep.
  a How would you colour-code the slopes in the pictures above?
  b Which colour would suit a beginner?

2 Solve these equations:
  a $2x-1 = 7$ **b** $3x+5 = 11$ **c** $x+3 = 2$

3 a Plot A(1, 3) and B(7, 6) on squared paper.
  b Draw lines through A parallel to the x-axis, and through B parallel to the y-axis, to meet at C.
  c Write down the lengths of AC and CB.

  d Calculate the value of $\dfrac{CB}{AC}$.

4 The point (3, 5) lies on the line $y = 2x-1$ because $5 = 2 \times 3 - 1$. Which of these points lie on the line $y = 2x-1$?
  a (1, 1)   **b** (0, −1)   **c** (4, 9)   **d** (−3, −7)

5 a On which part of the journey does the car travel: (i) fastest   (ii) slowest?
  b Explain how you knew this.

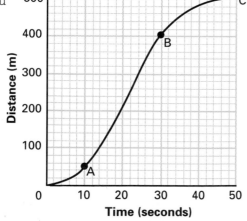

6 Calculate:
  a $5-6$ **b** $4-(-1)$ **c** $-3-4$ **d** $-1-(-1)$

7 Calculate: **a** $\dfrac{4}{-2}$ **b** $\dfrac{-9}{3}$ **c** $\dfrac{-1}{-2}$ **d** $\dfrac{0}{5}$

8 Find the coordinates of the points where these lines meet the x and y-axes, then sketch the lines:
  a $x+y = 4$ **b** $y = x-1$ **c** $3x+2y = 6$

9 Roger wants to find out if there is any link between a poor defence in a football team and the number of points the team has.

Number of goals against	7	28	19	10
Number of points	20	3	11	20

13	20	14	24	16	22
17	9	16	7	12	6

  a Use these axes and scales to plot the points, and make a scatter diagram.

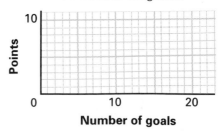

  b Draw the best-fitting straight line.
  c Does Roger find a link? If so, what is it?

10 Solve these pairs of simultaneous equations:
  a $y = 5x$ **b** $y = 10x$
   $y = 2x+6$ $y = 5x+30$

1

THE GRADIENT OF A STRAIGHT LINE

How can we measure the gradient of the flight-path of this climbing aircraft?

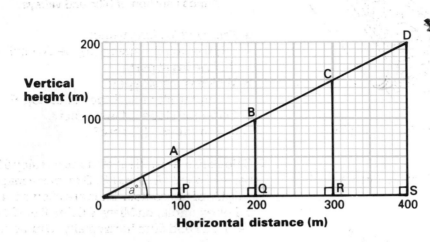

Vertical height (m)

Horizontal distance (m)

$\dfrac{PA}{OP} = \dfrac{50}{100} = \dfrac{1}{2}$. Also, $\dfrac{QB}{OQ} = \dfrac{100}{200} = \dfrac{1}{2}$, $\dfrac{RC}{OR} = \dfrac{150}{300} = \dfrac{1}{2}$, and $\dfrac{SD}{OS} = \dfrac{200}{400} = \dfrac{1}{2}$.

For *every* point on the flight-path, $\dfrac{\text{vertical height above O}}{\text{horizontal distance from O}} = \dfrac{1}{2}$.

The gradient of the flight-path $= \frac{1}{2}$.

The **gradient** of a slope $= \dfrac{\textbf{difference in vertical height} \text{ between each end}}{\textbf{horizontal distance} \text{ between each end}}$.

EXERCISE 1

1 For each *pair* of pictures:
  (i) first estimate, just by looking at them, which ladder has the greater gradient
  (ii) then calculate the gradients
  $\left(\dfrac{\text{vertical height}}{\text{horizontal distance}} \right)$.

a

b

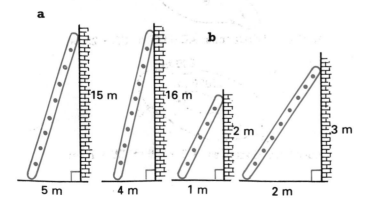

15 m   16 m   2 m   3 m

5 m   4 m   1 m   2 m

2 Calculate the gradient of each sloping line below.

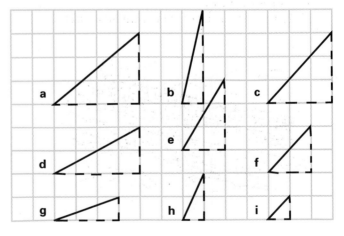

a   b   c

d   e   f

g   h   i

3 a Calculate the gradient of this escalator.

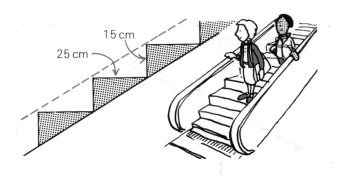

15 cm
25 cm

b What would the gradient be for a 24 cm by 16 cm step?

4 Calculate the gradient of each of the five parts of this fire escape.

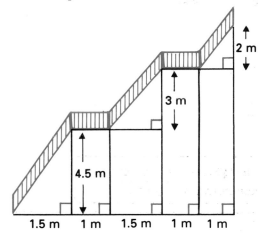

2 m

3 m

4.5 m

1.5 m   1 m   1.5 m   1 m   1 m

5 a A road rises five metres over a horizontal distance of 125 m.
b A railway line rises one metre over a horizontal distance of 250 m.
Calculate their gradients in decimal form.

6

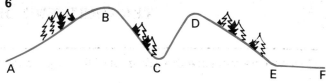

A cross-section of hills and valleys

a *From left to right*, name:
   (i) the uphill slopes   (ii) the downhill slopes
   (iii) the level part.
b Which is the steeper:
   (i) uphill slope   (ii) downhill slope?
c On which slope is the gradient:
   (i) greatest   (ii) zero?

7 Calculate the gradient of the rising slope between pairs of points A, B and C, D on these maps. The heights of the contour lines are shown in **a**, **b** and **c**. For example, on Misty Hill A to B is 100 m vertically and 50 m horizontally. Gradient of

$$AB = \frac{100}{50} = 2.$$

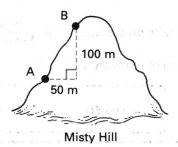

B

100 m

A

50 m

Misty Hill

a

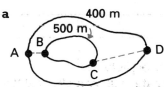

400 m
500 m
A   B   D
C

Horizontal distances: AB = 50 m   CD = 150 m

b

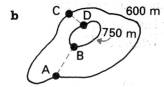

C   D   600 m
750 m
B
A

Horizontal distances: AB = 50 m   CD = 25 m

c

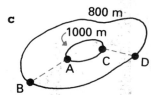

800 m
1000 m
C   D
A
B

Horizontal distances: AB = 100 m   CD = 75 m

In mathematics, the gradient of AB

$$= \frac{\text{change in } y \text{ from A to B}}{\text{change in } x \text{ from A to B}}$$

$$= \frac{y\text{-step}}{x\text{-step}}$$

$$= \frac{MB}{AM} = \frac{3}{6}, \text{ or } \frac{1}{2}.$$

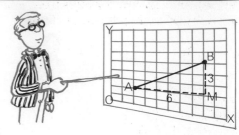

Note: the letter *m* is often used for the gradient. For the gradient of AB $= \frac{1}{2}$, we write $m_{AB} = \frac{1}{2}$.

Examples

a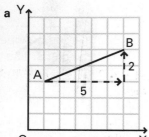

b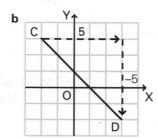

c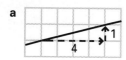

d

AB slopes **up from left to right**. It has a **positive gradient**.

CD slopes **down from left to right**. It has a **negative gradient**.

EF is parallel to the *x*-axis.

GH is parallel to the *y*-axis.

EXERCISE 2A

1 Calculate the gradient of each line.

a   **b**

c   **d**

2 Calculate the gradient of each line, $\frac{y\text{-step}}{x\text{-step}}$ (positive, negative or zero).

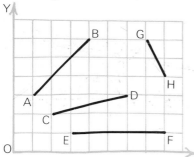

3 Calculate the gradient of each line.

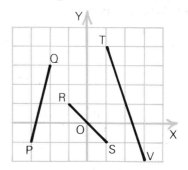

4 a Draw an OX axis. From O, draw lines with gradients which you estimate to be:

(i) 1   (ii) −1
(iii) 3   (iv) −3
(v) $\frac{1}{4}$ (vi) $-\frac{1}{4}$
(vii) 10   (viii) 0

b Which of your lines are at 45° to OX?

A gradient array

5 a On squared paper draw x and y-axes from -5 to 5, then draw lines joining the pairs of points listed below.

(i) A(2, 1), B(5, 2)
(ii) C(0, 3), D(3, 4)
(iii) E(2, -1), F(4, -4)
(iv) G(-2, 0), H(0, 2)
(v) J(-3, 3), K(-4, -2)
(vi) M(-3, -2), N(1, -4)

b Calculate the gradient of each line.

c What can you say about:
(i) the gradients
(ii) the directions
of AB and CD?

> Lines with the same gradient are **parallel**.

6 ABCD looks like a parallelogram, but is it? Check the gradients of opposite sides to find out.

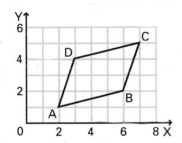

7 a Calculate the gradients of the sides of the quadrilaterals in this diagram.

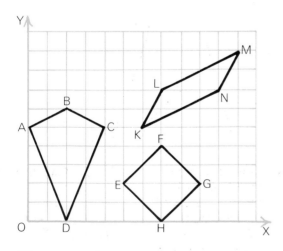

b What type of quadrilateral is:
(i) KLMN   (ii) EFGH?

c What do you notice about the gradients of the sides of the kite ABCD?

8 a Calculate:
(i) m_{AB} (ii) m_{AC} (iii) m_{AD} (iv) m_{AE}

b What can you say about A, B, C, D, E?

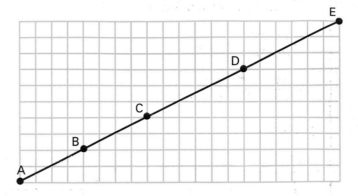

9 The fences joining P, Q, R and P, V, U and U, T, S should be straight. Are they?

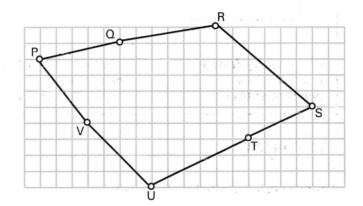

BRAINSTORMER

Calculate, as a fraction, the rising gradient of the seesaw when:
a *one end is on the ground*
b *it is horizontal.*

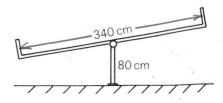

5

THE GRADIENT FORMULA

The gradient of AB $= \dfrac{\text{change in } y \text{ from A to B}}{\text{change in } x \text{ from A to B}}$

So $m_{AB} = \dfrac{y_2 - y_1}{x_2 - x_1}$

Example

For $A(-1, 2)$ and $B(3, -4)$, $m_{AB} = \dfrac{-4-2}{3-(-1)} = \dfrac{-6}{4} = -\dfrac{3}{2}$

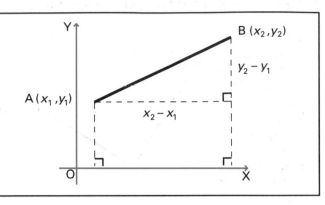

EXERCISE 2B

1 Calculate, in simplest form:

a $\dfrac{8}{4}$ **b** $\dfrac{6}{-2}$ **c** $\dfrac{-5}{10}$ **d** $\dfrac{-3}{-6}$

e $\dfrac{7-3}{1-3}$ **f** $\dfrac{-2-4}{5-3}$ **g** $\dfrac{0-2}{-1-(-3)}$

2 Use the formula to find the gradients of the lines joining:

a K(3, 4), L(7, 7)   **b** D(5, 2), E(2, 3)
c R(−4, 1), S(1, 6)   **d** P(−4, −2), Q(4, −2)

3 For which lines below is the gradient:
a positive **b** negative **c** zero
d none of these?

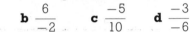

(i) 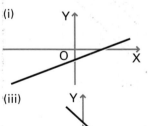   (ii)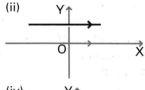

(iii) 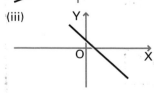   (iv)

4 △ABC has vertices A(−2, 1), B(1, 4) and C(2, 1).
Calculate the gradient of each side.

5 Quadrilateral PQRS has vertices P(−3, 0),
Q(0, 3), R(6, 1) and S(−2, −7).
a Calculate the gradient of each of its sides.
b What type of quadrilateral is it?

6 D is the point (−1, 1), E(1, 2) and F(5, 8).
a Calculate: (i) m_{DE} (ii) m_{EF} (iii) m_{DF}.
b What can you say about the three points?

7 An optical illusion! Use gradients to find which of the points R, S, T lies on PQ produced.

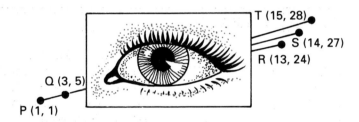

8 P is the point (−4, 2), Q(2, −1), R(3, 3), S(−3, 6).
Use gradients to show that PQRS is a parallelogram.

9 Surveyors fix flags at A(7, 9), B(45, 35), C(18, 20) and D(52, 34) to check whether the kerbs on the new road are parallel.
Which pairs of flags show that the kerbs *are* parallel?

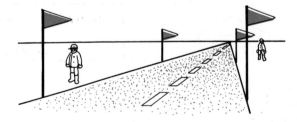

10 On squared paper, draw lines through O with gradients:
a 1 **b** 3 **c** −1 **d** $\frac{1}{2}$.
Which line has the steepest slope?

11 On squared paper, draw lines with gradient 1, through:
a (0, 2) **b** (0, 0) **c** (0, −2).

1 *P is the point (a, b). OP is rotated through 90° to OQ.*

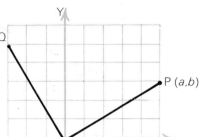

a *Write down the coordinates of Q in terms of a and b.*

b *Show that $m_{OP} \times m_{OQ} = -1$.*

c *Write down the gradients of lines perpendicular to lines with gradients $2, \frac{1}{3}, \frac{5}{8}$ and -4.*

2 $m_{AB} = \dfrac{MB}{AM} = \tan \theta°$, *where $\theta°$ is the angle AB makes with OX.*

a *Use your calculator to calculate θ, correct to the nearest degree.*

b *Calculate the sizes of the angles made by lines with gradients: (i) 1   (ii) 2   (iii) −0.5.*

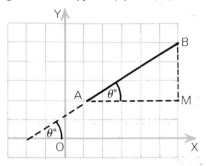

THE EQUATION OF A STRAIGHT LINE, $y = mx + c$

CLASS DISCUSSION

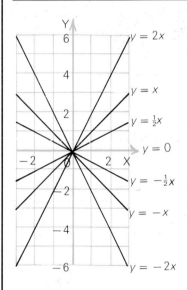

In Chapter 10 of Book 3B you discovered that lines through the origin had equations like $y = x, y = 3x, y = -2x, y = -\frac{1}{3}x, \ldots, y = ax$. Check that for each line in the diagram on the left, a is its gradient.

You also discovered that all straight lines (not parallel to the y-axis) had equations of the form $y = ax + b$. Check that for each line in the diagram on the right, b tells you how far from the origin the line cuts the y-axis.

It is traditional to write the equation of a straight line as $y = mx + c$, where m = gradient and c = y-intercept.

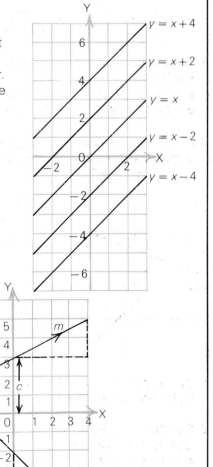

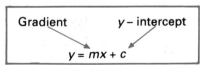

Gradient y − intercept

$y = mx + c$

Example

Find the equations of the two lines in this diagram.

Line (i)

$m = \frac{2}{4} = \frac{1}{2}$, and $c = 3$.

Using $y = mx + c$, the equation of the line is $y = \frac{1}{2}x + 3$, or $2y = x + 6$.

Line (ii)

$m = \frac{-4}{4} = -1$, and $c = -2$.

The equation of the line is $y = -x - 2$.

EXERCISE 3A

1 Write down the gradient and y-intercept of each of these lines:

a $y = 2x+5$ **b** $y = \frac{1}{2}x-4$ **c** $y = -x+1$
d $y = -8x-8$ **e** $y = 3x$ **f** $y = -2x$

2 Write down the gradient of each line and the coordinates of the point where it cuts the y-axis:

a $y = x+2$ **b** $y = -3x-1$ **c** $y = 5x-5$
d $y = -9x+1$ **e** $y = 2x$ **f** $y = 4$

3 Draw these pairs of lines on squared paper, and write down their gradients and y-intercepts.

a $y = x, y = x+4$ **b** $y = 2x, y = 2x-5$
c $y = -x, y = -x+3$ **d** $y = -2x, y = -2x-1$

4 Write down the equations of the lines through O with gradients:

a 5   **b** $\frac{1}{4}$ **c** $-\frac{1}{2}$ **d** 0   **e** $\frac{3}{2}$

5 Show that the straight line in:

a question **2a** cuts the x-axis at $(-2, 0)$
b question **2c** cuts the x-axis at $(1, 0)$.

6 Write down the gradient and y-intercept of each line, then find its equation.

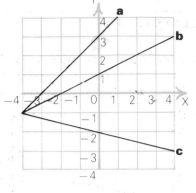

7 Write down the equations of the lines with gradient 3, cutting the y-axis at:

a $(0, 2)$ **b** $(0, -1)$
c $(0, 6)$ **d** $(0, -\frac{1}{2})$

8 In which of these pairs are the lines parallel?

a $\left.\begin{array}{l} y = 2x-5 \\ y = 2x-1 \end{array}\right\}$ **b** $\left.\begin{array}{l} y-x = 3 \\ y-x = 0 \end{array}\right\}$

c $\left.\begin{array}{l} x+y = 4 \\ x-y = 4 \end{array}\right\}$ **d** $\left.\begin{array}{l} y = 3x+4 \\ y = 4x+3 \end{array}\right\}$

EXERCISE 3B

Example
Find the equation of the line through the points A$(\frac{1}{2}, 8)$ and B$(2, 14)$.

$$m_{AB} = \frac{14-8}{2-\frac{1}{2}} = \frac{6}{1\frac{1}{2}} = 4.$$

Using $y = mx+c$, the equation of AB is
$y = 4x+c$.
$(2, 14)$ lies on AB, so $14 = 8+c$, and $c = 6$.
The equation of AB is $y = 4x+6$.

1 The equation of a line with gradient -2 is $y = -2x+c$. If the line passes through the point $(1, 4)$ then $4 = -2 \times 1 + c$.
Find c, and write down the equation of the line.

2 Find the equations of the lines with gradient 3, passing through the points:

a $(1, 5)$ **b** $(3, -1)$ **c** $(-2, 0)$

3 Using the method of the example in the box above, find the equations of the lines joining these pairs of points:

a A$(3, 6)$, B$(5, 8)$ **b** C$(2, 4)$, D$(6, 6)$
c E$(-2, -3)$, F$(3, 7)$ **d** G$(1, -2)$, H$(0, -3)$
e P$(\frac{1}{2}, 1\frac{1}{2})$, Q$(2, 6)$ **f** R$(0.4, 10)$, S$(0.9, 20)$

4 Rearrange each equation in the form $y = mx+c$. Then write down the gradient and y-intercept for each line.

a $x+y = 6$ **b** $2x-y = 3$ **c** $4y = 8x+12$
d $x+2y = -4$ **e** $3x+2y = 6$ **f** $x+y+1 = 0$
g $x-y = 3$ **h** $2x-y = 1$ **i** $x-y-5 = 0$
j $x+\frac{1}{2}y = 1$ **k** $x-\frac{1}{3}y = 0$ **l** $x-\frac{3}{4}y = 2$

5 Find the equations of the lines passing through these pairs of points.

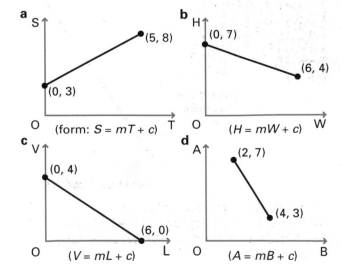

STRAIGHT LINES AND THEIR EQUATIONS AS MATHEMATICAL MODELS

EXERCISE 4A

1 For each of these lines, write down:
   (i) its gradient and its 'y-intercept'
   (ii) its equation in terms of C and T, or V and H.

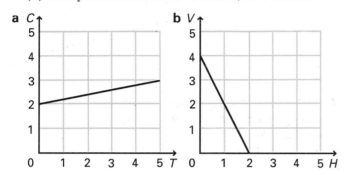

a   **b**

2 Calculate the gradient of each line—**watch the scales!**

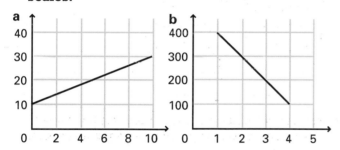

a   **b**

3 Did you know? The width of fabric in a curtain is usually much greater than the length of the curtain rail.

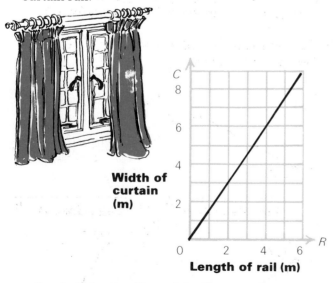

Width of curtain (m)

Length of rail (m)

a Read off the gradient of the line.
b Write down the equation of the line, $C = \ldots R$.
c Calculate the width of curtain fabric needed for a rail 8 m long.

4 Peter the plumber charges a call-out fee, plus an hourly charge for his work.

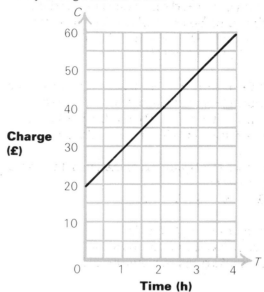

Charge (£)

Time (h)

a Write down:
   (i) the call-out fee   (ii) the hourly charge.
b What is:
   (i) the gradient of the line   (ii) its 'y-intercept'?
c Write down the equation of the line in the form $C = mT + c$.
d Calculate the charge for a 12 hour job.

5 Zoe's parachute drifts down from a height of 1200 metres.

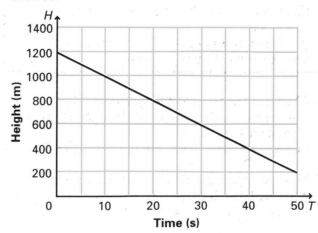

Height (m)

Time (s)

The graph is a mathematical model of the flight.
a Write down:
   (i) the gradient and 'y-intercept' of the line
   (ii) the equation of the line.
b Calculate the time Zoe takes to reach the ground.

6 Swift Delivery charge £25, plus £2 a mile.
  a Write down an equation for the charge £C for a delivery of M miles.
  b Calculate the charge for a 10 mile trip.
  c Draw a graph of charges up to 10 miles, using these scales.

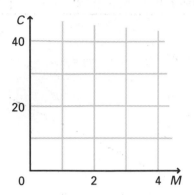

7 The value of Don's car falls each year by 10% of its original price of £8000.
  a Write down an equation for its value £V at the end of Y years.
  b After how long has it no value?
  c Draw a graph of value against time, using these scales.

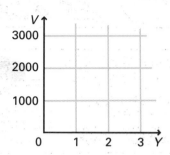

EXERCISE 4B

1 a Maximiles hire out motorbikes. They charge £20 deposit, and £5 a day.
  (i) Copy and complete this table, including the cost of the deposit:

Number of days (N)	0	1	2	3	4	5
Total cost (£C)	20	25	30			

  (ii) Copy and complete the graph.

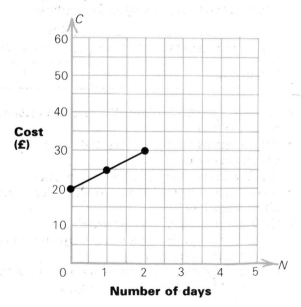

SPEEDWHEELS

b Speedwheels also hire out bikes. They charge £10 a day, but no deposit.
  (i) Copy and complete their table:

Number of days (N)	0	1	2	3	4	5
Total cost (£C)	0	10				

  (ii) Draw their graph on the same sheet.
c After how many days is the total cost the same? How much?
d Which company would you choose for:
  (i) a 2-day hire   (ii) a 5-day hire?
e (i) Write down an equation for each charge £C for N days hire.
  (ii) Solve these equations simultaneously to check when the total costs are equal.

2 a Make tables like those in question **1** for the cost of hiring these bicycles, including the deposit.

b Draw the two graphs of hire charges on the same sheet, using the same scales as in **1**.

c After how many days is the cost the same? How much is this?

d Which firm would you choose to use for:
   (i) 2 days   (ii) 4 days?

e (i) Write down an equation for each charge £C for N days hire.
   (ii) Solve these equations simultaneously to check when the total costs are equal.

3 Members of the school Enterprise Club estimate that they could produce a new video game at a cost of £200, plus £15 per cassette, and that they could then sell each cassette for £25.

a Taking $N = 10, 20, 30, 40, 50$ make tables for:
   (i) the cost (£C) of producing N cassettes
   (ii) the cost (£C) to anyone who buys N cassettes.

b Draw two graphs on the same diagram, using these scales.

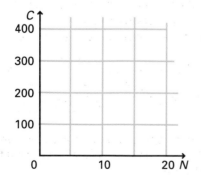

c What is the 'break-even' value for N?

d (i) Write down equations for the production cost and the cost to the buyer.
   (ii) Solve these equations simultaneously to check the break-even number of cassettes.

4 a North Gas Board has a standing charge of £10 per quarter, plus 10p per unit.
Using the graph, copy and complete this table.

Number of units (N)	0	50	100	150	200
Cost (£C)	10				

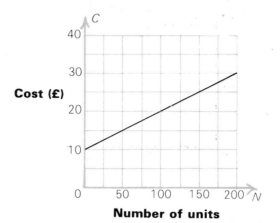

b South Gas Board has no standing charge, but each unit costs 20p. Copy and complete:

Number of units (N)	0	50	100	150	200
Cost (£C)	0	10			

c Draw graphs of C against N for both Boards on the same page.

d Where the two graphs cross, the Boards charge the same.
   (i) How much?   (ii) For how many units?

e Lynn Taylor uses 150 units. Which Board would charge her less?

f (i) The equation of the first graph is $C = 10 + \frac{1}{10}N$. Write down the equation of the second graph.
   (ii) Solve the equations simultaneously to check when the total charges are equal.

BEST-FITTING STRAIGHT LINE

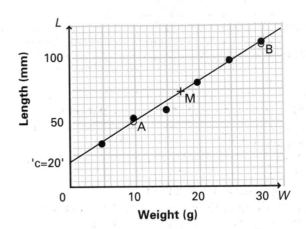

Mandy works in a cotton mill laboratory. She is testing the strength of a new elastic fibre by stretching it under different weights.

Weight (W g)	5	10	15	20	25	30
Length (L mm)	33	53	62	80	98	112

She calculates the *mean* point (mean weight, mean length), M(17.5, 73), and then plots it and the six points in the table.
Mandy draws the best-fitting straight line through M, and finds its equation.
The line is of the form $y = mx + c$, here $L = mW + c$. By choosing two well-separated points *on the line*, A(10, 50) and B(30, 110), she can find its equation.

$$m_{AB} = \frac{110 - 50}{30 - 10} = \frac{60}{20} = 3$$

The equation is $L = mW + c$
So $L = 3W + c$
From the graph, $c = 20$.
So the equation of the line is
$L = 3W + 20$.

EXERCISE 5

1 To check the maximum speed of a new plane a test-pilot fills in this table:

Time (T seconds)	1	2	3	4
Distance from marker (D m)	160	290	470	580

a Calculate the mean time and distance.
b Plot the mean point M and the four points in the table using these scales.

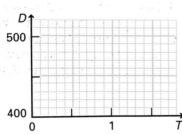

c Draw the best-fitting line through M.
d Calculate the gradient of the line.
e Write down the equation of the line in the form $D = mT + c$.
f The gradient gives the plane's speed (rate of change of distance with time). What is its speed?

2 Vic checks the rate of fall of the water level in the tank.

Time (T min)	3	5	6	9	12
Water depth (H cm)	85	72	68	58	42

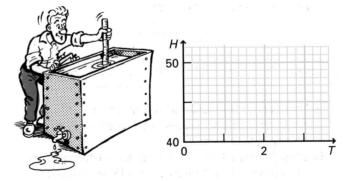

a Find the mean point M. Plot it, and the five points in the table.
b Draw the best-fitting straight line through M.
c Calculate the gradient of the line.
d Find the equation of the line, and use it to estimate the time needed to empty the tank.
e The gradient gives the rate of fall of the water level in cm/min. Write down this rate.

3 Surinder is given some pieces of iron, and asked to find the density of iron.
She measures the volume and mass of each piece, and puts the information in a table.

Volume (V cm³)	5	11	15	29	36	48
Mass (M g)	40	100	115	223	290	384

a Plot the mean point and the six points in the table on 2 mm squared paper, making the V-axis horizontal (scale 10 cm³ to 2 cm) and the M-axis vertical (scale 100 g to 2 cm).

b Draw your best-fitting straight line—why must it pass through $(0, 0)$?

c Find the equation of the line.

d Its gradient gives a measure of the density of iron in g/cm³. Write down the density.

4

Rory was stopped by the police and breathalysed. This table shows his blood alcohol level over the next five hours.

Time (T hours)	0	1	2	3	4	5
Alcohol (A mg/ml)	201	185	170	150	140	120

a Plot the mean point and the points in the table on 2 mm squared paper, and draw your best-fitting straight line.

b Find the equation of the line, and estimate how long it will take for his alcohol level to fall to 50 mg/ml.

c Write down the average rate of fall of his alcohol level in mg/ml per hour.

5 Michael carries out an experiment to find a toy car's acceleration down a slope.

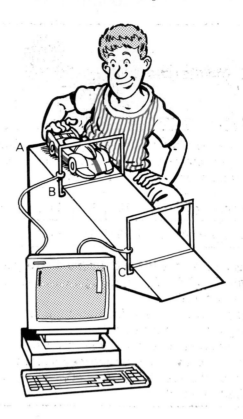

The car is released at A, and passes through electronic gates at B and C.
C can be moved to vary the distance BC.
A computer wired to gates B and C gives a 'read out' of the increase in the car's speed between B and C, and its time from B to C.

Time (T s)	1.1	2.1	3	3.9	5.2	5.7
Speed (S cm/s)	5	12	15	20	26	30

a Plot the points, and draw a line of best fit.

b Find the equation of the line.

c The gradient of the line gives the rate of change of speed with respect to time, or *acceleration* of the car. Estimate it.

CHECK-UP ON THE GRADIENT AND EQUATION OF A STRAIGHT LINE

1 Arrange these lines in three sets, with:
  a positive **b** negative **c** zero gradients.

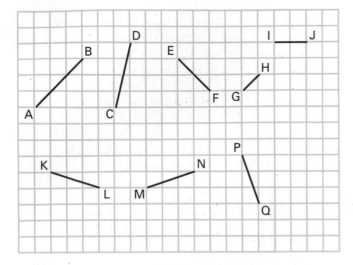

2 Calculate the gradient of each line in question **1**.

3 Match each line below with its equation.
  a $y = x$ **b** $y = -2x + 1$ **c** $y = 3x + 2$
  d $y = -x$

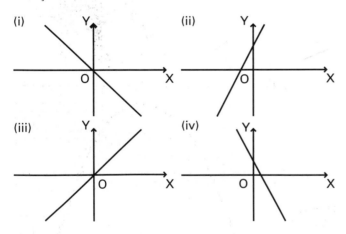

(i)   (ii)   (iii)   (iv)

4 Write down the gradient and the y-intercept of each line in question **3**.

5 Prove that ABCD is a parallelogram by calculating the gradients of its sides.

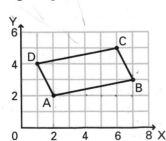

6 In question **5**, E is the point (18, 14). Show that A, C and E are in a straight line.

7 The angle which a ramp up to a car park makes with the horizontal has to be $20° \pm 2°$.
Which of these vertical heights/horizontal distances would be acceptable?
  a 35/100 **b** 25/76 **c** 21/49 **d** 85/221

8 Which of these lines are parallel?
  a $y = 2x + 3$ **b** $2x + y = 3$ **c** $2x - y + 3 = 0$

9 Draw these lines on squared paper, and write down their gradients and y-intercepts.
  a $y = x + 1$ **b** $y = -2x$ **c** $y = 3x - 2$

10 Write down the equation of the line:
  a with gradient 4, passing through (0, 1)
  b with gradient -3, passing through (0, -1)

11 Find the equation of the line joining:
  a P(-1, -1), Q(3, 7) **b** R(0, -2), S(-3, 4)

12

MINIBUS HIRE
CHARGE £2
PLUS £1.50 A MILE

  a Copy and complete the table of charges:

Distance (D miles)	0	1	2	3	4	5	6
Charge (£C)	2	3.5					

  b Draw the graph of C against D (with D on the horizontal axis).
  c Find the equation of the line, and use it to calculate the charge for 40 miles.

13 Karl measures the volume of water in a tank while it is being filled.

Time (T min)	1	2	3	4	5
Volume (V litres)	15.2	17.2	18.5	20.4	21.2

  a Find the mean point and plot it, along with the five points in the table.
  b Draw the best-fitting straight line.
  c Find the equation of the line, and use it to estimate the time taken to fill the tank, if it can hold 32 litres.

2 FUNCTIONS AND GRAPHS

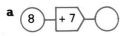
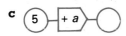

LOOKING BACK

1 Find the OUT entries in each of these:

a $8 \rightarrow +7 \rightarrow \bigcirc$ **b** $9 \rightarrow \times 6 \rightarrow \bigcirc$

c $5 \rightarrow + a \rightarrow \bigcirc$ **d** $5 \rightarrow \times a \rightarrow \bigcirc$

2 Find the value of each expression when $x = 3$.
a $2x+7$ **b** $x-5$ **c** $1-2x$ **d** $2x^2$

3 Solve these equations:
a $3y+1 = 16$ **b** $2t-1 = 4$ **c** $5u+3 = 13$

4 a On squared paper plot the points $(-5, -3)$, $(-3, -2)$, $(-1, -1)$, $(1, 0)$, $(3, 1)$, $(5, 2)$.
b Draw the straight line through these points.
c Write down the gradient and equation of the line.

5 The Gonzalez family are planning a winter holiday in Florida, and use this ready reckoner for currency exchange.

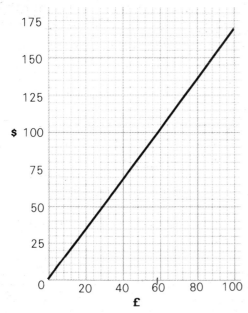

a How many dollars can they get for:
(i) £100   (ii) £1?
b Their hotel costs 100 dollars a night. How much is this in £s?
c If the exchange rate changes to $1.50 to the £, would the graph be steeper or less steep than at present?

6 a Find the coordinates of the point where the straight line with equation $x+2y = 4$ cuts:
(i) the x-axis   (ii) the y-axis.
b *Sketch* the line in your notebook.

7 Repeat question **6** for the line with equation $3x-y = 6$.

8 Plot the points in this table on squared paper, and join them by a smooth curve.

x	-3	-2	-1	0	1	2	3
y	7	2	-1	-2	-1	2	7

9 Find the value of $x^2 - 2x + 4$ when:
a $x = 1$ **b** $x = 3$ **c** $x = -2$

10 Angus takes his 4 iron at the 17th hole.

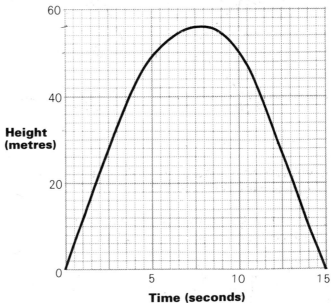

a How high does the ball go?
b How long does it take to land?
c (i) When is the ball 50 m above the ground?
(ii) Why are there two answers?
d What is the golf ball's height after 3 seconds?

ILLUSTRATING A FUNCTION

The **function** of a car assembly line is to take lots of different parts and put them together to make a motor car.

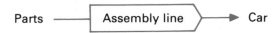

Parts ——— Assembly line ⟩ → Car

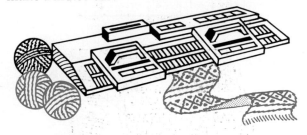

The knitting machine's function is to take separate balls of wool and use a pattern to knit a cardigan or scarf.

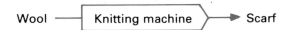

Wool ——— Knitting machine ⟩ → Scarf

The chef's function is to take the milk, flour, eggs and sugar, and use the recipe to prepare a plate of pancakes.

Ingredients ——— Recipe ⟩ → Pancakes

Each process can be summed up like this:

Input ——— **Function** ⟩ → **Output**

Each input has a definite output. For example, the chef would expect his ingredients and recipe to produce pancakes, not apple pie!

Example
Use diagrams to show how the mathematical function f, meaning 'times 2', links the input $\{1, 2, 3, 4\}$ with the output $\{2, 4, 6, 8\}$.

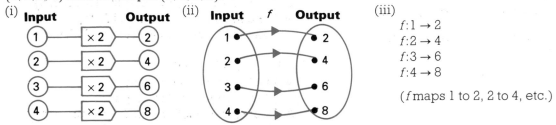

(i)
Input		Output
1	×2	2
2	×2	4
3	×2	6
4	×2	8

(ii) Input f Output
1 → 2
2 → 4
3 → 6
4 → 8

(iii)
$f: 1 \rightarrow 2$
$f: 2 \rightarrow 4$
$f: 3 \rightarrow 6$
$f: 4 \rightarrow 8$

(f maps 1 to 2, 2 to 4, etc.)

A **function** from a set A to a set B is a rule which links each member of A to one member of B.

EXERCISE 1

1 List the set of numbers in each output.

a
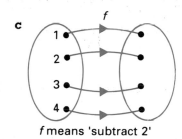

1 —[× 6]— ◯
2 —[× 6]— ◯
3 —[× 6]— ◯
4 —[× 6]— ◯

b

$f: 1 \to \ldots$
$f: 2 \to \ldots$
$f: 3 \to \ldots$
$f: 4 \to \ldots$
f means 'add 5'

c

f

1 ● → ●
2 ● → ●
3 ● → ●
4 ● → ●

f means 'subtract 2'

2 List the set of numbers in each input.

a

◯ —[÷ 3]— ②
◯ —[÷ 3]— ①
◯ —[÷ 3]— ④

b

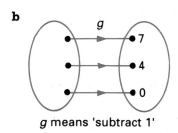

g

● → ● 7
● → ● 4
● → ● 0

g means 'subtract 1'

3 What function is involved in each of these?

a

18 —[   ]— 9
16 —[   ]— 8
12 —[   ]— 6
8 —[   ]— 4

b

$h: 10 \to 100$
$h: 20 \to 200$
$h: 30 \to 300$
$h: 40 \to 400$

4

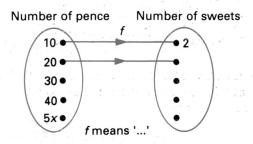

If you put in 10p, you get two sweets. Copy and complete the diagram below.

Number of pence   Number of sweets

f

10 ● → ● 2
20 ● → ●
30 ●   ●
40 ●   ●
5*x* ●   ●

f means '...'

5

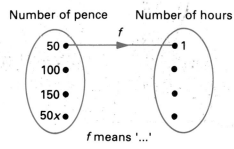

You pay 50p for each hour of parking. Copy and complete the diagram below.

Number of pence   Number of hours

f

50 ● → ● 1
100 ●   ●
150 ●   ●
50*x* ●   ●

f means '...'

6 Draw and complete mapping diagrams like the one in question **1c** for the following data.
  a Input {0, 1, 2, 3}, function *f* 'times 5'
  b Input {1, 3, 5}, function *g* 'square'
  c Input {21, 15, 9}, output {7, 5, 3}
  d Input {25, 20, 15, 10}, output {15, 10, 5, 0}
  e Function 'add 12', output {17, 27}
  f Function 'divide by 8', output {1, 5, 9}

7 $f: 1 \to 4, 2 \to 5, 3 \to 6$
  a List the set of numbers in:
    (i) the input   (ii) the output.
  b Describe a function which links the two sets.
  c Illustrate the function using the three types of diagram in question **1**.

NOTATION

Using the function 'times 5' again,
$$f:1 \rightarrow 5$$
$$f:2 \rightarrow 10$$
$$f:3 \rightarrow 15$$
$$f:x \rightarrow 5x$$
f can be defined by the formula $f(x) = 5x$, 'f of x equals $5x$'. (The function of x is $5x$.)
Then $f(1) = 5 \times 1 = 5$, and 5 is the value of f at 1
$\qquad f(2) = 5 \times 2 = 10$, and 10 is the value of f at 2
$\qquad f(a) = 5 \times a = 5a$, and so on.

Examples
a $g(x) = x^2 + 2$. Find the value of g at:
   (i) 3   (ii) -1.
   $g(x) = x^2 + 2$
(i) $g(3) = 3^2 + 2 = 9 + 2 = 11$
(ii) $g(-1) = (-1)^2 + 2 = 1 + 2 = 3$

b $h(x) = 2x - 5$. For what value of x is $h(x) = 4$?
$$2x - 5 = 4$$
$$2x = 9$$
$$x = 4\tfrac{1}{2}$$

EXERCISE 2A

1 a $f(x) = 8x$. Find the value of:
   (i) $f(1)$ (ii) $f(9)$ (iii) $f(0)$
   b $g(x) = x^2$. Find the value of:
   (i) $g(1)$ (ii) $g(10)$ (iii) $g(7)$

2 a $f(x) = 3x + 2$. Find the value of:
   (i) $f(2)$ (ii) $f(5)$ (iii) $f(8)$
   b $g(x) = 6x - 4$. Find the value of:
   (i) $g(0)$ (ii) $g(1)$ (iii) $g(-1)$

3 a $h(x) = 7 - x$. Find the value of:
   (i) $h(1)$ (ii) $h(0)$ (iii) $h(-1)$
   b $k(x) = 4 - 2x$. Find the value of:
   (i) $k(0)$ (ii) $k(2)$ (iii) $k(-2)$

4 For every bag of sand, the cement mixer makes three bags of concrete. The formula for its operation is $m(x) = 3x$. Calculate:
   a $m(2)$ **b** $m(4)$ **c** $m(6)$

5 The formula for the area (in square metres) of the front of the tent is $A(x) = \tfrac{3}{2}x$.
Calculate:
   a $A(1)$ **b** $A(2)$ **c** $A(4)$

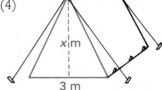

6 Margaret is buying a radio by hire purchase. She pays monthly. The amount she has paid so far, £C, is a function of the number of months, x, she has been paying. The formula for the function is $C(x) = 25 + 1.5x$.

SUPER STEREO
£25 Deposit
+£1.50 a month

   a Calculate the value of:
   (i) $C(2)$ (ii) $C(4)$ (iii) $C(6)$
   b How much will she have paid after one year?

7 $f(x) = x + 6$. For what value of x is $f(x) = 13$?

8 $g(x) = 2x - 3$. For what value of x is $g(x) = 7$?

9 $h(x) = 2x + 1$. For what value of x is $h(x) = 6$?

10 $p(x) = 1 - x$. If $p(t) = 3$, find t.

11 $q(x) = 2x + 3$. If $q(t) = 3$, find t.

12 $r(x) = 4 - 3x$. If $r(a) = 1$, find a.

Examples

1 $f(x) = 3x^2$. Find:
  a the value of f at 5
  b a formula for (i) $f(2t)$ (ii) $f(t+1)$.

  a $f(5) = 3 \times 5^2 = 3 \times 25 = 75$
  b (i) $f(2t) = 3 \times (2t)^2 = 3 \times 4t^2 = 12t^2$
     (ii) $f(t+1) = 3(t+1)^2$

2 $g(x) = 3x+1$. Find a formula for $g(a)+g(-a)$.

$$g(a)+g(-a) = 3a+1+3(-a)+1$$
$$= 3a+1-3a+1$$
$$= 2$$

EXERCISE 2B

1 $f(x) = 2x^3$. Find:
  a the value of f at: (i) 1   (ii) 10
  b formulae for: (i) $f(t)$ (ii) $f(a)$.

2 $f(x) = x^2 - 2x - 8$. Find the value of f at:
  a 0   **b** 2   **c** -2 **d** 4

3 $f : x \rightarrow (x+3)^2$. Find:
  a the value of f at: (i) 0   (ii) 3
  b a formula for $f(a)$.

4 Rajesh decides to hire a bicycle while he is on holiday. The amount he has to pay, £A, is a function of the number of days, n, he keeps it. The formula is $A(n) = 30 + 5n$.

  a Calculate:
     (i) $A(7)$ (ii) $A(14)$
  b For how many days does he hire the bicycle if he pays:
     (i) £75   (ii) £240?

5 A new challenge for the Land Speed Record! The time, t seconds, to cover the measured mile is a function of the speed, x mph, given by the formula $t(x) = \dfrac{3600}{x}$.

  a Calculate:
     (i) $t(60)$ (ii) $t(120)$ (iii) $t(180)$
  b What speed would be needed for a time of:
     (i) 18 seconds   (ii) 12 seconds?

6 A function f is defined by $f(x) = \dfrac{24}{x}$, where $x \neq 0$.
  a Calculate:
     (i) $f(1)$ (ii) $f(6)$ (iii) $f(-2)$
  b For what value of x is $f(x) = 8$?

7 The function f defined by $f(x) = \sqrt{x}$, where $x > 0$, gives the positive square root of x.
  a Calculate:
     (i) $f(1)$ (ii) $f(16)$ (iii) $f(81)$
  b For what value of x is $f(x) = 5$?

8 $f(x) = 5x$. Find a formula for:
  a $f(2a)$ **b** $f(a+1)$

9 $g(x) = x^2$. Find a formula for:
  a $g(2a)$ **b** $g(a-1)$

10 $h(x) = 4x - 2$. Find, in its simplest form, $h(a) + h(-a)$

11 $f(x) = ax+b$, $f(2) = 5$ and $f(1) = 4$.
  a Write down two equations in a and b.
  b Solve this pair of simultaneous equations.
  c Write down the formula for f.

12 $g(x) = ax+b$, $g(5) = 7$ and $q(1) = 3$.
  a Write down two equations in a and b, and solve them simultaneously.
  b Write down the formula for g.

13 Use the same method as in questions **11** and **12** to find formulae for $p(x)$ and $q(x)$.
  a $p(x) = ax+b$, $p(2) = 1$ and $p(0) = -3$.
  b $q(x) = ax+b$, $q(1) = 2$ and $q(-1) = -2$.

INVESTIGATION

Many of the keys on your calculator are function keys.
  a *List the ones you recognise. For some you have to operate the* ⬛2nd F⬛ *(second function) key first.*
  b *Choose a function, and make a table of values, using the calculator.*
  c *Draw a graph, and describe it.*
  d *Check the calculator instruction booklet to find if there is anything special about the function.*
  e *Investigate another function, and write a report.*

GRAPHS OF FUNCTIONS

(i) Linear and quadratic functions

A graph gives a picture of a function. It shows the link between the sets of numbers in the input (or **domain**) and the output (or **range**).

a The straight line shown here is the graph of the function f defined by $f(x) = 2x$, for $0 \leqslant x \leqslant 4$. $y = 2x$ is the equation of the graph of the function $f(0 \leqslant x \leqslant 4)$.

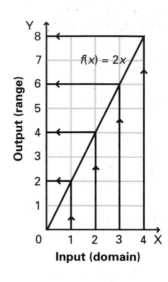
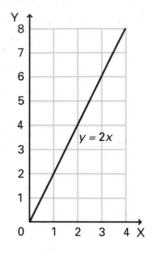

A function of the form $f(x) = ax + b$ is a linear function, and its graph is a straight line with equation $y = ax + b$.

b The parabola shown here is the graph of the function f defined by $f(x) = x^2$, for $-5 \leqslant x \leqslant 5$. Its equation is $y = x^2$.
From the graph:
  (i) the minimum value of f is 0, at $x = 0$
  (ii) $f(x) = 0$ at $x = 0$.
  (iii) the axis of symmetry of the parabola is the line
    $x = 0$.

A function of the form $f(x) = ax^2 + bx + c$ ($a \neq 0$) is a quadratic function, and its graph is a parabola with equation $y = ax^2 + bx + c$.

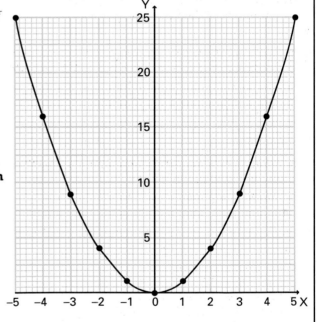

Some examples of parabolas are shown below.

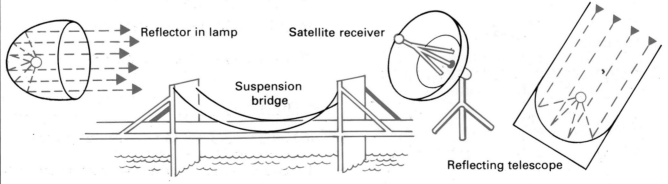

Reflector in lamp   Satellite receiver

Suspension bridge

Reflecting telescope

EXERCISE 3A

1 Draw the graph of the function f, where $f(x) = x + 2$, for $-3 \leqslant x \leqslant 3$. Its equation is $y = x + 2$. First, copy and complete this table:

x	-3	-2	-1	0	1	2	3
y							

2 *Sketch* the graphs of these linear functions. Remember that you only need to plot two points, and draw the straight line through them.
  a $g(x) = 2x - 4$ **b** $h(x) = 6 - x$ **c** $k(x) = 3x$

3 a Draw the graph $y = x^2$, for $-4 \leqslant x \leqslant 4$, using a table of values like this:

x	-4	-3	-2		3	4
y	16					16

  b Write down the equation of the axis of symmetry of the parabola.

4 a Draw the graph $y = x^2 - 4$, for $-4 \leqslant x \leqslant 4$, for the function $f(x) = x^2 - 4$. Use a table like this:

x	-4	-3	-2		3	4
y	12					12

  b Write down the minimum value of f, and the corresponding value of x.
  c For what values of x is $f(x) = 0$?

5 Use the graph of the function $f(x) = 6 + 4x - 2x^2$, shown below, to write down:
  a the maximum value of f, and the corresponding value of x
  b the values of x for which:
      (i) $f(x) = 0$ (ii) $f(x) = -10$

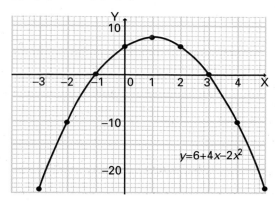

6 Use the graph of the function $g(x) = x^2 - 3x - 10$, shown below, to write down:
  a the minimum value of g, and the corresponding value of x
  b the values of x for which:
      (i) $g(x) = 0$ (ii) $g(x) = -10$

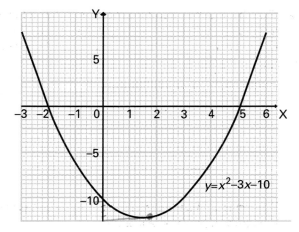

7 a Copy and complete this table for the graph of the function $g(x) = 3 + 2x - x^2$, for $-2 \leqslant x \leqslant 4$ (by calculator, when $x - -2$, $y = 3 + 2 \times (-2) - (-2)^2 = -5$).

x	-2	-1	0	1	2	3	4
y	-5						

  b Write down:
      (i) the maximum or minimum value of the function, and the corresponding value of x
      (ii) the values of x for which $f(x) = 0$.

Draw the graphs of the functions in questions **8–11**, and answer the two questions asked in **7b**.

8 $p(x) = x^2 - 2x$, for $-1 \leqslant x \leqslant 3$

9 $q(x) = 3 - 3x^2$, for $-2 \leqslant x \leqslant 2$

10 $u(x) = x^2 + 4x + 4$, for $-5 \leqslant x \leqslant 1$

11 $v(x) = 8 + 2x - x^2$, for $-3 \leqslant x \leqslant 5$

/ **CHALLENGE**

  a *Sketch the graphs:* (i) $y = -x^2$ (ii) $y = 2x^2$
      (iii) $y = x^2 + 1$ (iv) $y = (x - 1)^2$
  b *Explain how each can be obtained from the graph $y = x^2$.*

EXERCISE 3B

1 This graph shows the parabolic flight-path of a rocket on trial. Read off:
  a the maximum height, and the time taken to reach this height
  b the total flight time
  c the height after 35 seconds
  d the times for a height of 1500 m.

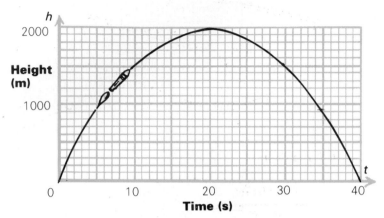

2

The life-raft falls a distance of *d* metres in *t* seconds, as shown in the table:

t	0	1	2	3	4
d	0	5	20	45	80

  a Draw the graph of *d* against *t*, for $0 \leqslant t \leqslant 4$, using the scales shown.

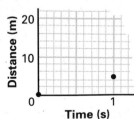

  b Read off:
    (i) *d* when $t = 1.5$ (ii) *t* when $d = 60$
  c The curve is part of the parabola $d = 5t^2$.
    Calculate:
    (i) *d* when $t = 6$ (ii) *t* when $d = 125$.

3 Jemma Thomson, a civil engineer, makes a model of her new bridge. It has a parabolic arch with equation $y = 25 - x^2$.

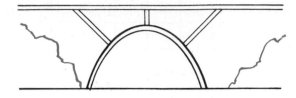

  a Draw the graph $y = 25 - x^2$ for $-5 \leqslant x \leqslant 5$.
  b From your graph read off *y* for *x* equal to:
    (i) -3.5 (ii) 1.5
  c On the model a horizontal support is placed at a height of 15 units. Read off the length of this support from your graph, correct to 1 decimal place.

4 The braking distance, *D* feet, for a car travelling at *S* mph is given by the formula $D = \dfrac{S^2}{20}$.

  a Copy and complete:

S	0	20	40	60	80	100
D	0					500

  b Draw the graph $D = \dfrac{S^2}{20}$, using scales of 20 mph to 2 cm horizontally, and 100 ft to 2 cm vertically.
  c Use your graph to find:
    (i) braking distances at 30 mph and 70 mph
    (ii) speeds for braking distances of 200 feet and 400 feet.

a Look at these two graphs. For what values of *x* on the parabolas is:
 (i) *f*(*x*) = 0   (ii) *f*(*x*) > 0   (iii) *f*(*x*) < 0
 (iv) *f*(*x*) increasing as *x* increases
 (v) *f*(*x*) decreasing as *x* increases?
b Write down a possible equation for each graph.

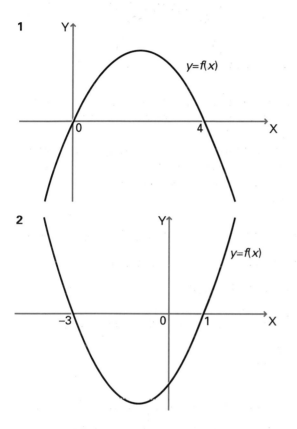

Roger's job is to take a sheet of metal 20 cm wide and bend the sides up to make a channel for carrying water. The ends have to be rectangular. He's also been told to make the channel as big as possible. How can he do this? Trial and error? A mathematical model?

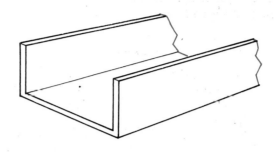

a Trial and error

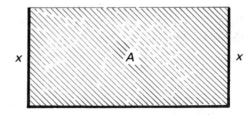

Copy Roger's sketches, and draw some more. Investigate the maximum area, and the height and width of that channel.

b A mathematical model

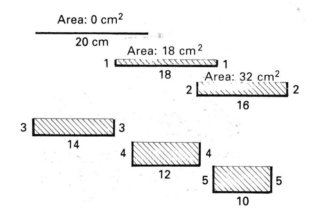

(i) $A = x(20 - 2x)$. Why?
(ii) Draw the graph of *A* against *x*, and find the dimensions of the channel with the greatest cross-sectional area.
c Investigate the dimensions of a V-shaped channel made from the same sheet of metal, which gives maximum cross-sectional area.

(ii) Cubic functions

A function of the form $f(x) = ax^3 + bx^2 + cx + d$
($a \neq 0$) is called a **cubic function**. Why?
Putting $a = 1$, and $b = c = d = 0$, $f(x) = x^3$.
Using this table of values we can draw the
graph of f, with equation $y = x^3$.

x	-3	-2	-1	0	1	2	3
y	-27	-8	-1	0	1	8	27

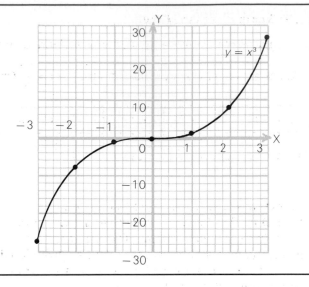

EXERCISE 4

1 a Draw the graph $y = x^3$, using the table of
values, axes and scales shown above.
b Where is its centre of symmetry?
c Does the graph have an axis of symmetry?

2 a On your diagram for question **1**, draw the
graph $y = -x^3$.
b Where do the graphs cross?
c Name two axes of symmetry for the whole
diagram.

3 a Draw the graph of the function $g(x) = x^3 - 4x$,
using a table of values like this:

x	-3	-2	-1	0	1	2	3
y							

b (i) Estimate, to 1 decimal place, the maximum
and minimum values of g, and the
corresponding values of x, for $-2 \leqslant x \leqslant 2$.
(ii) State the values of x for which g is zero.

4 a Draw the graph of the function $h(x) = x^3 - 3x^2$,
for $-2 \leqslant x \leqslant 4$.
b State:
(i) the maximum and minimum values of h and
the corresponding values of x, for
$0 \leqslant x < 3$
(ii) the values of x for which h is zero.

5 The Marzipan Metal Company makes *open* water
tanks. Their design is based on square sheets of
metal with squares of side x metres cut from the
corners.
a Prove that the formula for the volume, $V\,m^3$, of
such a tank is $V = x(10 - 2x)^2$.

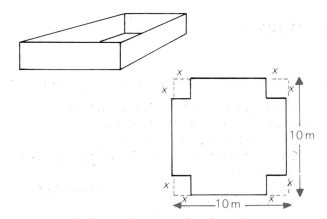

The Company realises that tanks can be many
different shapes—short and fat, tall and skinny.
How do they find the one with the greatest
volume? Can mathematics help? Can you help?
b Graph V against x, for $x = 0, 0.5, 1, 1.5, 2, 3, 4,$
5.
c From the graph read off, as accurately as you
can, the greatest value of V and the
corresponding value of x. Now write down the
dimensions of the tank with the greatest
volume.

(iii) Reciprocal functions

The simplest reciprocal functions are of the form $f(x) = \dfrac{a}{x}$.

This table of values is for the function $f(x) = \dfrac{24}{x}$ (where $a = 24$).

x	-24	-16	-12	-8	-6	-4	-3	-2	-1.5	-1	0	1	1.5	2	3	4	6	8	12	16	24
y	-1	-1.5	-2	-3	-4	-6	-8	-12	-16	-24	$-$	24	16	12	8	6	4	3	2	1.5	1

This graph is called a **hyperbola**; it has two **branches**. You'll see a curve like this on the wall of a room lit by a standard lamp, for example. The further you go along the axes in either direction the closer the curve approaches them. The axes are called **asymptotes** to the curve.

(*Note:* the **reciprocal** of x is $\dfrac{1}{x}$.

Hence the name of the function.)

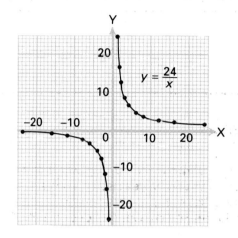

EXERCISE 5

1 a Draw the graph with equation $y = \dfrac{24}{x}$, using the table of values, axes and scales above.

  b Mark: (i) the axes of symmetry
          (ii) the centre of symmetry.

  c Calculate y when $x = 100, 1000, 1\,000\,000$. Copy and complete:
'As x increases, $y \ldots\ldots\ldots\ldots$, and the graph gets closer and closer to $\ldots\ldots\ldots\ldots$.'

  d Calculate y when $x = 0.01, 0.001, 0.000\,001$. Copy and complete:
'As x decreases, $y \ldots\ldots\ldots\ldots$, and the graph $\ldots\ldots\ldots\ldots$.'

2 a Draw the graph of the hyperbola $y = \dfrac{20}{x}$, by making a table of values with $x = -20, -10, -5, -4, -2, -1, 1, \ldots, 20$.

  b Describe any lines or points of symmetry.

3 a This time the equation of the hyperbola is disguised as $xy = -20$. Draw the graph, using the same values of x as in question **2**.

  b Describe its symmetry.

4

To check its petrol consumption, Steve drove the Ranger Group's new model XX round the test track at different speeds.

Speed, s m/s	6	10	20	30	40	50	60
Time, t seconds	200	120	60	40	30	24	20

  a Draw the graph of t against s, for $6 \leqslant s \leqslant 60$ (scale 10 units to 20 mm on s-axis, 50 units to 20 mm on t-axis).

  b From your graph, estimate the time for a speed of: (i) 15 m/s (ii) 25 m/s.

5

The new Town Hall carpark has to be rectangular, with an area of 240 m². Its length is L m and its breadth is B m. Teresa Jones, the council planner, drew up a table with $L = 5, 6, 8, 10, 12, 15, 16, 20, 24, 30, 40, 48$.

Length (L m)	5	6	8	10
Breadth (B m)	48	40	30	24

a Copy and complete the table.
b Draw a graph of B against L (scale 10 units = 10 mm on each axis).
c $B \times L = \ldots$. Is this graph part of a hyperbola?

CHALLENGE

Sketch the kinds of graph given by:
a $y = ax$ **b** $y = ax^2$ **c** $y = ax^3$
d $y = \dfrac{a}{x}$
for: (i) $a > 0$ (ii) $a < 0$ in each case.

MAKING SURE

1 Examine this notice board, and check that each function is linked to the correct graph.

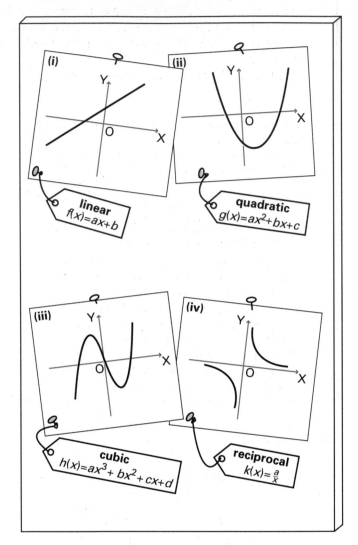

2 Which graph in question **1** would you link with each of the following equations?

a $y = \dfrac{12}{x}$ **b** $y = x + 4$ **c** $y = x^2 - 2x - 3$

d $y = x^3 - 4x$ **e** $y = 5 - x$ **f** $y = x^3 - 9x$

g $y = \dfrac{1}{x}$ **h** $y = 2x^2 - 3x - 2$

i $y = \frac{1}{2}x + 1$ **j** $y = \dfrac{100}{x}$

RESEARCH AND MATHEMATICAL MODELS

Scientists looking for a connection between two or more quantities:
(i) collect data, using experiments, surveys, measurements, etc.
(ii) organise the data by means of tables, calculations and graphs
(iii) analyse the data, perhaps by matching it with graphs like those on the notice board opposite
(iv) use the results to predict further results.

Example
(i) Fast Car Research are testing a new racing car.

Time (x seconds)	0	0.5	1.0	1.5	2.0	2.5
Distance (y metres)	0	2	8	18	32	50

(ii) They draw a graph of the data, and decide that it is like the parabola $y = ax^2$.
(iii) They then choose the point $(1, 8)$ on the graph, and put it in the equation $y = ax^2$, giving $8 = a \times 1^2$, so $a = 8$.
So the equation of their graph is $y = 8x^2$.
They check this for other points on the graph, for example $(2, 32)$: $32 = 8 \times 2^2$.
(iv) They are now able to *use* the equation: at $t = 2.2$, $y = 8 \times 2.2^2 = 38.72$, so the car travels nearly 39 m in 2.2 seconds.

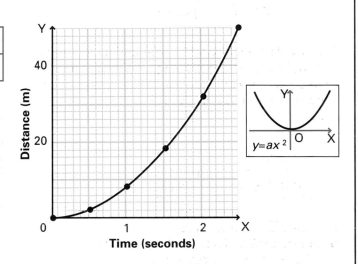

EXERCISE 6

1 Use the given data to find the actual equations of these graphs.

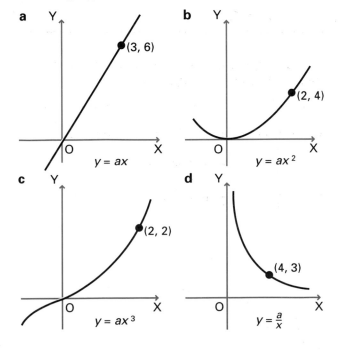

a $y = ax$ with point $(3, 6)$

b $y = ax^2$ with point $(2, 4)$

c $y = ax^3$ with point $(2, 2)$

d $y = \frac{a}{x}$ with point $(4, 3)$

2 Lucy is experimenting to find the connection between the current and the voltage in a circuit.

Current (x amps)	0	2.5	3.5	7	9.5
Voltage (y volts)	0	7.5	10.5	21	28.5

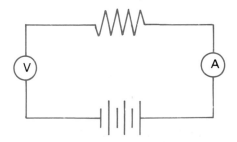

a Draw a graph.
b Is it like one of the graphs in question **1**? Which one? Use the equation of that graph to find the actual equation of Lucy's graph.
c Calculate the voltage for a current of:
  (i) 5 amps (ii) 10 amps.

3 Jamie drops stones from different heights and measures how long each one takes to reach the ground.

Time (x seconds)	0	0.5	1	1.5	2
Height (y metres)	0	1.25	5	11.25	20

a Draw a graph.
b Assuming the graph is like **b** in question **1**, find its equation.
c Calculate the height for times of:
   (i) 1.2 seconds   (ii) 1.8 seconds.

4 This table shows the volumes of gas needed to blow up balloons of different radii.

Radius (x cm)	0	1	2	3	4
Volume (y cm³)	0	4	32	108	256

a Draw a graph.
b Matthew tried to fit this to a parabola, but couldn't. So he tried to fit it to a cubic curve, as in question **1c**. Was he successful? If so, find the equation of the curve.
c How much gas is needed for a balloon with a radius of: (i) 2.5 cm   (ii) 3.5 cm?

5 Lucy's next experiment is to find out the current needed to drive a light bulb.

Bulb size (x watts)	40	60	100	120
Current (y amps)	6	4	2.4	2

a Draw a graph.
b Which graph in question **1** would suit Lucy's data?
c Find the equation of her graph.
d Estimate the current that would be needed for bulbs of: (i) 20 watts   (ii) 150 watts.

6 The area on the screen lit up by the projector is a function of the distance between the projector and the screen.

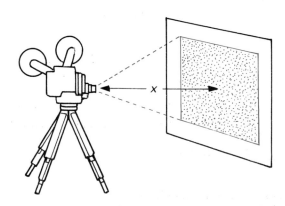

Distance (x m)	0	1	2	3
Area lit up (y m²)	0	9	36	81

a Draw a graph.
b Which graph in question **1** fits here?
c Find the equation of the graph.
d Calculate the area lit up when the distance is: (i) 2.5 m   (ii) 4 m.

CHECK-UP ON FUNCTIONS AND GRAPHS

1 Use the graph of the function $f(x) = 6x - x^2$, shown below, to write down:
  a the maximum value of f, and the corresponding value of x
  b the values of x for which:
   (i) $f(x) = 0$ (ii) $f(x) = 8$.

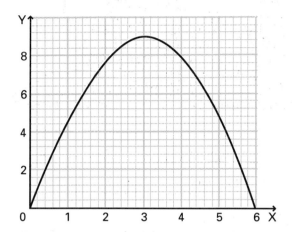

2 List the sets of numbers in the input and output for each of these functions:

a
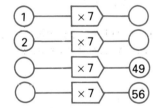

b $f: 64 \to \ldots$
$f: 48 \to \ldots$
$f: \ldots \to 5$
$f: \ldots \to 1$
f means '$\div 8$'

c
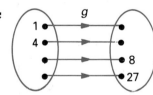
g means 'cube'

d $h: \quad 5 \to$
$h: -5 \to$
$h: \ldots \to 5$
$h: \ldots \to 12$
h means 'subtract 5'

3 a $f(x) = 5x - 2$. Calculate:
   (i) $f(3)$ (ii) $f(0)$ (iii) $f(-1)$
  b $g(x) = x^2 - 9$. Calculate:
   (i) $g(0)$ (ii) $g(3)$ (iii) $g(-1)$

4 $h(x) = 2x + 1$. For what value of x is:
  a $h(x) = 7$ **b** $h(x) = 2$?

5 a Show that the formula for the perimeter $P(x)$ metres of this rectangular fence (without the gate) is $P(x) = 4x + 3$.

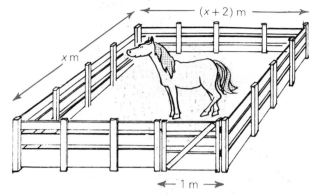

  b Calculate $P(12)$.
  c Given $P(a) = 27$, find a.

6 a Copy and complete this table for the function f with formula $f(x) = x^2 - 2x - 8$.

x	-3	-2	-1	0	1	2	3	4	5
$f(x)$	7								7

  b Draw the graph of the function:
  c Write down the minimum value of f, and the corresponding value of x.
  d For what values of x is $f(x) = 0$?

7 Match each graph below with its equation.
  a $y = ax^2 + bx + c$ **b** $y = \dfrac{a}{x}$
  c $y = ax + b$ **d** $y = ax^3 + bx^2 + cx + d$

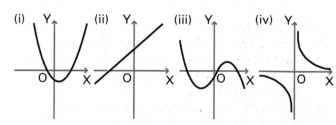

8 In a 'Spot the Ball' competition the prize money varies, depending on the number of winners. Here are some examples of numbers of winners and their prizes, in £1000s.

Number of winners (N)	6	3	12	18	9	8	4	2
Each receives (£C)	12	24	6	4	8	9	18	36

  a Draw a graph of C against N.
  b What type of graph is it? Write down its equation.
  c What is the prize money for:
   (i) 5 winners (ii) 10 winners?

3 SYMMETRY IN THE CIRCLE

LOOKING BACK

Circles are everywhere. Some everyday examples are shown above.

1 Draw a circle, then mark in, and name: the centre, a radius, a diameter, the circumference and an arc.

2 a What is the sum of the angles at a point (making a complete turn)?
b Find x in each circle. The dot marks the centre.

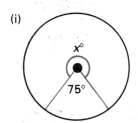

(i)

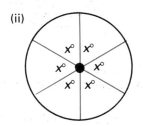

(ii)

3 a What is the sum of the angles of a triangle?
b Calculate x in each triangle below ($\triangle$ABC is isosceles; $\triangle$DEF is right-angled).

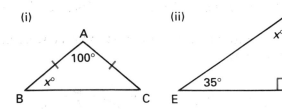

(i)

(ii)

4 a Write down formulae for:
  (i) the circumference C cm of a circle with diameter D cm
  (ii) the area A cm² of a circle with radius r cm.
b Calculate, correct to 1 decimal place:
  (i) the circumference (ii) the area
  of a circle with radius 25 cm.

5 Calculate the length of AC in each right-angled triangle, using Pythagoras' Theorem.

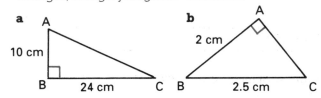

a   A
10 cm
B   24 cm   C

b   A
2 cm
B   2.5 cm   C

6 Calculate $\angle$ KMN, correct to 1 decimal place, in the triangle below, using trigonometry. (Remember SOH − CAH − TOA?)

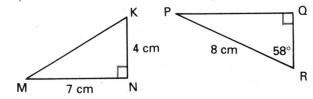

K
4 cm
M   7 cm   N

P   Q
8 cm   58°
R

7 In $\triangle$PQR above, calculate, correct to 1 decimal place: **a** PQ **b** QR.

8 The circle has two kinds of symmetry which you have seen before.

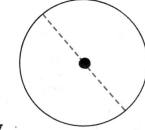

a Rotational symmetry
Make a tracing of this circle. Rotate it about its centre. The tracing always fits its outline. **The circle has rotational symmetry about its centre.**

b Line symmetry
Draw the dotted diameter on your tracing. Flip the tracing over and match the dotted line on it with the one on the page. The circle fits its outline perfectly. This is true for every diameter. **The circle has line symmetry about every diameter.**

ANGLES IN A CIRCLE

O is the **centre** of the circle, OA and OB are **radii**, and AB is a **chord**.
Since OA = OB, △OAB is isosceles.
∠OBA = ∠OAB = 30°, and
∠AOB = 180° − 30° − 30° = 120°.

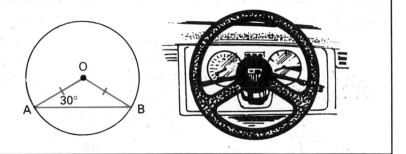

Note
Throughout this chapter:
 (i) O is the centre of each circle
(ii) give answers correct to 1 decimal place, where necessary.

EXERCISE 1

Hint: spot the isosceles triangles.

In questions **1–3**, calculate $a, b, c, \ldots$

1 a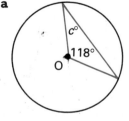

b

2 a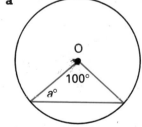

b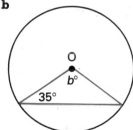

3 a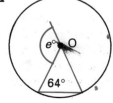

b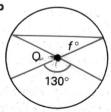

4 Eight wedges of cheese-spread fill a circular box.

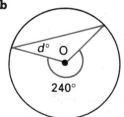

Calculate:
 a x, at the centre **b** y.

5 a Copy this diagram, and fill in the sizes of all the angles.

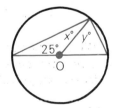

 b Check that $x° + y° = 90°$.

6 Copy these diagrams and mark in the sizes of all the angles.

a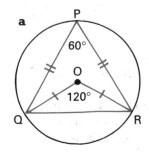

b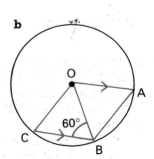

ANGLES IN A SEMI-CIRCLE

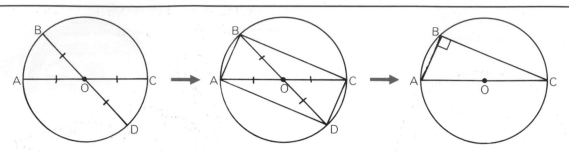

This circle has centre O, and diameters AC and BD.

AC and BD have the same length and bisect each other, so ABCD is a rectangle.

∠ABC, in a semi-circle, is a right angle.

Every angle in a semi-circle is a right angle.

PRACTICAL PROJECTS

1 **a** *Draw a semicircle, with radius at least 4 cm long.*
  b *Mark any point P on the circumference.*
  c *Join PA and PB.*
  d *Measure ∠APB.*

2 *Repeat for different sizes of semi-circles, and different points on the circumference. What do you find about ∠APB each time?*

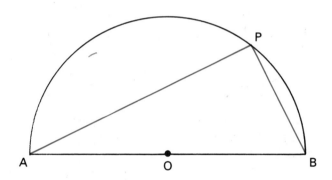

EXERCISE 2

Hint: spot the right angles in semi-circles.

1 Calculate *x*.

a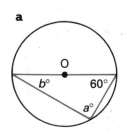

b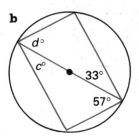

2 Calculate *a*, *b*, *c* and *d*.

a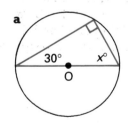

b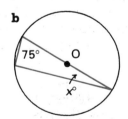

3 Calculate *e*, *f* and *g*.

a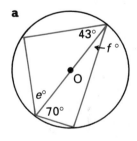

b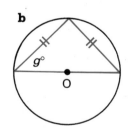

4 Calculate *x* and *y*.

a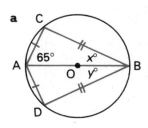

b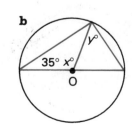

5 *Using Pythagoras' Theorem*
Copy and complete this for the diagram below:

$\angle ACB = 90°$ ($\angle$ in a . . . .)
$d^2 = 4^2 + 2^2$ (. . . . .)
$\quad = \ldots$
$d = \ldots$

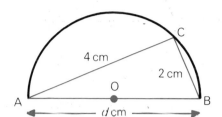

6 Calculate y.

a   **b**

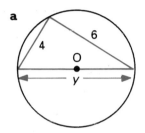 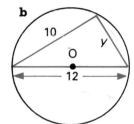

7 *Using trigonometry*
Copy and complete:

$\angle PRQ = 90°$ ($\angle$ in a . . . . . .)
$\cos m° = \dfrac{6}{8}$
$\quad m = \ldots$

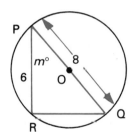

8 Calculate d and m in each drawing.

a   **b**

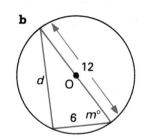

9 Calculate x.

a   **b**

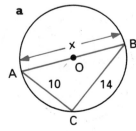 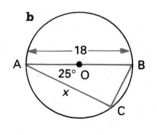

10 Mrs Williams' circular tablecloth just covers a square table of side 80 cm. Calculate:
  a the diameter of the tablecloth
  b the area of the tablecloth, to 3 significant figures.

11 Another proof that an angle in a semi-circle is 90°:

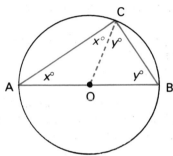

  a Why are the $x°$ angles equal?
  b Why are the $y°$ angles equal?
  c Why is $2x° + 2y° = 180°$?
  d So $x° + y° = \ldots$.

12 Alice was using the kitchen mixer. Its whisks traced out congruent circles which she drew. She was surprised to find that when she drew diameters AB and AC, and joined B, D and C, BDC was always a straight line. Can you explain why?

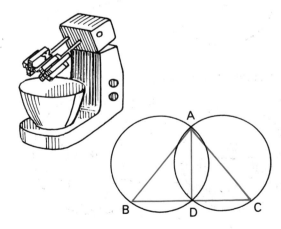

TANGENTS TO A CIRCLE—MORE RIGHT ANGLES

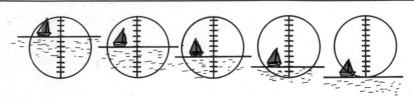

Margo sights a yacht on the horizon (seen as a chord in the viewing circle). A vertical diameter is marked on the circle. As she tilts the telescope up, the horizon appears to move down, always remaining at right-angles to the vertical line. It cuts the circle in two points that come closer and closer together. Eventually the horizon cuts the circle at only one point. The horizon is then a **tangent** to the circle.

A tangent is at right angles to the radius through the point of contact.

Example
AB is a tangent to the circle, centre C.
Calculate: (i) d (ii) $x°$ (iii) $y°$
$\angle ABC = 90°$ (Tangent-radius)
  (i) By Pythagoras' Theorem, $d^2 + 2.5^2 = 6.5^2$
$d^2 + 6.25 = 42.25$
$d^2 = 36$
$d = 6$

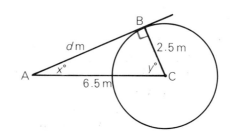

(ii) $\sin x° = \dfrac{2.5}{6.5}$

$x° = 22.6°$, correct to 1 decimal place
(iii) $y° = 180° - 90° - 22.6° = 67.4°$.

PRACTICAL PROJECTS

1 a *Use compasses to draw a circle, centre O.*
  b *Mark any point T outside the circle.*
  c *Draw a tangent TA, touching the circle at A.*
  d *Join OA, and measure $\angle OAT$.*

2 *Repeat for one or two different circles. What do you find?*

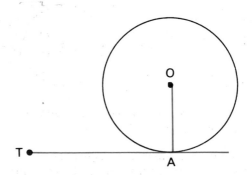

EXERCISE 3

Hint: spot the right angles between tangents and radii.

Copy the diagrams in questions **1–3**, and fill in the sizes of all the angles.
The lines touching the circles are tangents at A.

1 a

b

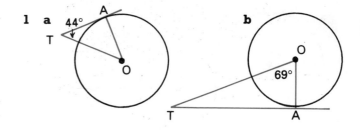

2 a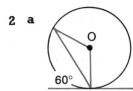

b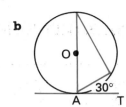

3 a

b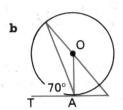

4 Calculate *d*.

a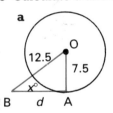

b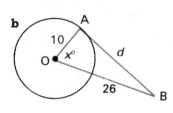

5 Calculate *d* and *x*.

a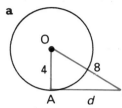

b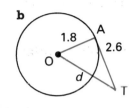

6 In diagram (i) below, BA and BC are tangents.
  a Calculate AB and CB.
  b What type of quadrilateral is OABC?

(i) 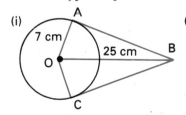 **(ii)**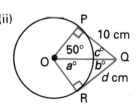

7 Write down the values of *a*, *b*, *c* and *d* in the tangent-kite in diagram (ii) above.

8 In metalwork, Sam designs a cake slice. It is based on a circle of radius 35 mm. The cutting edges are tangents which meet 125 mm from the centre of the circle. Calculate the length of each cutting edge.

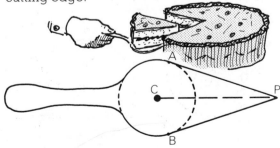

9 This wall clock hangs from D by a cord which is fixed at the '10' and '2', and makes tangents at A and C.
  a Sketch the tangent kite ABCD, and fill in the sizes of its angles.
  b Draw ABCD's axis of symmetry. If AB = 16 cm, calculate AD.

10 A wheel of radius 1 metre stands against the wall in the blacksmith's shop.

  a How far above the ground is A?
  b How far is the centre of the wheel from the corner C?

BRAINSTORMER

A 2p coin has a diameter of 25 mm. Four 2p coins are placed with their centres at the corners of a square, so that each coin touches two others. Calculate the diameter of the smallest circular tray that can hold the coins, without overlapping.

CHALLENGE

A mountain peak is 8 km above sea-level. A climber at the top sees the horizon at A.
  a *Which line is a tangent in the diagram?*
  b *Calculate:*
    (i) *BA, the distance from the climber to the horizon, to the nearest km.*
    (ii) *∠BOA, to the nearest degree.*

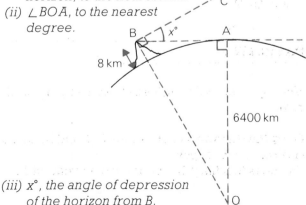

    (iii) *x°, the angle of depression of the horizon from B.*

SYMMETRY ABOUT A DIAMETER—AND MORE RIGHT ANGLES

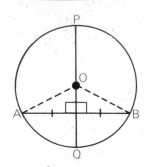

PQ is a diameter of the circle, centre O.
Under reflection in PQ, B is the image of A.
Therefore PQ bisects AB at right-angles.
If any one of the statements below is true then the other two statements are true also.

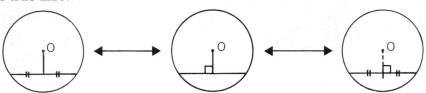

Line from centre O to midpoint of chord is at right angles to chord.

Line from centre O at right angles to chord bisects the chord.

Line bisecting chord at right angles goes through the centre O.

Example
The radius of the circle is 5 cm.
Calculate the distance from the centre to a chord 8 cm long.
Draw OM perpendicular to AB. So AM = MB = 4 cm.
By Pythagoras' Theorem,
$$d^2 + 4^2 = 5^2$$
$$d^2 + 16 = 25$$
$$d^2 = 9$$
$$d = 3$$
The distance is 3 cm.

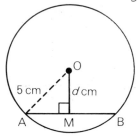

EXERCISE 4A

1 Copy these diagrams, and fill in all the angles.

a

O
100°

b

O
35°

c

30°
O

d

30°
60°
O

2 Calculate the distance from O to each chord.

a

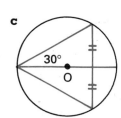

O
20
32

b

24
O
13

3 Calculate the length of each chord.

a

O
7.5   4.5

b

O
5
8

4 Calculate *x*.

a

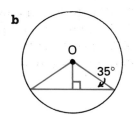

x
O
2.5
12

b

O
9
x ←12→

5 Calculate *x* and *y*.

a

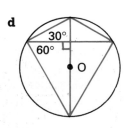

O
8
x° *y*°
12

b

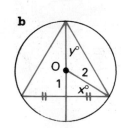

y°
O
2
1
x°

6 Calculate the height of the tunnel from the roadway to the highest part of the roof, to the nearest centimetre.

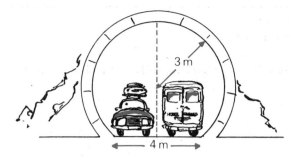

3 m

4 m

7 The diameter of the cylindrical oil tank is 50 cm, and the depth of the oil is 10 cm.
Calculate the width PQ of the oil surface.

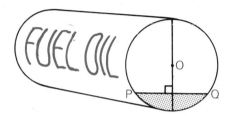

8

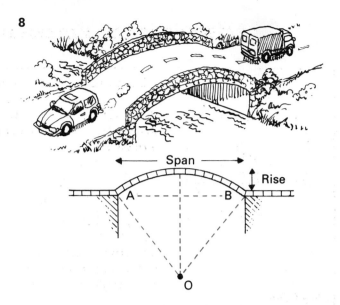

Span

Rise

A — — — — B

O

The span of this bridge is 100 m, and the radius of its curve is 200 m. Sketch OAB, and calculate the rise in the bridge, to the nearest metre.

EXERCISE 4B

1 This picture shows the cross-section of a toy. The radius of the circle, centre O, is 25 mm.
AB = 30 mm and CD = 40 mm. Calculate the distance between the parallel chords AB and CD.

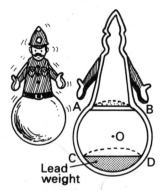

A   B

·O

C   D

Lead weight

2

A   B

Alfred is operating a circular saw. Its radius is 300 mm. The depth of the centre of the saw below the work-surface AB can be changed. Calculate:

a the depth d mm for AB to be 480 mm long

b the length AB when the depth d mm is set at 84 mm.

3 A small cask has circular ends made from four strips of wood, each 10 cm wide.
Calculate:

a the diameter of the cask

b the lengths of the edges of the strips where they meet in pairs.

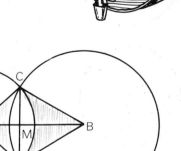

10 cm

4

C

A   M   B

D

CD is the 'common chord' of the two circles with centres A and B.

a Name: (i) the axis of symmetry
(ii) a right angle
(iii) three pairs of equal lines.

b What kind of quadrilateral is ACBD? Why?

5 Adele, who is a keen astronomer, took a sequence of photographs of a total eclipse of the sun by the moon. The images of the sun and moon in the photographs have diameters of 20 mm. By measuring the common chord, Adele could calculate the distance between the centres of the discs.

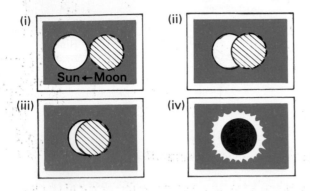

(i)   (ii)

(iii)   (iv)

Sun ← Moon

Calculate this distance for common chords of lengths: **a** 5 mm **b** 10 mm **c** 15 mm.
(*Note:* never look at the sun directly!)

6 The radius of each circle is 10 cm.
  a Which chord is longer in **a**, and by how much?
  b Which chord is nearer the centre in **b**, and by how much?

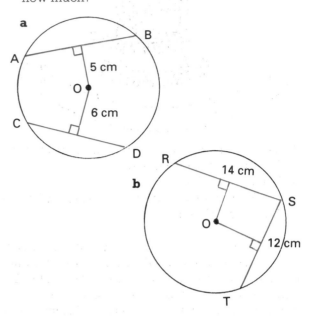

FINDING THE CENTRE OF A CIRCLE

CLASS DISCUSSION

Pam uses a saucer to draw a circle. How can she find the centre of the circle? She draws two chords. Then, using ruler and compasses, she draws the perpendicular bisector of each chord.

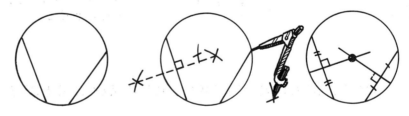

Why does this give her the centre of the circle? Would any two chords give this result?

EXERCISE 5

1 a Draw round a circular object such as a tin, or cup, or saucer. (If these are not available, use the edge of a protractor, or draw a circle with compasses.)
  b Use Pam's method to find the centre of this circle.
  c Check, by drawing a third chord and its perpendicular bisector.

2 Ben thought of another way.

Make a tracing of the circle. Fold the circle in half twice. The folds will cross at the centre.

Try his method. Why does it work?

3

The edges of the chair's rocker are arcs of circles which have the same centre.

a Trace the rocker.
b Use Pam's method for chords AC and BD to find the centre of the circle.

4 Three friends live in the countryside, and wish to meet at a place which is the same distance from each of their homes. Taking their homes at A, B and C, find the position on a tracing of the meeting place. Check that it is equidistant from A, B and C.

5 Stone circles interest archaeologists. Often there are only a few stones of the circle left. Three of the stones in Newton Circle are shown in the sketch-map.

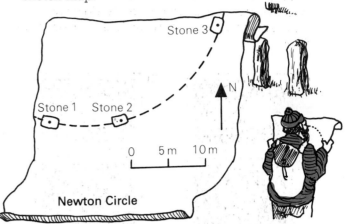

Newton Circle

a Make a tracing, and draw the original circle.
b It is thought that there were 12 equally spaced stones altogether. Mark them all on your plan to show where the archaeologists should dig to find remains of the others.

INVESTIGATION

Draw three different kinds of triangle, with:
a all angles acute   b one angle right
c one angle obtuse.
Investigate the positions of the centres of the circumcircles of the triangles, which pass through the vertices of the triangles. Write a report of your investigation.

LENGTHS OF ARCS AND AREAS OF SECTORS OF CIRCLES

CLASS DISCUSSION/EXERCISE 6

It's Carmen's birthday and she has invited five friends to her party. Her mother has made a circular cake for her. There's marzipan on top, and icing round the edge. She cuts it into six equal portions and gives each girl her share.

1 a What fraction does each girl have of:
   (i) the cake   (ii) the marzipan on top
   (iii) the icing round the edge?
   b What size is the angle at the centre of each piece of cake?

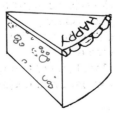

2 Seven of Andrew's friends come to his party. His mother bakes a circular cake too.

a What fraction do Andrew and each of his friends get of:
  (i) the cake
  (ii) the marzipan on top
  (iii) the icing round the edge?
b What size is the angle at the centre of each piece of cake?

3 List the entries in this table, row by row.

Number at party	4	6	8	10	12
Angle of each portion of cake		60°			
Fraction of a complete turn		$\frac{1}{6}$			
Fraction of area of marzipan on top		$\frac{1}{6}$			
Fraction of length of icing round the edge		$\frac{1}{6}$			

A 'slice' of a circle made by two radii and an arc is called a **sector** of the circle.

Using the rotational symmetry of a circle, questions **1**, **2** and **3** suggest that:

(i) Length of arc = angle fraction × circumference of circle
(ii) Area of sector = angle fraction × area of circle

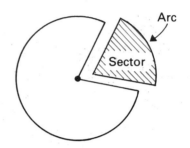

Example
A cheese slice has a sector angle of 30°. Its straight edge (the radius of the circle) is 5 cm long. Calculate the length of its curved edge.

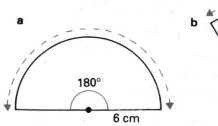

$$\frac{\text{Sector angle}}{\text{Complete turn}} = \frac{30°}{360°} = 0.083\ldots$$

So length of arc
$= 0.083\ldots \times$ circumference of circle
$= 0.083 \times \pi D$ cm
$= 0.083 \times \pi \times 10$ cm
$= 2.6$ cm, correct to 1 decimal place.

EXERCISE 7

1 In each diagram below calculate:
  (i) the fraction the sector angle is of a complete turn
  (ii) the length of the arc of the sector.

c

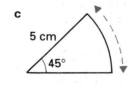

5 cm
45°

d

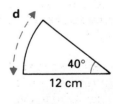

40°
12 cm

a

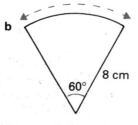

180°
6 cm

b

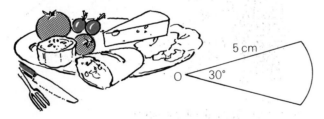

60°
8 cm

e

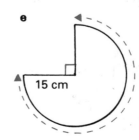

15 cm

f

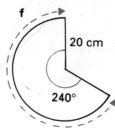

20 cm
240°

2 a What fraction of a complete turn is the angle in the fan?

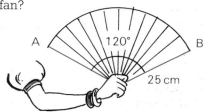

b Calculate the length of the curved edge AB of the fan.

3 Calculate the length of the circular curve AB on Gordon's rocking horse, to the nearest cm.

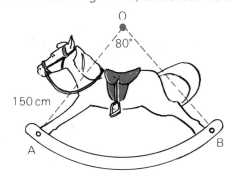

4 The radius of the Big Wheel is 10 m.
a What size is the smallest angle at the centre O?
b Naima is in chair A. How far does she travel:
(i) in moving from A to B
(ii) in one complete turn of the wheel?

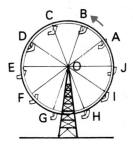
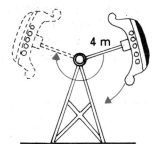

5 Aboard the pirate ship at the fairground, Naima and her friends swing through 216°. See the diagram above. What distance do they turn through?

6 Tim measured part of his curved rail track. Do you think that the inner and outer rails have the same length? Calculate, and find out.

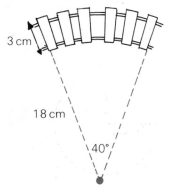

7

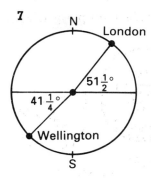

The latitude of London is $51\frac{1}{2}$° N, and that of Wellington, New Zealand, is $41\frac{1}{4}$° S. The cross-section of the Earth is roughly circular, with radius 4000 miles. Which flight from London to Wellington will be shorter—over the North pole, or over the South pole? By how many miles?

8 Calculate x. In **a**, $10 = \frac{x}{360} \times \pi \times 24$, so $\pi \times 24 \times x = 3600$, etc.

a

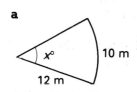

b

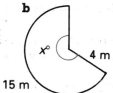

9 Ian and Irma make and sell party hats. They make the cones from sectors of card. The sector arc is the circumference of the bottom of the hat.

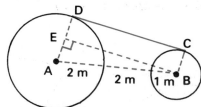

Calculate:
a the arc length of the sector.
b the angle at the centre of the sector.

<hr>

CHALLENGE

A driving belt passes round two wheels. In the diagram, DC is a common tangent to the circles which represent the wheels.

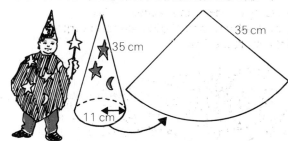

a *What shape is CDEB?*
b *Write down the lengths of:*
(i) BC (ii) DE (iii) AD (iv) AE
c *Calculate: (i) BE (ii) ∠BAE (iii) the total length of the driving belt.*

AREAS OF SECTORS

Example

Laura and John have just finished helping to put up a new 'solar' greenhouse. They want to calculate the area of glass in one end, which is a sector of a circle.

$$\frac{\text{Sector angle}}{\text{Complete turn}} = \frac{90°}{360°} = 0.25$$

Area of glass sector
$= 0.25 \times$ area of circle
$= 0.25 \times \pi r^2 \, \text{m}^2$
$= 0.25 \times \pi \times 2.5^2 \, \text{m}^2$
$= 4.9 \, \text{m}^2$, correct to 1 decimal place.

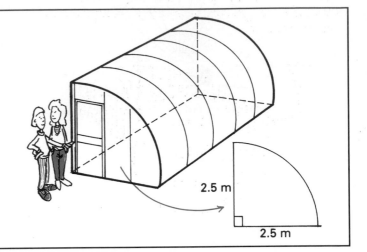

2.5 m

2.5 m

EXERCISE 8

1 Calculate the area of each sector.

a

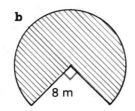

40°
5 cm

b

8 m

2 Calculate the area of the label on top of the cheese portion.

5 cm

30°

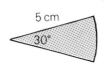

3 Calculate the area of one end of this bookshelf, which is a sector of a circle.

20 cm

20 cm

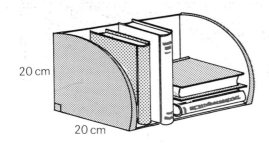

4 Calculate the area of the shaded sector in each picture below.

a

100°

20 cm

b

2 m

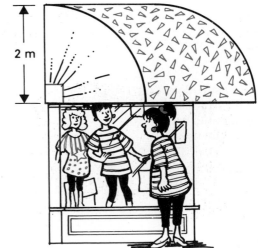

5 Paul is a DIY fanatic. He has bought a portable circular saw. The safety guard has a sector angle of 160°, and the radius of the blade is 60 mm. Calculate the area of blade which is exposed, to the nearest mm².

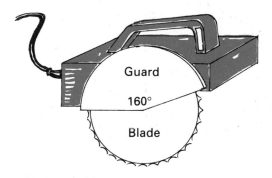

6 This small truck has only one windscreen-wiper, which sweeps through 111°. Calculate the area, to the nearest cm², of:
a the large sector covered (radius 60 cm)
b the small sector (radius 17 cm)
c the actual area of windscreen cleared.

7 Calculate the area of the end, and the volume, each to 3 significant figures, of this magazine rack.

8 AB 'subtends' (or faces) a right angle at centre O. Calculate the area of:
a sector OAB
b triangle OAB
c the shaded segment of the circle.

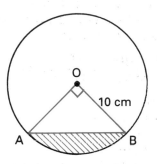

9 The areas of these sectors are given. Calculate the angles marked at the centres of the sectors.

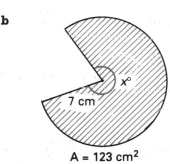

a 12 m, A = 42 m²

b 7 cm, A = 123 cm²

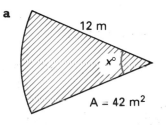

10 Calculate, to 3 significant figures:
a the length of the arch of the bridge
b the area of the opening between the bridge and the river.

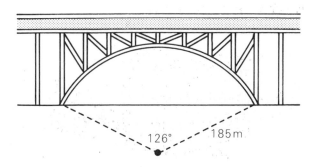

126°   185 m

CHECK-UP ON SYMMETRY IN THE CIRCLE

1 On a circle with centre O, draw and name:
- **a** a radius OA
- **b** a diameter BOC
- **c** a chord CD
- **d** an arc DE
- **e** a sector EOF (shade it).

2 Name the right angles in these diagrams. Give a reason why each one is a right angle.

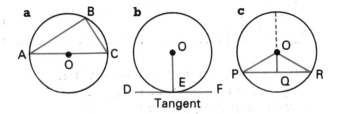

3 Calculate x in each diagram below.

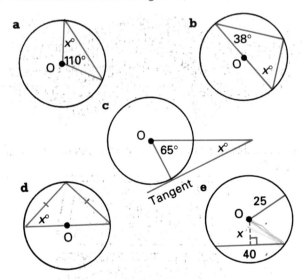

4 Calculate d and m.

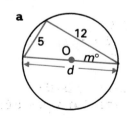

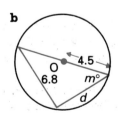

5 Calculate:
- **a** $x° + y°$
- **b** the length of the diameter.

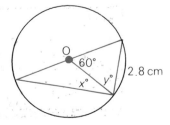

6 AB and AC are tangents to the circle. Calculate:
a AO **b** AC **c** ∠BAC

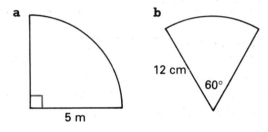

7 Calculate: (i) the length of each arc
                   (ii) the area of each sector.

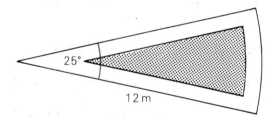

8 A traffic island is a sector of a circle of radius 12 m. Calculate the length of the curved edge.

9 The ends of the canopy are sectors of a circle.

Calculate:
- **a** the length of the curved edge AB
- **b** the area of each end, to the nearest cm².

10 The pendulum is 1.5 m long, and swings through an angle of 8°. Calculate:
- **a** the length of the arc, in cm, traced out by the weight
- **b** the area of the sector, in cm², covered by the pendulum.

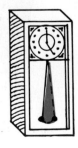

4 INEQUALITIES

Reminders

Symbols:
> 'is greater than' $(1 > 0)$
⩾ 'is greater than or equal to'
< 'is less than' $(0 < 1)$
⩽ 'is less than or equal to'

For the set $\{0, 1, 2, 3\}$ the solution of the inequality:
$x > 2$ is 3
$x ⩾ 2$ is 2, 3
$x < 2$ is 0, 1
$x ⩽ 2$ is 0, 1, 2

LOOKING BACK

1 Solve the equations:
  a $3x + 2 = 14$　　**b** $2(x + 7) = 24$
  c $5x - 7 = 3x - 15$　**d** $1 - x = 3$

2 In your notebook draw x and y-axes, and sketch the lines with equations:
  a $x = 6$　　**b** $y = 4$　　**c** $x + y = 5$
  d $y = 2x + 4$　**e** $y = 4 - 2x$

3 a Draw a number line, and mark it from -6 to $+6$.
  b Say whether each of the following is true (T) or false (F):
  (i) $5 > 1$　　(ii) $2 < 4$　　(iii) $3 < 0$
  (iv) $3 > 0$　　(v) $1 < -1$　　(vi) $-3 < -2$
  (vii) $4 > -1$　(viii) $0 > -6$

4 Put the correct symbol > (is greater than) or < (is less than) between the numbers in each pair, in the order given:
  a 5, 3　**b** 1, 2　**c** 1, 0　**d** $-1, 0$
  e $2, -2$　**f** $-2, 2$　**g** $-3, -4$　**h** $5, -1$

5 This lift can take up to 8 persons. For p persons, $p ⩽ 8$. How many could it take if:
  a $p ⩽ 12$　**b** $p < 10$?

Max. 8 persons

6 Write down an inequality for each of these:
  a the maximum exam mark, m, is 100
  b the minimum age for entry, a, is 14
  c the maximum weight, w tonnes, which the bridge can support is 7.5 tonnes

  d the minimum number of paper fasteners, n, is 200.

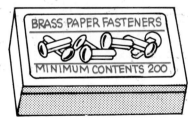
BRASS PAPER FASTENERS
MINIMUM CONTENTS 200

7 List all the solutions from the set $\{-2, -1, 0, 1, 2\}$ for:
  a $x > 1$　**b** $x < -1$　**c** $x ⩾ 0$
  d $x ⩽ 0$　**e** $x + 1 > 2$　**f** $2x + 1 < 3$
  g $x > 1$ or $x < -1$　**h** $3x < -3$

8 Write down inequalities which describe the range of temperature $t°$C between the pointers on this thermometer.

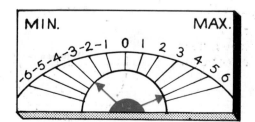
MIN.　　　MAX.
-6 -5 -4 -3 -2 -1 0 1 2 3 4 5 6

INEQUALITIES ON THE NUMBER LINE

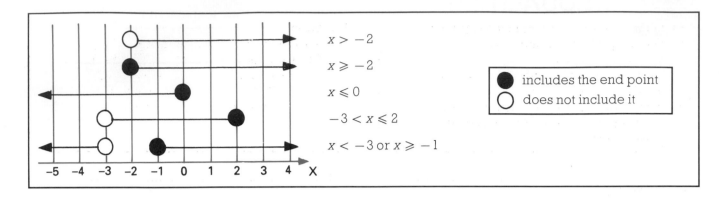

$x > -2$

$x \geqslant -2$

$x \leqslant 0$

$-3 < x \leqslant 2$

$x < -3 \text{ or } x \geqslant -1$

● includes the end point
○ does not include it

EXERCISE 1

1 Write down the inequality represented by each line.

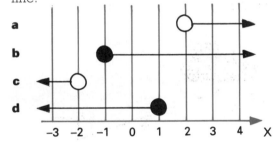

2 Repeat question **1** for these inequalities:

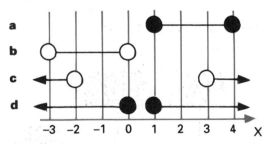

3 Illustrate these inequalities on the number line:
  a $x \leqslant 5$ **b** $x > -1$ **c** $-3 \leqslant x \leqslant 1$
  d $-2 < x < 2$ **e** $x \leqslant 0 \text{ or } x \geqslant 3$
  f $-2 \leqslant x \leqslant 2$ **g** $x \geqslant 1 \text{ or } x \leqslant -1$

4 Write down the inequality represented by each line.

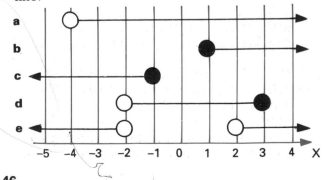

5 Write down an inequality for each of these, and illustrate it on the number line.

  a Dose, d ml, must not exceed 5 ml.

  b The weight, w kg, of each bag of potatoes must be more than 2 kg.

  c The height, h m, of the door can be from 2 m to 3 m.

  d For these plants to grow, the temperature, t°C, must be less than 3°C or more than 10°C.

  e The range of temperatures where the plants in **d** will not grow.

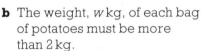
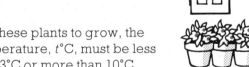
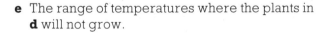

6 These two signs are fixed at the entrance to the Clyde Tunnel.

Number in a blue circle: minimum speed

Number in a red circle: maximum speed

  a Write down an inequality to show the possible speed, s mph, of a motorist obeying:
    (i) the blue sign   (ii) the red sign
    (iii) both signs.
  b Illustrate all three inequalities on a number line.

SOLVING INEQUALITIES

All the rules for solving equations apply to solving inequalities, except one: Is $5 > 3$? Is $(-2) \times 5 > (-2) \times 3$, that is, $-10 > -6$? Is $-10 < -6$? If you multiply (or divide) each side by a negative number, you must reverse the inequality symbol.	*Examples*

Examples

a $4(x+1)-16 \geqslant x$
$4x+4-16 \geqslant x$
$4x-12 \geqslant x$
$3x \geqslant 12$
$x \geqslant 4$

b $7-2y < 5$
$-2y < 5-7$
$-2y < -2$
$2y > 2$
$y > 1$

EXERCISE 2A

Solve the inequalities in questions **1–10**.

1 a $y+1 > 3$ **b** $x+5 < 4$ **c** $m+3 > 8$
d $n-1 < 0$ **e** $k+7 \geqslant 8$ **f** $t+1 \leqslant -1$
g $u-3 \geqslant 0$ **h** $v-2 \leqslant -1$ **i** $w-4 > 2$
j $p+5 \leqslant 5$ **k** $z+6 \leqslant 3$ **l** $t+5 < 1$

2 a $2y < 6$ **b** $3x < 12$ **c** $5m > 10$
d $6n < -6$ **e** $4k \geqslant 8$ **f** $7t \leqslant -14$

3 a $2y+3 > 9$ **b** $3x-2 < 7$ **c** $5m-4 > 21$
d $6n+6 < 0$ **e** $4k+1 \geqslant 9$ **f** $7t+2 \leqslant 23$
g $3u+6 \geqslant 0$ **h** $5v+5 \leqslant 5$ **i** $2p+1 < -3$

4 Solve each of these three inequalities, then write down the smallest whole number which makes it true.
a $3x+7 \geqslant 16$ **b** $5x-6 > 19$ **c** $2x+4 > 11$

5 a $4x+5 > 17$ **b** $2x-2 > 18$ **c** $3x-1 < 11$
d $5y-3 \leqslant 27$ **e** $7y+4 \leqslant 4$ **f** $8y+3 \geqslant 59$

6 a $3t+4 > 1$ **b** $6u+14 < 2$ **c** $3v+2 > -16$
d $5w+1 \leqslant -34$ **e** $2x+7 \geqslant 3$ **f** $4y-1 \leqslant -25$

7 Remember that if $-x < 5$, then $x > -5$.
a $-x < 2$ **b** $-y > 1$ **c** $-t > -2$
d $-2u > 4$ **e** $-3y < 9$ **f** $-4z \geqslant -4$
g $7-x < 11$ **h** $4-y \geqslant 2$ **i** $3-p \leqslant 5$

8 a $3p+1 > p+7$ **b** $5q+6 < 3q+24$
c $7r-3 > 3r+13$ **d** $3s+1 \geqslant 13-s$
e $13-2t \geqslant 3t-2$ **f** $24-3u \leqslant u+4$

9 a $2(x+1)+3 > 15$ **b** $3(y+5)-4 < 29$
c $5(2z-1)+4 \leqslant 9$ **d** $6-2(x-1) > 12$
e $3-(1-y) < 7$ **f** $1-3(t-2) \geqslant -5$

10 a $5-2t \leqslant 11$ **b** $1-5x < 11$ **c** $3-3y \geqslant -9$
d $25-5p \leqslant 0$ **e** $8-4u > -8$ **f** $4-2r \geqslant -4$

/ **BRAINSTORMERS**

1 *Each bag can hold x weights, and each weight weighs 1 kg.*

a

Can you find anything wrong?

b

x is the same in each picture. How many weights are in a bag? (Use both pictures.)

2 a *Write down two values of x for which $x^2 = 9$.*
b *Solve these inequalities, and illustrate the solutions on the number line:*
(i) $x^2 \leqslant 9$ (ii) $x^2 > 9$.
c *Solve, and illustrate, on the number line, the solution of: (i) $x^2 \leqslant 16$ (ii) $x^2 > 16$.*

EXERCISE 2B

1 Helen has a blank 3 hour video tape. She records x half-hour programmes.

   a Can you see that $0.5x \leqslant 3$?
   b Solve the inequality to find the number of programmes she can record.

2 Sanjay pours 200 ml of orange concentrate and 5 cups of water, each holding x ml, into a litre jug.
   a Show that $200 + 5x \leqslant 1000$.
   b Solve the inequality, and write down the maximum capacity of a cup.

3 Mr Allen, head of English, has £100 to spend on textbooks which cost £5 each. The delivery charge is £10. He orders x books.
   a Make an inequality, and solve it.
   b What is the greatest number of books he can buy?

4 A carpark covers $840 \, \text{m}^2$. Each car needs $20 \, \text{m}^2$, and space for turning, etc., takes up $40 \, \text{m}^2$.
   a Make an inequality for x cars in the carpark, and solve it.
   b Can the carpark hold:
       (i) 30 cars   (ii) 40 cars   (iii) 50 cars?

5 Tom loads his barrow with 4 kg blocks. He weighs 70 kg, and his barrow weighs 40 kg. The plank can bear no more than 160 kg. Make an inequality for x blocks, solve it, and describe the number of blocks he can take safely up the plank.

6 Ruth's essay has to be at least 1000 words long. It is in two parts, the main part of 750 words and a summary x lines long.
   a If she writes an average of 15 words per line in the summary, make an inequality, and solve it.
   b What is the least number of lines in her summary?

7 The school disco costs £200 to run. A raffle raises £36, and x tickets are sold at £2 each.
   a Make an inequality and solve it.
   b What is the minimum number of tickets that must be sold to avoid a loss?

8

   a Write down the hire cost for x miles with each firm.
   b Make an inequality in which Otto's cost is less than Carl's for the x miles, and solve it.
   c Which firm would you choose for a journey of:
       (i) 9 miles   (ii) 10 miles   (iii) 11 miles?

9

   a Write down the cost of ordering x calculators from each firm.
   b Make an inequality in which School Supplies are cheaper than Calculator Contracts, and solve it.
   c What sizes of orders are cheaper from School Supplies?

REGIONS OF THE COORDINATE PLANE

Inequalities can be used to describe regions of the XOY plane, like this:
 (i) draw the boundary line—full if it is included in the region, dotted if not
(ii) shade the part of the plane you don't want, **leaving the part you want clear.**

Example
Show the regions:

a $x > 2$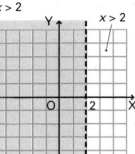

b $x \geqslant 2$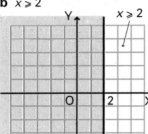

c $y \geqslant -2$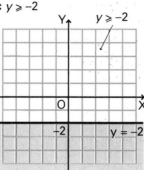

d $y \geqslant 2$ and $y > -2$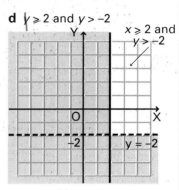

EXERCISE 3

1 Use an inequality to describe each unshaded region.

a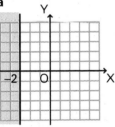

b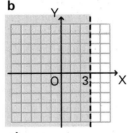

c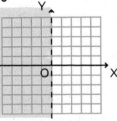

d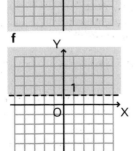

e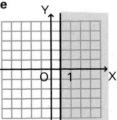

f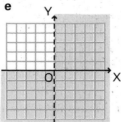

2 Use two inequalities to describe each unshaded region.

a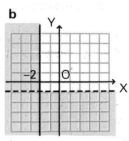

b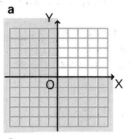

c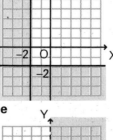

d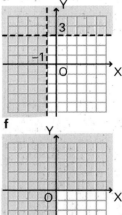

e

f

3 Make coordinate sketches in your notebook to show the unshaded regions of the XOY plane defined by these inequalities.

a $x > 1$ **b** $x \geqslant 3$ **c** $x < -1$ **d** $x < 1$

e $y \geqslant 2$ **f** $y \geqslant -1$ **g** $y < 4$ **h** $y < -1$

4 For every point in this unshaded region, $x \geqslant 2$ and $x \leqslant 4$, that is $2 \leqslant x \leqslant 4$.

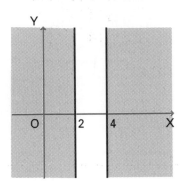

Draw sketches to show the unshaded regions defined by:

a $x > 1$ and $x < 4$ **b** $x > 0$ and $x \leqslant 5$

c $-1 \leqslant x \leqslant 1$ **d** $y > 2$ and $y < 4$

e $y \geqslant 1$ and $y \leqslant 5$ **f** $0 \leqslant y \leqslant 2$

g $-2 \leqslant y < 2$

5 Use inequalities to describe these unshaded regions.

a

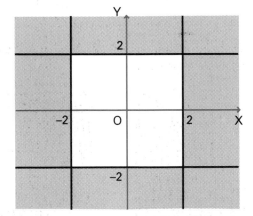

b

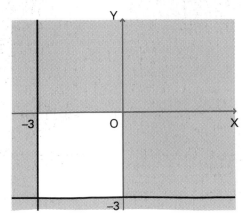

6 Alpha Beta oil-field is split into squares for drilling.

Use x, y and the symbols $\geqslant$ and $\leqslant$ to describe these parts of the 'field':

a square C, allocated to Universe Oil

b the block made up of squares M, N and O, belonging to Galaxy Oil

c the block of squares F, G, K, L, P and Q given to Cosmos Oil.

7 Stellar Oil is allocated these regions of the oil-field:

a $2 \leqslant x \leqslant 3$ and $2 \leqslant y \leqslant 3$

b $1 \leqslant x \leqslant 3$ and $-2 \leqslant y \leqslant 0$

Name the squares allocated to it.

EXERCISE 4

The line $y = x$ divides the coordinate plane into the two regions where $y > x$ and $y < x$.
Using the same methods as before, we can illustrate these inequalities by *unshaded regions* of the plane.

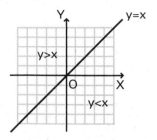

a $y > x + 2$

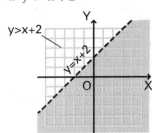

b $y \leqslant x + 2$

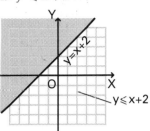

1 Write down inequalities which describe the unshaded regions.

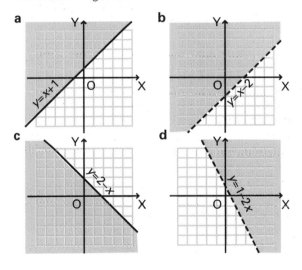

2 Write down inequalities for the unshaded regions below.

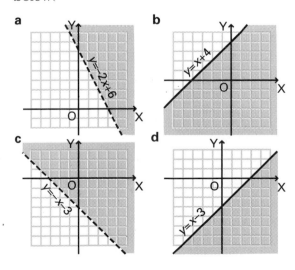

3 In each of the following:
  (i) use the equation $y = mx + c$ to find the equation of the boundary line

Reminder
$$m = \frac{-4}{4} = -1; c = 4$$
So $y = -x + 4$,
or $y = 4 - x$

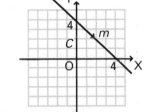

  (ii) write down an inequality which describes the unshaded region.

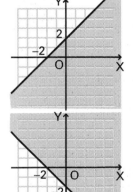

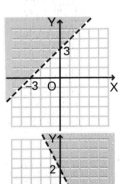

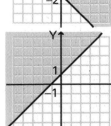

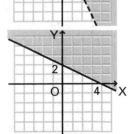

ENCLOSED REGIONS

Examples

a Illustrate the inequality $3x + 2y < 12$ on the coordinate plane.

Step 1
Draw the boundary line
$3x + 2y = 12$.
If $x = 0$, $y = 6$. $(0, 6)$ is on it.
If $y = 0$, $x = 4$. $(4, 0)$ is on it.

Step 2
Is the origin in the region?
Test $(0, 0)$ in the inequality.
$0 + 0 < 12$. True, so the origin
is in the required (unshaded)
region.

Step 3
Shade the unwanted region.

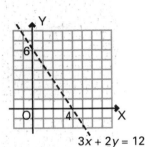

$3x + 2y = 12$

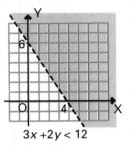

$3x + 2y < 12$

b Show the region defined by the inequalities $y \geqslant 0$, $x \geqslant 0$ and $3x + 2y < 12$.

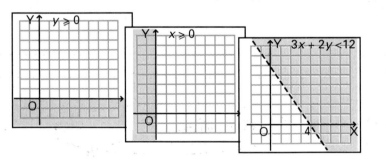

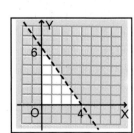

EXERCISE 5A

1 Illustrate these inequalities on the coordinate plane.

a $x + y > 5$ **b** $5x - 2y < 10$
c $x + 4y \geqslant 8$ **d** $3y - 2x \geqslant -6$
e $y \geqslant x - 7$ **f** $3x + 4y > 12$
g $3x - 4y < 12$ **h** $2x + 5y \leqslant 20$

2 Write down a set of inequalities which defines each unshaded region below.

a
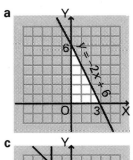

b
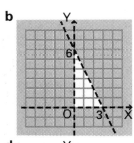

c
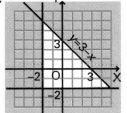

d
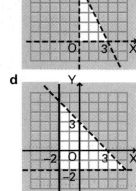

3 Show the regions defined by the inequalities:

a $x < 2$, $x > -2$, $y < x + 1$ and $y > x - 1$
b $x \geqslant 0$, $y \geqslant 0$, $y < 3$ and $x + y \leqslant 5$
c $x \geqslant 1$, $y \geqslant -1$, $x + y \leqslant 6$ and $y \leqslant x + 2$

4 Find the equations of these boundary lines, then write down a set of inequalities which defines each unshaded region.

a
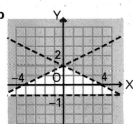

b
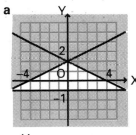

c
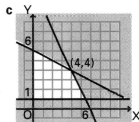

d
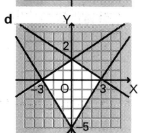

EXERCISE 5B

1 Mr Slickman is having a business lunch. He can spend up to £15, and wants to have a starter and a main course. Starters cost less than £5, and main courses cost at least £8.
Take the cost of a starter as £x (so $x > 0$ and $x < \ldots$).
Take the cost of a main course as £y (so $y \geqslant \ldots$).
a Write down four inequalities.
b Illustrate them on a coordinate diagram.

2 Central High's social committee has ten members, some Seniors, some Juniors. At any meeting there must be:
at least five members present; not more than ten present; more than two Seniors, and more than two Juniors present.
Take x for the number of Seniors present, and y for the number of Juniors.
a Write down four inequalities.
b Illustrate these in a diagram.
c x and y must be whole numbers. From your diagram, list all possible attendances at a committee meeting.

3
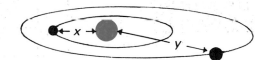

Two satellites orbit the Earth at distances of x units and y units, respectively.
x is always at least 1, and y is always at least 2.
The sum $x + y$ never exceeds 8, and the difference $y - x$ is never more than 3.
Write down four inequalities and illustrate them in a diagram.

4 Niall is training for a mountain bike race. He decides to cover up to 12 miles, walking at least 3 miles, cycling at least 5 miles, but cycling no more than twice the distance he walks.
Take x miles walked and y miles cycled.
a Write down four inequalities, and illustrate them in a diagram.
b Which of these training plans would suit him?
(i) (4, 6), that is, 4 miles walked, 6 cycled
(ii) (5, 6)   (iii) (6, 7)   (iv) (8, 4).

MAXIMUM AND MINIMUM VALUES OF $ax + by$

Example

Find: **a** the maximum value of $3x + 2y$
      b the minimum value of $2x - 5y$
in the region defined by:
$x \geqslant 0, y \geqslant 0, x + y \leqslant 10, y \leqslant x + 4$.

This is a table of values at the vertices of the region:

	(0, 0)	(10, 0)	(3, 7)	(0, 4)
$3x + 2y$	0	30	23	8
$2x - 5y$	0	20	-29	-20

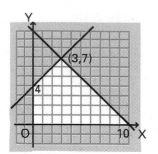

The maximum and minimum values occur at vertices of the region, so:
a the maximum value of $3x + 2y$ is 30, when $x = 10$ and $y = 0$
b the minimum value of $2x - 5y$ is -29, when $x = 3$ and $y = 7$.

EXERCISE 6B

In questions **1–4**, the maximum and minimum values refer to the unshaded regions of the plane.

1

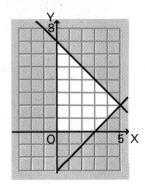

Find the maximum and minimum values of:
a $x + 2y$ **b** $2x + y$ **c** $2y - x$

2

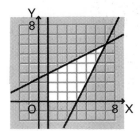

Find the maximum value of:
a $x + y$ **b** $x - y$ **c** $2x + 3y$

3

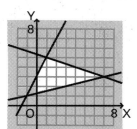

Find the minimum value of:
a $x + y$ **b** $x - y$ **c** $x + 2y$

4

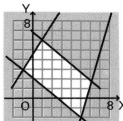

Find the maximum and minimum values of:
a $x + y$ **b** $x - y$
c $3y - x$ **d** $3y + 5x$

5 Illustrate the regions defined by these inequalities, and find the maximum value of $x + y$ in each region.
    a $x \geqslant 0, y \leqslant 4, 2y \geqslant x$
    b $x \geqslant 0, y \geqslant 0, x \leqslant 5, y \leqslant 6$
    c $x \geqslant 0, y \geqslant 0, 2x + 3y \leqslant 12$
    d $x \geqslant 0, y \geqslant 0, 2x + y \leqslant 6, x + 2y \leqslant 6$

6 Find the maximum and minimum values of $2x + 4y$ in the region defined by:
    $x \geqslant 1, x \leqslant 4, y \geqslant 0, x + y \leqslant 6, 2x + y \geqslant 3$.

CHECK-UP ON INEQUALITIES

1 Write down the inequality represented by each line.

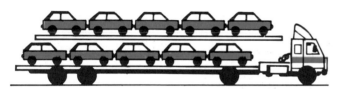

2 Solve these inequalities:
  a $x - 6 \geqslant 4$ **b** $3y + 5 < 29$ **c** $4z + 5 > 1$
  d $2t \geqslant 5$ **e** $-2p < 8$ **f** $6 - 3u \leqslant 12$

3 Each platform on the transporter can hold up to five cars. A space of 1 metre is left at the front and back of the row of cars, and the platform is 22 m long.

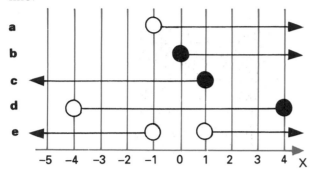

  a Taking a car to be x metres long, make an inequality in x.
  b Solve it to find the longest car that can be carried.

4 Solve:
  a $3x + 4 \leqslant x - 10$ **b** $2(y + 3) - 5 < 1$
  c $13 - 2n \geqslant 5n - 8$ **d** $2k - 3(1 - k) \geqslant 2$

5 These business cards show the cost of video rental.

  a Taking x for the number of videos rented, make an inequality which shows that Video Hire's cost is less than Movie Rental's.
  b Solve the inequality.

6 Find the smallest whole number for which:
  a $5x - 8 \geqslant 7$ **b** $4y + 1 > 15$ **c** $5 - 2z < -1$

7 Write down a set of inequalities which describes the *unshaded* region.

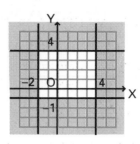

8 Write down an inequality that defines each *unshaded* region.

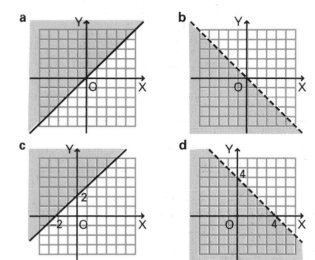

9 Illustrate each of these inequalities in a diagram.
  a $y \geqslant \frac{1}{2}x$ **b** $x + y < 6$

10 Draw a diagram which shows the region defined by:
  $x \geqslant 0,\ y \geqslant 0,\ x + y \leqslant 10$ and $y \leqslant x + 5$.

11 Find the maximum and minimum values of $x + 2y$ and $y - 3x$ in the unshaded region.

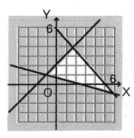

12 Find the maximum value of $2x + y$, given:
  $x \geqslant 1,\ y \geqslant 2,\ y - x \geqslant 0$ and $x + y \leqslant 8$.

TRIGONOMETRY – CALCULATIONS, GRAPHS AND EQUATIONS

Reminders

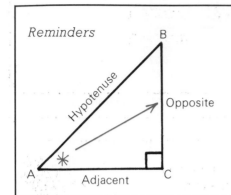

In right-angled $\triangle ABC$,

$$\sin A = \frac{\text{Opposite side}}{\text{Hypotenuse}}$$

$$\cos A = \frac{\text{Adjacent side}}{\text{Hypotenuse}}$$

$$\tan A = \frac{\text{Opposite side}}{\text{Adjacent side}}$$

Memory aid:

SOH–CAH–TOA

Note: In this chapter give answers correct to 1 decimal place, unless there are other instructions.

LOOKING BACK

1 Use Pythagoras' Theorem to calculate *d* in each triangle.

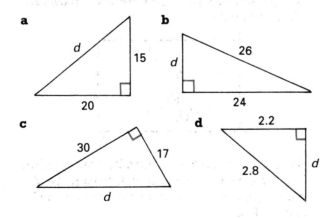

2 Write down ratios for sin A, cos A and tan A in each triangle below.

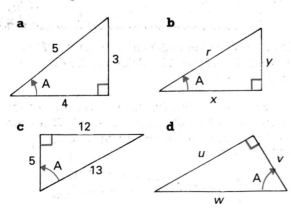

3 Calculate *d*.

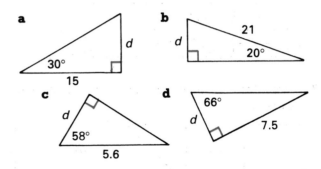

4 Calculate *x*.

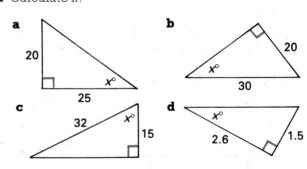

5 Calculate the height *h* cm and the area of the isosceles triangle and the parallelogram. The lengths are in cm.

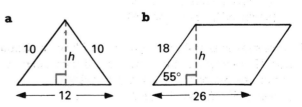

2-D CALCULATIONS

Given $\tan A = \frac{15}{8}$, and $0° < A < 90°$, we can draw this right-angled $\triangle ABC$, and calculate the exact value of $\sin A$, etc, in ratio form.

$AB^2 = 8^2 + 15^2$ (Pythagoras' Theorem)
So $AB = 17$.

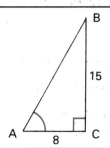

Then:

$\sin A = \frac{15}{17}$ $\sin B = \frac{8}{17}$

$\cos A = \frac{8}{17}$ $\cos B = \frac{15}{17}$

$\tan B = \frac{8}{15}$

EXERCISE 1

1 In each part, sketch a right-angled triangle, calculate the third side, and find the required ratios.

	Given	Write down ratios for:
a	$\tan A = \frac{3}{4}$	$\sin A$, $\cos A$
b	$\sin P = \frac{5}{13}$	$\cos P$, $\tan P$
c	$\cos X = \frac{24}{25}$	$\sin X$, $\tan X$

2 Sketch this 45°, 45°, 90° triangle, made from half of a square.

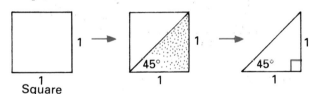

Square

Show that the length of the hypotenuse is $\sqrt{2}$, and write down ratios for $\sin 45°$, $\cos 45°$ and $\tan 45°$.

3 Sketch this 30°, 60°, 90° triangle.

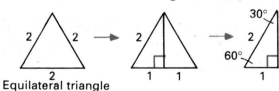

Equilateral triangle

a Show that the length of the third side is $\sqrt{3}$.
b Write down ratios for:
   (i) $\sin 30°$, $\cos 30°$, $\tan 30°$
   (ii) $\sin 60°$, $\cos 60°$, $\tan 60°$.

4 A trawler sets sail on a course 035° from its home port H. It keeps to this course for 22 km. How far, to the nearest km, is the trawler then:
a east of H   **b** north of H?

5 To reach the observation platform Graeme and Martin have to climb the steps and then the ladder. What height is the platform above the ground, to one tenth of a metre?

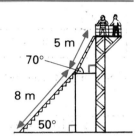

6 A hole is drilled in the metal sheet at A. Another hole has to be drilled at B. Calculate the coordinates of B, giving answers to the nearest whole number.

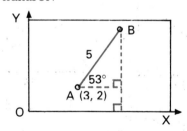

7 Avril is checking the distance between marker buoys for a yacht race. She is at the top of a cliff 85 m high, and the two buoys are both directly ahead of her.

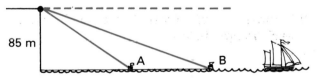

She measures the angles of depression of the buoys to be 35° and 20°. Calculate the distance between them.

8 The Sun is 9.3×10^7 miles from the Earth, and the Moon is 2.4×10^5 miles from the Earth. Calculate $\angle ESM$, correct to 2 decimal places, when $\angle SEM = 90°$.

3-D CALCULATIONS

If a line, like OP, is perpendicular to a plane, it is perpendicular to *all* the lines it meets in the plane.

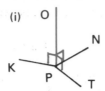

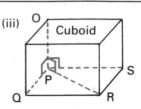

EXERCISE 2

1 Name the right angles at P in diagrams (i) and (iii) above which have OP as one arm.

2 The mast OP is supported by wires fixed in horizontal ground at A, B and C.
a Sketch OAP, OBP and OCP as right-angled triangles.
b Calculate the angles between the wires and the ground at A, B and C.

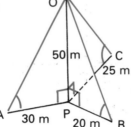

3

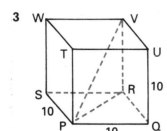

This cube has edges 10 cm long.
a Sketch right-angled △PQR, and calculate the length of PR.
b Sketch right-angled △PRV, and calculate ∠RPV.

4 This goods container is in the shape of a cuboid.

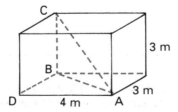

Calculate:
a AB **b** AC **c** ∠BAC

5 The cone has a circular base, and its vertex H is vertically above the centre of the base. Calculate:
a the slant height HJ
b the angle between HJ and the base
c the apex angle, JHL.

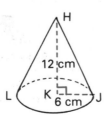

6 For this cone, calculate:
a the vertical height, HK
b the radius of the base, KJ.

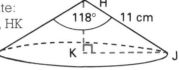

7 The drilling rig has a vertical pole OA rising from the centre of a square base. Calculate:
a BD **b** BO **c** AO **d** ∠ABO

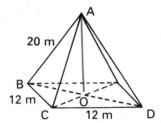

8

This pyramid is made from four isosceles triangles on a horizontal rectangular base. TB is vertical, and 12 cm long. Calculate:
a PR **b** PB **c** ∠TPR

9 An observer in the balloon, 1500 m above O on the ground, spots a fire F due south. The ranger's hut R is due east. The angles of depression of F and R are 40° and 30° respectively. Calculate, to the nearest 100 m:
a OF **b** OR **c** FR.

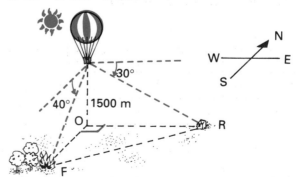

SINES, COSINES AND TANGENTS OF ALL SIZES OF ANGLES

Coordinates help trigonometry to break free from the shackles of the right-angled triangle.

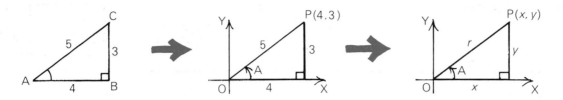

Using coordinates, for any angle A, $\sin A = \dfrac{y}{r}$, $\cos A = \dfrac{x}{r}$, $\tan A = \dfrac{y}{x}$.

Examples

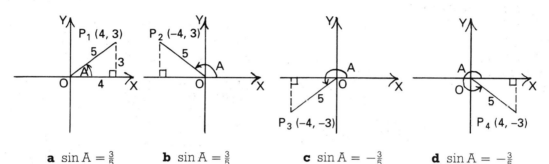

a $\sin A = \frac{3}{5}$ **b** $\sin A = \frac{3}{5}$ **c** $\sin A = -\frac{3}{5}$ **d** $\sin A = -\frac{3}{5}$

Note (i) If OP rotates *anti-clockwise* from OX through an angle A, the angle is positive.
(ii) *r* is always positive.

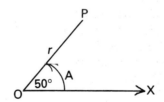

EXERCISE 3A

1 Copy and complete this table, using the diagrams in the examples above.

P	x	y	r	$\sin A\left(\dfrac{y}{r}\right)$	$\cos A\left(\dfrac{x}{r}\right)$	$\tan A\left(\dfrac{y}{x}\right)$
P_1	4	3	5	$\frac{3}{5}$	$\frac{4}{5}$	$\frac{3}{4}$
P_2	−4	3	5			
P_3						
P_4						

2 Look again at your table in question **1**. In which quadrants are these positive?
a $\sin A$ **b** $\cos A$ **c** $\tan A$
d $\sin A$, $\cos A$ *and* $\tan A$

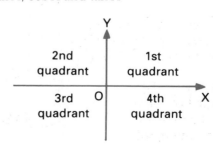

3 a Make sketches for angle B = ∠ XOP, where:
  (i) P₁ is (5, 12) (ii) P₂ is (−5, 12)
  (iii) P₃ is (−5, −12) (iv) P₄ is (5, −12)

b Make and complete a table like the one in question **1**.

c Answer question **2** for sin B, cos B and tan B.

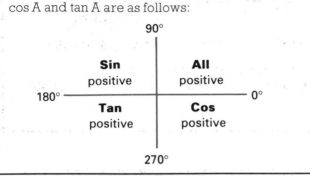

In fact, for every angle A, the signs of sin A, cos A and tan A are as follows:

90°

Sin positive | **All** positive
180° — 0°
Tan positive | **Cos** positive

270°

4 Using the diagram above, say which of these are positive and which are negative:
  a sin 100° **b** cos 100° **c** tan 100° **d** sin 200°
  e cos 200° **f** tan 200° **g** cos 300° **h** sin 300°

5 Use your calculator to find the values (including signs), correct to 3 decimal places, of the sines, cosines and tangents in question **4**. Then check that your answers to **4** were correct.

6 Write down the sign of each of these:
  a tan 123° **b** cos 333° **c** sin 85° **d** tan 350°
  e cos 235° **f** sin 95° **g** cos 106° **h** tan 210°

7 Use your calculator to find the values, correct to 3 decimal places, of the sines, cosines and tangents in question **6**. Then check your answers to question **6**.

8 Write down the sign of:
  a the tangent of every acute angle
  b the cosine of every obtuse angle
  c the sine of every reflex angle.

9 a Using the definitions $\sin A = \dfrac{y}{r}$ and $\cos A = \dfrac{x}{r}$, copy and complete this table.

A	0°	90°	180°	270°	360°
sin A	0	1			
cos A					

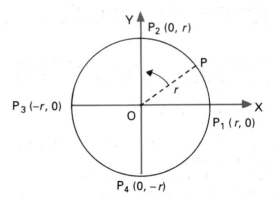

b Check your answers by calculator.

c Add a row for tan A. Again check with your calculator, explaining the error messages.

10 Suppose $\sin x° = \frac{3}{5}$ and 0 < x < 90. Sketch a suitable right-angled triangle with x° as one angle. Write down ratios for cos x° and tan x°.

11 Suppose $\tan y° = \frac{8}{15}$ and 0 < y < 90. Find ratios for sin y° and cos y°.

EXERCISE 3B

Example

Express in terms of acute angles: **a** $\sin 150°$ **b** $\cos 200°$ **c** $\tan 315°$

(i)

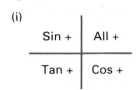

Sin +	All +
Tan +	Cos +

(ii)

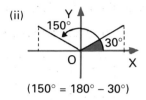

$(150° = 180° - 30°)$

(iii)

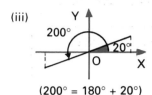

$(200° = 180° + 20°)$

(iv)

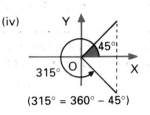

$(315° = 360° - 45°)$

a From (i), the sign of $\sin 150°$ is $+$.
From (ii), the related acute angle is $30°$.
So $\sin 150° = \sin 30°$ (the sine of an
angle $=$ the sine of its supplement).

In the same way, from (iii) and (iv):
b $\cos 200° = -\cos 20°$ **c** $\tan 315° = -\tan 45°$

---

1 Express each angle in terms of a related acute
angle $a°$, using $(180-a)°$, $(180+a)°$ or $(360-a)°$:
a $100°$ **b** $170°$ **c** $190°$
d $220°$ **e** $300°$ **f** $330°$

2 Express each of these in terms of the sin, cos or
tan of an acute angle.
a $\sin 100°$ **b** $\cos 100°$ **c** $\tan 100°$
d $\sin 220°$ **e** $\cos 220°$ **f** $\tan 220°$
g $\sin 300°$ **h** $\cos 300°$ **i** $\tan 300°$
j $\sin 110°$ **k** $\cos 160°$ **l** $\tan 340°$
m $\sin 125°$ **n** $\cos 335°$ **o** $\tan 145°$

3 Using this triangle, you found that
$\sin 45° = \dfrac{1}{\sqrt{2}}$, $\cos 45° = \dfrac{1}{\sqrt{2}}$, $\tan 45° = 1$.

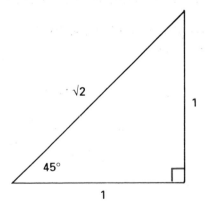

Now write down ratios for:
a $\sin 135°$, $\cos 135°$ and $\tan 135°$
b $\sin 225°$, $\cos 225°$ and $\tan 225°$
c $\sin 315°$, $\cos 315°$ and $\tan 315°$

4 With the help of this triangle, write down ratios
for:
a $\sin 120°$, $\sin 240°$, $\sin 300°$
b $\cos 120°$, $\cos 240°$, $\cos 300°$
c $\tan 120°$, $\tan 240°$, $\tan 300°$

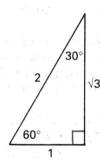

CHALLENGE

a *Copy the diagram, which is symmetrical about
both axes, and fill in the coordinates of P_2, P_3 and
P_4 in terms of x and y.*

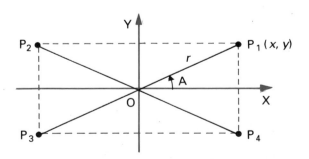

b *Use the definitions of $\sin XOP$, $\cos XOP$ and
$\tan XOP$ to justify the quadrant rule:*
All-sin-tan-cos positive.

THE TRIGONOMETRIC FUNCTIONS AND THEIR GRAPHS

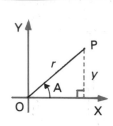

For each angle A, there is only one position of OP, so there is only one value of sin A. This value lies between 1 and −1.

So there is a function which maps the set of all angles to the set of all numbers from −1 to 1. This function is called the **sine function**.

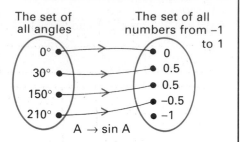

Similarly, the **cosine function** maps the set of all angles to the set of all numbers from −1 to 1.

EXERCISE 4

1 The graph of the sine function

a Copy and complete this table, using your calculator (correct to 1 decimal place):

x	0	30	60	90	120		360
sin x°							

b Plot all the points in the table, using these scales and axes.

c Join the points by a smooth curve, called a **sine curve** or **sine wave**.

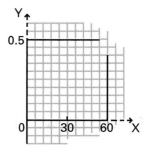

(i) As OP rotates through angles from 360° to 720°, another complete sine wave is produced—one wave or cycle in 360°, two in 720°, . . .

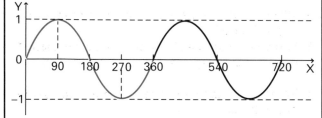

For this reason, **the sine function is a periodic function with period 360°.**

(ii) The maximum value of sin x° is 1, and the minimum value is −1; so **−1 ⩽ sin x° ⩽ 1.**

(iii) Each 'hump' or 'hollow' on the curve has an axis of symmetry. For the first hump it is x = 90, and for the first hollow x = 270.

2 This diagram shows the graph of the sine function for 0 ⩽ x ⩽ 720.

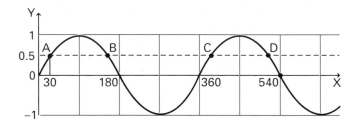

a For what values of x, 0 ⩽ x ⩽ 360, is:
  (i) sin x° = 0   (ii) sin x° = 1
  (iii) sin x° = −1?

b The point A(30, 0.5) is shown. Use the symmetry and periodicity of the curve to deduce the coordinates of B, C and D.

3 The graph of the cosine function
Make a table similar to the one in question **1** which allows you to draw the graph of y = cos x° for 0 ⩽ x ⩽ 360.

(i) **The cosine function also has a period of 360°.**

(ii) Its graph is similar to that of the sine function, but 90° 'out of phase'. If you cover up the part of the sine graph from x = 0 to x = 90, you'll see the form of the cosine graph starting at x = 90.

(iii) The maximum value of cos x° is 1 and the minimum value is −1; **so −1 ⩽ cos x° ⩽ 1.**

4 a For what values of x, 0 ⩽ x ⩽ 360, is:
  (i) cos x° = 0   (ii) cos x° = 1   (iii) cos x° = −1?

b What is the equation of the curve's axis of symmetry for the part from x = 0 to x = 360?

5 The graph of the tangent function

a Copy and complete this table, with values of tan $x°$ correct to 1 decimal place where necessary.

x	0	30	60	75	105	120	150
tan $x°$							

180	210	240	255	285	300	330	360

b Plot the points, using these scales and axes.

c Join the points to form three parts of the tangent graph.

d Key in tangents of angles near 90°, for example, 89°, 89.9°, 89.999 999°, 90.000 001°. Draw vertical lines at $x = 90$ and $x = 270$. As x increases from zero, the graph gets closer and closer to these lines, or asymptotes.

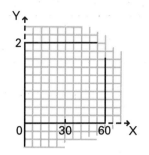

The graph of $y = \tan x°$ consists of an endless number of branches. These occur at intervals of 180°, so the period of the tangent function is 180°. Tan $x°$ has no value at $x = 90, 270, \ldots$ so the function is undefined at these points.

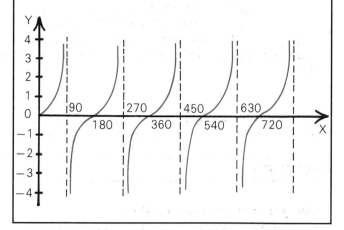

SKETCHING TRIGONOMETRIC GRAPHS

EXERCISE 5A

The graph of $y = 2 \sin x°$

Compared to $y = \sin x°$, each value of $\sin x°$ is *multiplied by 2*.

Its maximum value is $1 \times 2 = 2$; its minimum value is $-1 \times 2 = -2$.

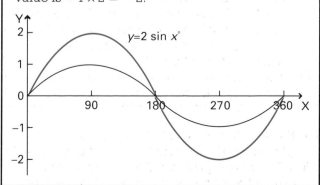

Note: All the sketches here are for $0 \leqslant x \leqslant 360$.

1 a Write down the maximum and minimum values of $y = 3 \sin x°$.

b Sketch the graphs of $y = \sin x°$ and $y = 3 \sin x°$ on the same diagram.

2 a Write down the maximum and minimum values of $y = 2 \cos x°$.

b Sketch the graphs of $y = \cos x°$ and $y = 2 \cos x°$ on the same diagram.

c Add a sketch of $y = 3 \cos x°$ to your diagram.

3 For $y = -\sin x°$, each value of y in $y = \sin x°$ is multiplied by -1. Sketch the graph of $y = -\sin x°$.

The graph of $y = \sin 2x°$

(i) Its maximum value is 1, and its minimum value is -1, as it is a sine curve.

(ii) The period of the function $y = \sin x°$ is 360°, given by $0 \leqslant x \leqslant 360$.

The period of the function $y = \sin 2x°$ is given by $0 \leqslant 2x \leqslant 360$,
$0 \leqslant x \leqslant 180$, and so is 180°.

So its graph has 2 complete cycles between 0 and 360.

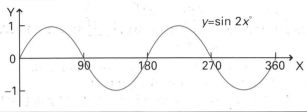

4 $y = \cos 2x°$ has two complete cycles for $0 \leqslant x \leqslant 360$. Sketch its graph.

5 How many complete cycles has $y = \sin 3x°$ for $0 \leqslant x \leqslant 360$? Sketch the graph.

6 $y = \sin \frac{1}{2}x°$ has half a complete cycle for $0 \leqslant x \leqslant 360$. Sketch the graph.

Summary

For the graphs of $y = a \sin nx°$ and $y = a \cos nx°$:

(i) a gives the maximum and minimum values

(ii) n gives the number of cycles for $0 \leqslant x \leqslant 360$,
and the period of the function is $\dfrac{360°}{n}$.

---

7 For each of the following:
(i) write down the maximum and minimum values of y, and the number of cycles in the graph for $0 \leqslant x \leqslant 360$
(ii) sketch the graph.

  a $y = \sin x°$ **b** $y = \cos x°$ **c** $y = 4 \sin x°$
  d $y = 4 \cos x°$ **e** $y = \sin 2x°$ **f** $y = 3 \sin 2x°$
  g $y = \cos 2x°$ **h** $y = 4 \cos 2x°$ **i** $y = 5 \cos \frac{1}{2}x°$

8 Find the equations of these graphs; they are of the form $y = a \sin nx°$ or $y = a \cos nx°$.

a

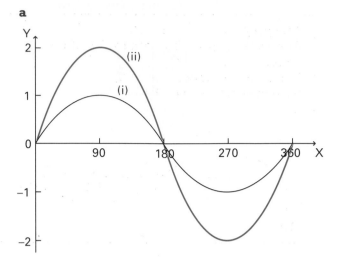

b

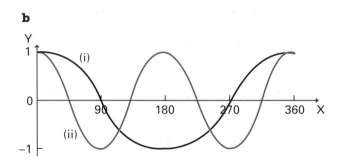

c

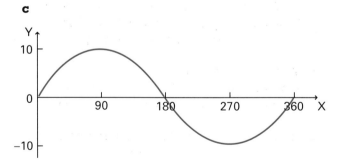

d

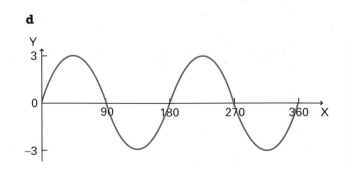

EXERCISE 5B

The graph of $y = 1 + \sin x°$.
Compared to $y = \sin x°$, each value of y is *increased by 1*.
Its maximum value is $1 + 1 = 2$;
its minimum value is $-1 + 1 = 0$.

1 a Write down the maximum and minimum values of $y = 2 + \sin x°$.
   b Sketch the graphs of $y = \sin x°$ and $y - 2 + \sin x°$ on the same diagram.

2 a Write down the maximum and minimum values of $y = -1 + \sin x°$.
   b Sketch the graphs of $y = \sin x°$ and $y = -1 + \sin x°$ on the same diagram.

3 a Write down the maximum and minimum values of: (i) $y = 1 + \cos x°$ (ii) $y = -1 + \cos x°$.
   b Sketch the graphs of $y = 1 + \cos x°$ and $y = -1 + \cos x°$ on the same diagram.

4 Sketch the graphs of:
   a $y = 2 + \sin 3x°$ **b** $y = -5 + \cos 3x°$
   c $y = 4 + 2\sin 2x°$ **d** $y = -4 + 3\cos 2x°$

5 Find the equation of this trigonometric graph.

6 As the windmill rotates, the height h m of A above the ground at time t seconds is given by $h = 10 + 6\sin 2t°$.

   a Write down the maximum and minimum heights of A above the ground.
   b Calculate the height when timing began ($t = 0$).
   c Sketch the graph of $h = 10 + 6\sin 2t°$.

7 The lighthouse beam shines across the bay. Its power P, t minutes after midnight, is given by $P = 10 + 10\cos 6t°$.

   a Calculate:
      (i) the maximum and minimum powers
      (ii) the power of the beam at 12.30 am.
   b Sketch the graph of P.

8 The height h km of the space capsule above the Earth after x hours is given by:
$h = 1000 + 50\sin 10x°$.

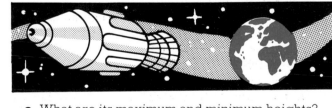

   a What are its maximum and minimum heights?
   b What is the period of h?
   c Sketch the graph of h.

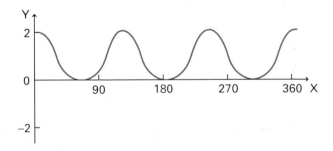

INVESTIGATION

Investigate the graphs of $y = a + b\sin nx°$ and $y = a + b\cos nx°$ with the aid of a computer or graphics calculator. Write a report on your findings.

TRIGONOMETRIC EQUATIONS

Examples

a Solve $\sin x° = 0.6$, to the nearest degree, for $0 \leqslant x \leqslant 360$.

(i) By calculator,

$$\boxed{2\text{nd F}}\ \boxed{\sin}\ 0.6 = 37$$

(ii) $\sin x°$ is positive, so x is in the first or second quadrant.
So $x = 37$ or $180 - 37 = 143$

Sin +	All +
$(180 - x)°$	$x°$
$(180 + x)°$	$(360 - x)°$
Tan +	Cos +

All - sin - tan - cos positive

b Solve $3 \cos x° + 1 = 0$, for $0 \leqslant x \leqslant 360$.
$\cos x° = -\frac{1}{3}$

(i) By calculator,

$$\boxed{2\text{nd F}}\ \boxed{\cos}\ \boxed{(}\ 1\ \boxed{\div}\ 3\ \boxed{)} = 71$$

(ii) $\cos x°$ is negative, so x is in the second or third quadrants.
So $x = 180 - 71$ or $180 + 71$
$= 109$ or 251

EXERCISE 6

Solve these equations, giving answers to the nearest degree, for $0 \leqslant x \leqslant 360$.

1 a $\sin x° = 0.5$ **b** $\cos x° = 0.5$ **c** $\tan x° = 1$

2 a $\sin x° = -0.5$ **b** $\cos x° = -0.5$
  c $\tan x° = -1$

3 a $\sin x° = 0.7$ **b** $\cos x° = 0.2$ **c** $\tan x° = 2$

4 a $2 \sin x° = 0.4$ **b** $4 \cos x° = -3$

5 a $4 \sin x° + 1 = 0$ **b** $3 \tan x° - 2 = 0$

6 a $7 \cos x° - 4 = 0$ **b** $10 \sin x° - 1 = 0$

7 a $5 \tan x° + 12 = 0$ **b** $12 \tan x° - 5 = 0$

8 a $3 \sin x° + 2 = 1$ **b** $4 \cos x° - 2 = 1$

9 Sketch the sine and cosine curves for
$0 \leqslant x \leqslant 360$, and use them to solve:
  a $\sin x° = 1$ **b** $\cos x° = 1$ **c** $\sin x° = -1$
  d $\cos x° = -1$ **e** $\sin x° = 0$ **f** $\cos x° = 0$

10 Remembering that:
  (i) $\sin^2 x° = (\sin x°)^2$, and
  (ii) if $a^2 = 4$, $a = 2$ or -2,
  solve these equations, for $0 \leqslant x \leqslant 360$.
  a $\sin^2 x° = 0.25$ **b** $\cos^2 x° = 0.25$
  c $\tan^2 x° = 81$

11 Solve, for $0 \leqslant x \leqslant 360$:
  a $5 \sin x° - 1 = \sin x°$ **b** $8 \cos x° + 3 = \cos x°$

/ CHALLENGE

As the piston P travels up and down it moves the connecting rod PA, which turns the crankshaft OA. OA = 6 cm, and is horizontal at the start.

a *In the first three turns of OA, how often is A:*
  (i) at the 'top dead centre' B
  (ii) 3 cm to the left of the centre line BOP
  (iii) 4 cm to the right of the centre line?

b *Calculate the angles turned through by OA to the positions in **a**(i), (ii) and (iii), giving angles in (iii) correct to the nearest degree.*

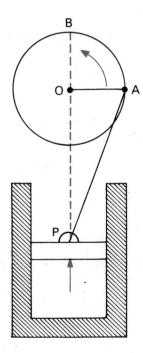

TWO FORMULAE

(i)

$$\frac{\sin A}{\cos A} = \frac{\frac{y}{r}}{\frac{x}{r}}$$

$$= \frac{y}{r} \times \frac{r}{x}$$

$$= \frac{y}{x}$$

$$= \tan A$$

So $\mathbf{\tan A = \dfrac{\sin A}{\cos A}}$

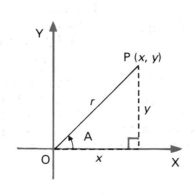

(ii) $\sin^2 A + \cos^2 A$

$$= \left(\frac{y}{r}\right)^2 + \left(\frac{x}{r}\right)^2$$

$$= \frac{y^2}{r^2} + \frac{x^2}{r^2}$$

$$= \frac{y^2 + x^2}{r^2}$$

$$= \frac{r^2}{r^2} \text{ (By Pythagoras' Theorem)}$$

$$= 1$$

So $\mathbf{\sin^2 A + \cos^2 A = 1}$

EXERCISE 7B

1 Check with your calculator that:

a $\dfrac{\sin 50°}{\cos 50°} = \tan 50°$ **b** $\dfrac{\sin 88°}{\cos 88°} = \tan 88°$

c $\sin^2 45° + \cos^2 45° = 1$ **d** $\sin^2 100° + \cos^2 100° = 1$

2 To find $\sin x°$, for $0 \leqslant x \leqslant 90$, when $\cos x° = 0.7$, copy and complete:

$\sin^2 x° + \cos^2 x° = 1$

$\sin^2 x° + 0.7^2 = 1$

$\sin^2 x° = 1 - \ldots$

$\sin x° = \sqrt{\ldots} = \ldots$, correct to 1 decimal place.

3 Calculate $\cos x°$, $0 \leqslant x \leqslant 90$, when:

a $\sin x° = 0.8$ **b** $\sin x° = 0.6$

4 Calculate $\sin x°$, $0 \leqslant x \leqslant 90$, when:

a $\cos x° = 0.4$ **b** $\cos x° = 0.5$

5 Calculate $\tan x°$, $0 \leqslant x < 90$, when $\sin x° = \cos x°$

6 $\sin^2 x° = 0.64$. Calculate:

a $\cos^2 x°$ **b** $\tan^2 x°$

7 To solve the equation $2 \sin x° - 3 \cos x° = 0$, for $0 \leqslant x \leqslant 360$, copy and complete:

$2 \sin x° - 3 \cos x° = 0$

$\dfrac{2 \sin x°}{\cos x°} - \dfrac{3 \cos x°}{\cos x°} = 0 \ (\cos x° \neq 0)$

$2 \tan x° - 3 = 0$

$\tan x° = \ldots$

$x° = \ldots$ or $180° + \ldots$

$\ = \ldots$ or $\ldots$

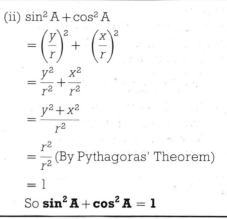

8 Solve, for $0 \leqslant x \leqslant 360$:

a $3 \sin x° - 4 \cos x° = 0$ **b** $\sin x° - \cos x° = 0$

c $\sin x° - 3 \cos x° = 0$ **d** $5 \sin x° = 2 \cos x°$

> **BRAINSTORMER**
>
> Use the formula $\sin^2 A + \cos^2 A = 1$ to prove that:
>
> **a** $5 \sin^2 A + 5 \cos^2 A = 5$
>
> **b** $\sin X \sin^2 A + \sin X \cos^2 A = \sin X$
>
> **c** $(\sin A + \cos A)^2 = 1 + 2 \sin A \cos A$
>
> **d** $(\sin A + \cos A)^2 + (\sin A - \cos A)^2 = 2$
>
> **e** $\cos^2 A - \sin^2 A = 1 - 2 \sin^2 A$
>
> **f** $\cos^2 A - \sin^2 A = 2 \cos^2 A - 1$
>
> **g** $(x \cos A + y \sin A)^2 + (x \sin A - y \cos A)^2 = x^2 + y^2$

**CHECK-UP ON TRIGONOMETRY—
CALCULATIONS, GRAPHS AND
EQUATIONS**

1 Calculate x in each triangle below.

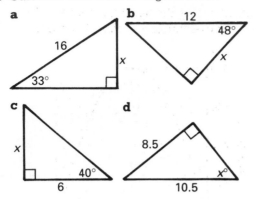

a

16

33°

b

12

48°

x

c

x

40°

6

d

8.5

10.5

$x°$

2 Calculate, to $\frac{1}{10}$ m, the distance
between the points where the
wires are fixed to this mast.

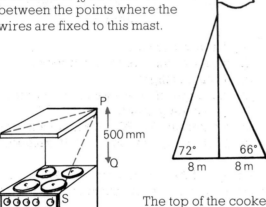

72°   66°

8 m   8 m

3

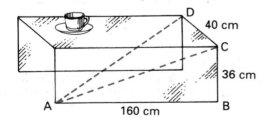

P

500 mm

Q

R

S

500 mm

The top of the cooker
and the hood are
horizontal. Calculate
the angle between the
vertical PQ and:
a PR **b** PS.

4 The glass coffee table has a metal strut from A to
D. Calculate:
a AC **b** AD **c** ∠CAD

D

40 cm

C

36 cm

A

160 cm

B

5 a Sketch the x and y-axes, mark the points
P(8, 6) and Q(−8, 6), and calculate the lengths
of OP and OQ.
b Write down ratios for:
(i) sin XOP, cos XOP, tan XOP
(ii) sin XOQ, cos XOQ, tan XOQ.

6 a Sketch the all-sin-tan-cos quadrant diagram.
b Use it to say whether each of these is positive
or negative:
(i) sin 200° (ii) cos 85° (iii) tan 240°
(iv) cos 323°
c Use your calculator to find the values of (i), (ii),
(iii) and (iv) above, correct to 3 decimal places.

7 Sketch the graphs for $0 \leqslant x \leqslant 360$, of:
a $y = \sin x°$ **b** $y = \sin 2x°$ **c** $y = 2 \sin x°$

8 Sketch the graphs, for $0 \leqslant x \leqslant 360$, of:
$y = \cos x°$ and $y = 2 + \cos x°$ on the same
diagram.

9 Write down the equations of these trigonometric
curves:

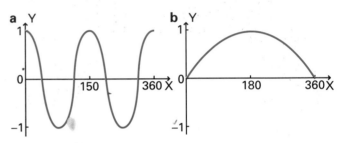

a

b

10 This curve shows the brightness of a double star,
as one star circles in front and behind the other.

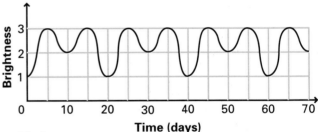

Find:
a the period of the curve
b the maximum and minimum brightnesses.

11 Solve these equations, correct to 0.1, for
$0 \leqslant x \leqslant 360$.
a $\cos x° = 0.7$ **b** $\sin x° = 0.2$
c $\tan x° = -7$ **d** $4 \sin x° = 1$
e $3 \cos x° + 1 = 0$ **f** $5 \tan x° = 8$

12 The equation of this curve is $y = a + b \sin nx°$.
Find a, b and n.

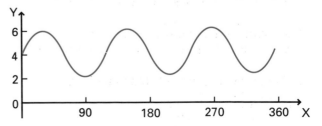

6 QUADRATIC EQUATIONS

LOOKING BACK

1 The hang-glider drifts gently down. Its height, h metres, after t minutes, is given by the formula $h = 30 - 6t$.

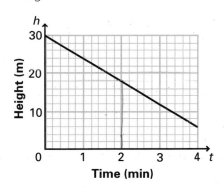

  a Using the graph:
  (i) What is the hang-glider's height after 2 minutes?
  (ii) For how long was it more than 12 m above the ground?

  b Use the formula to calculate the total time of flight.

2 Calculate the value of $2x^2 - 3x + 5$ when:
  a $x = 5$ **b** $x = -2$

3 Solve these equations:
  a $2x = 5$ **b** $3y + 6 = 0$ **c** $4t - 2 = 0$

4 Rearrange in the form $y = mx + c$:
  a $2x + y = 6$ **b** $x - y = 1$ **c** $y - 3x + 4 = 0$

5 Calculate, correct to 1 decimal place:
  a $\dfrac{4 + \sqrt{33}}{2}$ **b** $\dfrac{2 - \sqrt{14}}{6}$

6 The graph shows the height, h metres, of a firework rocket t seconds after it is fired.

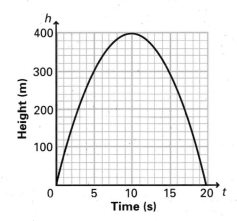

  a Use the graph to find:
  (i) the maximum height of the rocket
  (ii) its time of flight
  (iii) the length of time it was 300 m or more above the ground.
  b Use the formula $h = 80t - 4t^2$ to calculate its height after: (i) 1 second (ii) 16 seconds.

7 The graph of the function $f(x) = x^2 + 2x - 3$ is shown below. For what values of x is $f(x) = 0$?

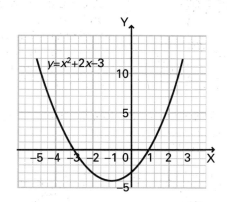

8 Multiply out:
  a $x(x - 2)$ **b** $(y + 1)^2$ **c** $(p - 3)^2$
  d $(t + 1)(t + 3)$ **e** $(u - 3)(u - 2)$ **f** $(v + 1)(v - 4)$

9 Factorise:
  a $x^2 - x$ **b** $2u - 2u^2$ **c** $a^2 - b^2$
  d $x^2 + 4x + 3$ **e** $y^2 - 2y + 1$ **f** $2c^2 + c - 1$

10 Use your calculator to show that if $x^3 = 14$, then:
  a x lies between 2 and 3
  b x lies between 2.4 and 2.5

WHAT IS A QUADRATIC EQUATION?

1 The area of this football pitch can be calculated using the formula $A = x(x+20)$.
If $A = 12\,000$, $x(x+20) = 12\,000$,

$$\text{so } x^2 + 20x - 12\,000 = 0$$

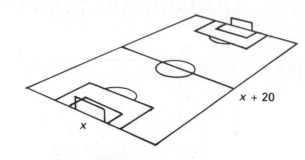

2 The distance travelled by the train can be calculated using the formula $D = t^2 - 5t$.
If $D = 750$, $750 = t^2 - 5t$,

$$\text{so } t^2 - 5t - 750 = 0$$

3 The line $y = 2x + 1$ cuts the curve $y = 3x^2$ at points A and B. The x-coordinates of A and B are given by $3x^2 = 2x + 1$,

$$\text{so } 3x^2 - 2x - 1 = 0.$$

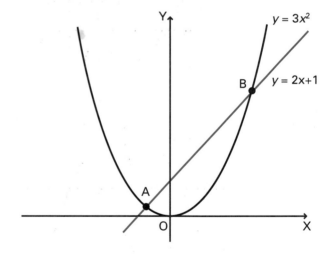

These are all quadratic equations, of the form $ax^2 + bx + c = 0$, $a \neq 0$. They contain second degree terms like x^2 or t^2, and occur widely in mathematics and its applications.

SOLVING QUADRATIC EQUATIONS: (i) USING GRAPHS

Chapter 2 described **quadratic functions** like $f(x) = x^2 + 2x - 3$ and its graph $y = x^2 + 2x - 3$.

To find the solution of the **quadratic equation** $x^2 + 2x - 3 = 0$, you must find the values of x for which $y = 0$, where the graph crosses the x-axis.

At A, $x = -3$, and at B, $x = 1$.

The solution of the quadratic equation $x^2 + 2x - 3 = 0$ is $x = -3$ and 1.

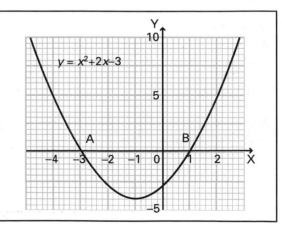

EXERCISE 1

Use the quadratic graphs to solve the quadratic equations in questions **1–3**.

1 Solve
$x^2 - 4x = 0$.

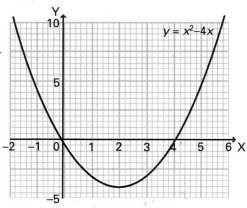

2 Solve
$2x^2 + 3x - 5 = 0$.

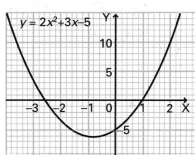

3 Solve
$4 - x^2 = 0$.

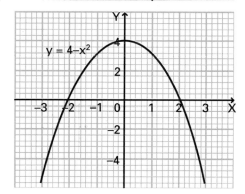

4 It's November 5th. Ranjit sets off a rocket. Its height h metres after time t seconds is given by the formula $h = 18t - 3t^2$.
Write down:
a the values of t when the rocket:
(i) takes off
(ii) lands
b the solution of the quadratic equation $18t - 3t^2 = 0$.

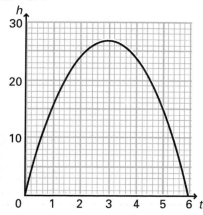

5 This graph is drawn of the flight formula $h = 8t - t^2$. Write down:
a the values of t when the rocket:
(i) takes off   (ii) lands
b the solution of the quadratic equation $8t - t^2 = 0$.

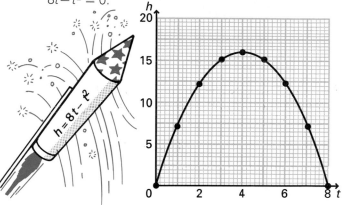

6 The curve on the suspension bridge is part of the parabola $y = x^2 - 2500$ (x is in metres).
a Write down the coordinates of A and B.
b What is the length of the road from P to Q?

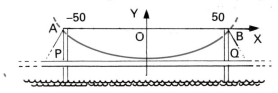

7 The top of a roller coaster is part of the parabola $y = 400 - x^2$ (x is in metres).
a Write down the coordinates of M and N.
b What is the length of the strut MN?

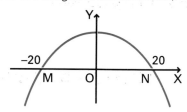

8 a Copy and complete this table. Then use it to draw the parabola $y = x^2 - 8x + 7$.

x	0	1	2			7	8
y	7	0	−5				

b Use your graph to solve the quadratic equation $x^2 - 8x + 7 = 0$.

9 a Draw the graph $y = 5 - x^2$, using $x = -3, -2, -1, 0, 1, 2, 3$.
b Use the graph to solve the equation $5 - x^2 = 0$, correct to 1 decimal place.

71

SOLVING QUADRATIC EQUATIONS: (ii) USING FACTORS

It's obvious!
If $a \times b = 0$
then $a = 0$
or $b = 0$
or a and $b = 0$

Examples
a Solve $(x+3)(2x-1) = 0$.
  $x+3 = 0$ or $2x-1 = 0$
  $x = -3$ or $x = \frac{1}{2}$

b Solve $3t - t^2 = 0$.
  $t(3-t) = 0$ (common factor)
  $t = 0$ or $3-t = 0$
  $t = 0$ or $t = 3$

EXERCISE 2

1 Solve:
  a $x-5 = 0$ **b** $3-y = 0$ **c** $4k = 0$
  d $2x-3 = 0$ **e** $4y+8 = 0$ **f** $3t+4 = 0$

2 Find the *two* values of x in the solution of each equation.
  a $(x-1)(x-2) = 0$ **b** $(x+4)(x-7) = 0$
  c $x(x-8) = 0$ **d** $2x(x+4) = 0$
  e $3x(x+5) = 0$ **f** $(x+3)(x-3) = 0$
  g $x(2x-1) = 0$ **h** $(2x-1)(3x+2) = 0$

3 Solve:
  a $(x+6)(2x-3) = 0$ **b** $6t(1-t) = 0$
  c $(3r+4)(5r-8) = 0$ **d** $(4x-1)(4x+1) = 0$
  e $(x-1)^2 = 0$ **f** $(2y+1)^2 = 0$
  g $(4t+1)(2t+3) = 0$ **h** $(2-3m)(1+2m) = 0$

4 Find the coordinates of the points A and B where these parabolas cross the x-axis.

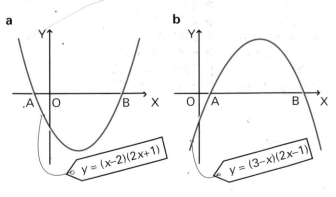

a $y = (x-2)(2x+1)$
b $y = (3-x)(2x-1)$

c $y = x(4-x)$
d $y = (3x+2)(2x-5)$

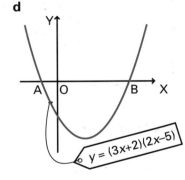

5 Find the coordinates of the points where these parabolas meet the x-axis.
  a $y = (x-1)(2x-9)$ **b** $y = x(5-x)$
  c $y = (3x-2)(2x+5)$ **d** $y = 2(x+7)(3x-5)$
  e $y = x^2$ **f** $y = (x+2)^2$

6 a Find the coordinates of the points where the parabola $y = (x+2)(x-2)$ crosses:
  (i) the x-axis   (ii) the y-axis.
  b Sketch the parabola.

7 Repeat question **6** for the parabola $y = (3+x)(3-x)$.

Reminder (about factorising an expression)

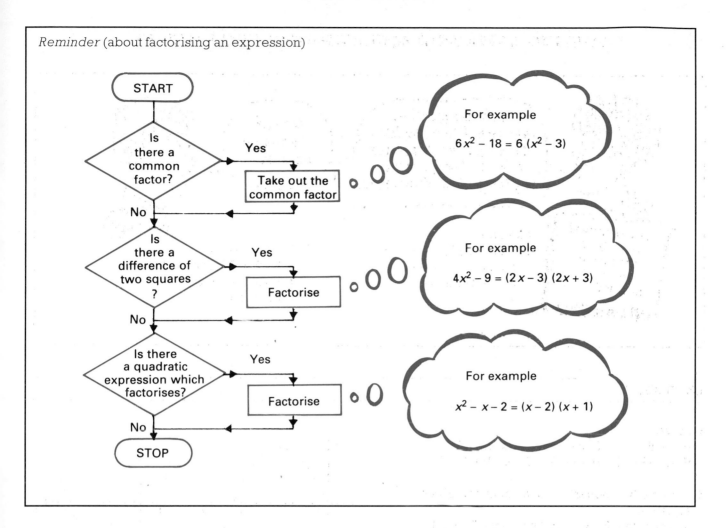

EXERCISE 3A

Common factors

1 Factorise these:

a $3x^2+6$ **b** $5y^2-10$ **c** $6z^2+8$ **d** $4-2k^2$

e $12-12m$ **f** a^2+3a **g** b^2-5b **h** x^2+x

i $2d^2+4d$ **j** $8y-12y^2$ **k** p^2-p **l** $3q^2+9q$

Difference of squares

2 Factorise these:

a x^2-y^2 **b** p^2-q^2 **c** m^2-4 **d** x^2-16

e k^2-1 **f** $4x^2-1$ **g** $9y^2-4$ **h** $16-z^2$

i y^2-100 **j** $16c^2-25$ **k** t^2-81 **l** $4t^2-81$

Quadratic expressions

3 Factorise these:

a x^2+3x+2 **b** $x^2+7x+10$ **c** y^2+2y+1

d y^2+6y+9 **e** a^2-2a+1 **f** $b^2-8b+16$

g c^2-c-6 **h** $d^2+3d-10$ **i** $2x^2+3x+1$

j $3y^2+5y+2$ **k** $2x^2-7x+3$ **l** $8y^2+10y-3$

EXERCISE 3B

1 Factorise:

a $2x^2-3x$ **b** x^2-9 **c** $x^2+8x+16$

d t^2-4t+4 **e** $25x^2-4$ **f** $5x^2+15x$

g a^2-a **h** m^2-2m+1 **i** $9y^2+6y+1$

j $9-4n^2$ **k** $5x-20x^2$ **l** $4x^2-11x+6$

m $6+x-x^2$ **n** $6-y-y^2$ **o** $6-5z+z^2$

2 Factorise—remember to look for a common factor first.

a $2x^2-8$ **b** $5y^2-5$

c $3a^2-3$ **d** $4c^2-36$

e $4x^2+10x+4$ **f** $8y^2+8y+2$

g $2x^2-5x-3$ **h** $6x^2-13x+6$

i $32-2x^2$ **j** $12y^2+10y-12$

k $4t^2+14t-8$ **l** $30a^2+30a-60$

EXERCISE 4A

1 Copy and complete these solutions:

a
$$x^2 + 5x = 0$$
$$x(\ldots) = 0$$
$$x = 0 \text{ or } \ldots = 0$$
$$x = 0 \text{ or } \ldots$$

b
$$y^2 - 16 = 0$$
$$(y-4)(\ldots) = 0$$
$$y - 4 = 0 \text{ or } \ldots$$
$$y = 4 \text{ or } \ldots$$

c
$$2x^2 - 3x - 5 = 0$$
$$(2x-5)(x + \ldots) = 0$$
$$2x - 5 = 0 \text{ or } \ldots$$
$$2x = 5 \text{ or } \ldots$$
$$x = 2\tfrac{1}{2} \text{ or } \ldots$$

d
$$3t^2 - 3 = 0$$
$$3(t^2 - 1) = 0$$
$$3(t-1)(t + \ldots) = 0$$
$$t - 1 = 0 \text{ or } \ldots$$
$$t = 1 \text{ or } \ldots$$

2 Solve these quadratic equations by factorising their left-hand sides first.

a $x^2 - 2x = 0$ **b** $y^2 + y - 2 = 0$
c $a^2 - 9 = 0$ **d** $b^2 - 2b - 8 = 0$
e $k^2 + 6k = 0$ **f** $t^2 - 8t - 20 = 0$
g $u^2 + 9u = 0$ **h** $6x^2 - 6 = 0$
i $m^2 - 3m + 2 = 0$ **j** $x^2 - 7x + 12 = 0$
k $c^2 - 6c + 5 = 0$ **l** $x^2 - x - 6 = 0$
m $r^2 + 2r - 15 = 0$ **n** $x^2 + 5x + 4 = 0$
o $16 - x^2 = 0$ **p** $4x^2 - 1 = 0$
q $2y^2 - y = 0$ **r** $5m^2 - 2m = 0$
s $x^2 + 10x + 21 = 0$ **t** $9 - 6y + y^2 = 0$
u $100 + 20z + z^2 = 0$ **v** $2t^2 - 5t + 2 = 0$
w $2a^2 + 5a - 3 = 0$ **x** $2x^2 - 5x + 3 = 0$

EXERCISE 4B

1 Find the coordinates of the points where these parabolas cross the x-axis.

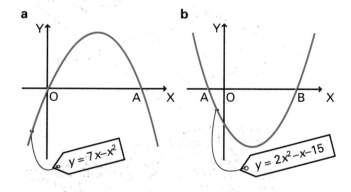

a $y = 7x - x^2$

b $y = 2x^2 - x - 15$

2 Find the coordinates of the points where these parabolas meet the x-axis.

a $y = x^2 - 9$ **b** $y = 4x - x^2$
c $y = 6x^2 - x - 2$ **d** $y = (4x - 3)^2$

3 The road surface is cambered (curved) to let water run away. The equation of the curve is $y = 21 + 4x - x^2$, where y is in millimetres and x is in metres.

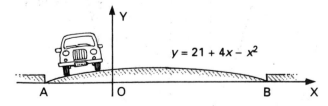

$y = 21 + 4x - x^2$

a Solve the equation $21 + 4x - x^2 = 0$ to find the points A and B where the road meets the kerbs.
b How wide is the road?

4 The curve on a satellite dish has equation $y = x^2 - 1600$. The pick-up point P(0, 30) is held by two arms AP and BP (units are cm).

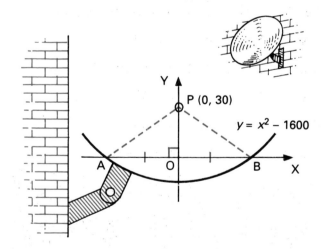

P (0, 30)

$y = x^2 - 1600$

a Solve the equation $x^2 - 1600 = 0$ to find A and B.
b Use Pythagoras' Theorem to calculate the length of AP.

5 Solve these quadratic equations:

a $2x^2 + 5x + 3 = 0$ **b** $3y^2 - 10y + 3 = 0$
c $9x^2 + 6x + 1 = 0$ **d** $6y^2 - 5y + 1 = 0$
e $2x^2 - 2x = 0$ **f** $2x^2 - 18 = 0$
g $2x^2 - 2x - 4 = 0$ **h** $2x^2 = 0$

6 Solve:

a $4x^2 + 8x + 3 = 0$ **b** $10 + y - 2y^2 = 0$
c $25 - 10z + z^2 = 0$ **d** $3y^2 + 12y + 12 = 0$
e $5w^2 - 30w + 45 = 0$ **f** $2x^2 + 6x - 56 = 0$

SKETCHING A PARABOLA

Example

Sketch the parabola $y = x^2 - 2x - 3$.

a If $x = 0$, $y = -3$ (A)
b If $y = 0$, $x^2 - 2x - 3 = 0$
$(x + 1)(x - 3) = 0$
$x = -1$ or 3 (B, C)
c The axis of symmetry is the line $x = 1$.
d When $x = 1$, $y = 1^2 - 2 \times 1 - 3 = -4$, so the minimum turning point is D(1, -4).

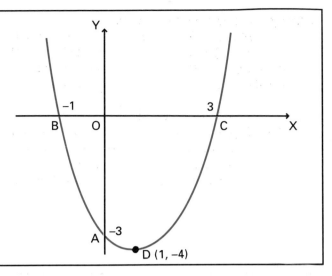

EXERCISE 5

Sketch the following parabolas, by first finding:
 (i) where they cut the axes
 (ii) their axes of symmetry
 (iii) their maximum or minimum turning points.

1 a $y = x^2 - 2x$ **b** $y = 6x - x^2$

2 a $y = x^2 - 2x - 8$ **b** $y = 3 - 2x - x^2$

3 a $y = 9 - x^2$ **b** $y = (x + 1)^2$

4 a $y = (5 - 2x)^2$ **b** $y = x^2 + 4$

5 a $y = 6x^2 - x - 2$ **b** $y = 4x - 6x^2$

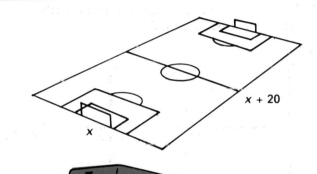

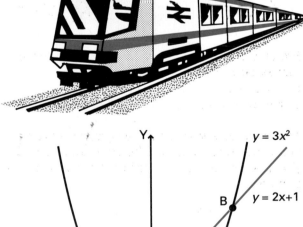

CHALLENGE

Solve the three quadratic equations in the section headed 'What is a quadratic equation?' on page 70. Then find the dimensions of the pitch, the time of travel and the coordinates of A and B.

THE STANDARD FORM OF A QUADRATIC EQUATION

The standard form of a quadratic equation is $ax^2 + bx + c = 0, a \neq 0$. Before solving any quadratic equation, make sure that it is in standard form.

Example
Solve $x(2x-3) = -1$
$2x^2 - 3x = -1$
$2x^2 - 3x + 1 = 0$ ... standard form
$(2x-1)(x-1) = 0$
$x = \frac{1}{2}$ or 1

EXERCISE 6

1 Rearrange each equation in standard form, $ax^2 + bx + c = 0$, then solve it:
a $x^2 + 5x = -4$ **b** $x^2 - 2x = 8$
c $x^2 - 7x = -6$ **d** $x^2 + x = 12$
e $x^2 = x$ **f** $x^2 = 4$
g $x^2 = 12x - 36$ **h** $x^2 = -8x - 15$
i $3x^2 + 3 = 10x$ **j** $x^2 + 4 = 4x$
k $1 + 6x^2 = 5x$ **l** $4x^2 + 1 = 5x$

2 Rearrange, then solve, these equations.
a $x^2 - x - 1 = x + 2$ **b** $2x^2 - x = 2x - 1$
c $x^2 - 5x + 6 = 2 - x$ **d** $x^2 + 3x - 1 = 2x + 11$

3 The equation of the model bridge support is $y = 41 + 6x - x^2$, and the equation of the road is $y = 1$ (x and y are in centimetres).

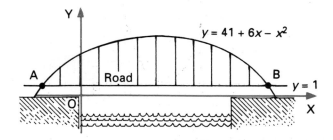

a Rearrange the equation $41 + 6x - x^2 = 1$ to find the points A and B.
b What is the length of the road AB on the model?

4 On this plan, the cross-section of *SS Surprise* is a parabola with equation $y = x^2 - 8x + 12$. Use:
a $y = 0$ to find points A and B on the waterline
b $y = 5$ to find points C and D where the deck meets the hull.

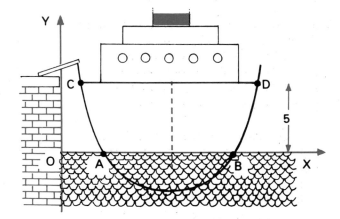

5 Multiply out the brackets, rearrange the terms and then solve these equations.
a $x(x+4) = 32$ **b** $x(x-5) = 24$
c $4x(x+1) = 15$ **d** $(x+2)(x+3) = 6$
e $(x+1)^2 = 1$ **f** $x^2 + (x-1)^2 = 1$
g $(2x-3)^2 = 4$ **h** $(x-3)(2x+3) = 5$

6 Solve:
a $(m+1)(m-1) = 5(m+1)$
b $(y+1)(3y-2) = y+1$
c $(2t+3)(3-t) = 2(t-3)$
d $(p+1)^2 + 6(p+1) + 8 = 0$

SOLVING QUADRATIC EQUATIONS: (iii) USING A FORMULA

The solution (or roots) of the quadratic equation $ax^2 + bx + c = 0$ can be found by using the **quadratic formula**

$$x = \frac{-b + \sqrt{b^2 - 4ac}}{2a} \text{ or } \frac{-b - \sqrt{b^2 - 4ac}}{2a}$$

$$\boxed{x = \frac{-b \pm \sqrt{b^2 - 4ac}}{2a}}$$

(In the Investigation on page 78, you can discover how to work out this formula.)

Example Solve the equation $2x^2 - 5x - 1 = 0$

$$2x^2 - 5x - 1 = 0$$

Compare $ax^2 + bx + c = 0$

$$a = 2, b = -5, c = -1$$
$$\sqrt{b^2 - 4ac} = 5.74, \text{ to 2 decimal places}$$

$$x = \frac{-(-5) + 5.74}{2 \times 2} \text{ or } \frac{-(-5) - 5.74}{2 \times 2}$$

$= 2.7$ or -0.2, correct to 1 decimal place.

EXERCISE 7A

1 Solve each of these quadratic equations:
(i) using factors (ii) using the formula.
  a $x^2 + 3x + 2 = 0$ **b** $x^2 + 6x + 8 = 0$
  c $x^2 + 3x - 4 = 0$ **d** $x^2 + 4x - 12 = 0$
  e $x^2 - 3x + 2 = 0$ **f** $x^2 - 5x + 6 = 0$
  g $x^2 - x - 2 = 0$ **h** $x^2 - 2x - 8 = 0$

2 Use the quadratic formula to solve these equations. Give the solutions correct to 1 decimal place.
  a $x^2 + 2x - 1 = 0$ **b** $x^2 - 5x + 2 = 0$
  c $2x^2 + 8x + 1 = 0$ **d** $2x^2 - 5x + 1 = 0$
  e $3x^2 - 4x - 5 = 0$ **f** $4x^2 - x - 1 = 0$
  g $2x^2 + 3x - 4 = 0$ **h** $5x^2 - 8x + 2 = 0$

3 (i) Solve each equation below, using factors and the formula, where possible.
 (ii) Explain the connection between the solution and the graph in each case.
  a Graph $y = 2x^2 + 3x - 5$
    Solve $2x^2 + 3x - 5 = 0$

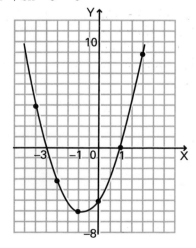

b Graph $y = 4x^2 - 12x + 9$
   Solve $4x^2 - 12x + 9 = 0$

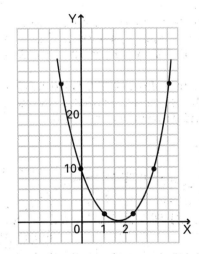

c Graph $y = 4x^2 - 4x + 5$
   Solve $4x^2 - 4x + 5 = 0$

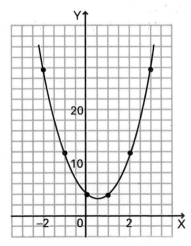

EXERCISE 7B

1 Rearrange each equation in standard form, and solve it, correct to 1 decimal place.

a $x^2 + 8x = 16$ **b** $x^2 = 12x + 5$

c $1 - x - x^2 = 0$ **d** $5 = 3x(x+1)$

e $7 - 4x^2 = 0$ **f** $4x^2 = 3(4x+5)$

g $(x+1)(x-1) = 6$ **h** $(2x+3)^2 = 2$

2 Find the x-coordinates of A and B, correct to 2 significant figures.

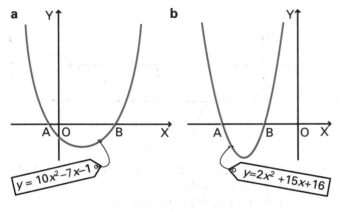

a $y = 10x^2 - 7x - 1$

b $y = 2x^2 + 15x + 16$

3 a Copy and complete the table of values for $y = 2x^2 + 3x - 7$ for $x = -4$ to $x = 2$.

x	-4	-3			1	2
y	13	2			-2	7

b Draw the graph $y = 2x^2 + 3x - 7$.

c Solve the equation $2x^2 + 3x - 7 = 0$, giving x correct to 2 significant figures by means of:
(i) the graph   (ii) the formula.

INVESTIGATION

1 Copy and complete the lines below to investigate the method of 'Completing the Square' for solving quadratic equations.

$$x^2 - 6x + 1 = 0$$
$$x^2 - 6x = \ldots$$
$$x^2 - 6x + (-3)^2 = \ldots + \ldots \text{ (Add ($\frac{1}{2}$ coefficient}$$
$$(x-3)^2 = \ldots \qquad \text{of x)}^2 \text{ to each side)}$$
$$x - 3 = \pm\sqrt{8}$$
$$x = 3 \pm \sqrt{8} = \ldots \text{ or} \ldots$$

2 Solve these equations, correct to 1 decimal place, by 'Completing the Square'.

a $x^2 + 2x - 8 = 0$ **b** $x^2 - 2x - 3 = 0$

c $x^2 + 4x + 1 = 0$ **d** $x^2 - 6x + 3 = 0$

e $2x^2 + 6x - 1 = 0$ *(Divide each term by 2 first.)*

---

3 *As a real challenge complete the square for*

$$ax^2 + bx + c = 0 \text{ to get } x = \frac{-b \pm \sqrt{b^2 - 4ac}}{2a}.$$

Begin $ax^2 + bx + c = 0$

$$x^2 + \frac{b}{a}x = -\frac{c}{a}$$

Add $\left(\dfrac{b}{2a}\right)^2$ *to each side* ......

BRAINSTORMER

The arches of this unique bridge are arcs of circles with radii as follows:

5 m for arches 1 and 2;

13 m for arch 3;

39 m for arch 4.

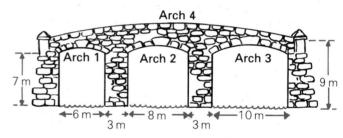

Find the maximum clearance for arches 1, 2 and 3, and the maximum height of arch 4 above the river.

Hint: using Pythagoras' Theorem, $(5-x)^2 + 3^2 = 5^2$.

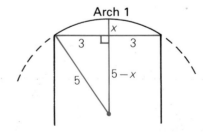

Arch 1

Go on to show that the maximum clearance above the river for arch 1 is 8 m.

Then try the other parts of the problem.

STRAIGHT LINES AND PARABOLAS

Example
Find the coordinates of the points where the
line $y = x + 1$ cuts the parabola $y = x^2 - 5x + 6$.
At the points of intersection, A and B,
$y = x^2 - 5x + 6$ *and* $y = x + 1$

So $x^2 - 5x + 6 = x + 1$
$x^2 - 6x + 5 = 0$
$(x - 1)(x - 5) = 0$
$x = 1$ or 5
$y = x + 1 = 2$ or 6

A is the point $(1, 2)$ and B is $(5, 6)$.

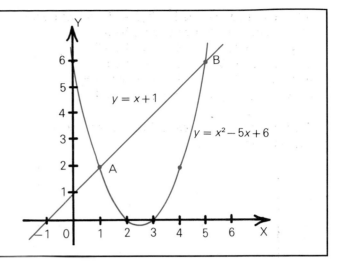

EXERCISE 8

1 Another rocket is set off on Bonfire Night. Find the
times at which it is at a height of 12 m by:
a noting where the line $h = 12$ cuts the parabola
$h = 8t - t^2$
b solving the quadratic equation $8t - t^2 = 12$.

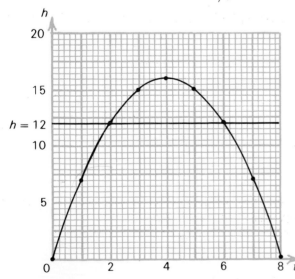

2 Find the times when the rocket in question **1** is at
heights of:
a 7 m   **b** 15 m   **c** 16 m.

3 Find the coordinates of the points where the lines
meet the parabolas by:
  (i) reading them from the graphs
  (ii) forming quadratic equations, and solving
    them.

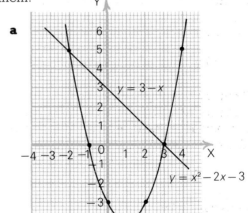

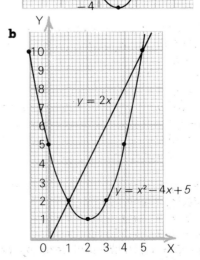

4 Find the coordinates of the points of intersection of these straight lines and parabolas.

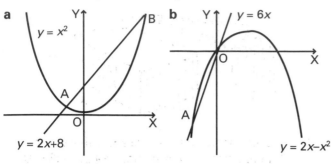

a $y = x^2$, $y = 2x+8$

b $y = 6x$, $y = 2x-x^2$

5 A machine robot is programmed to cut along the line $y = x$ from O to A, then along the parabola to B, finally back to O. Find the coordinates of the points that must be programmed into it.

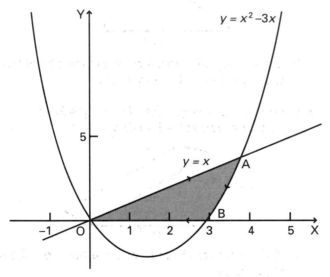

$y = x^2 - 3x$

$y = x$

6 The equation of the reflector on the electric fire is $y = x^2 - 25$, and that of the guard is $y = 5 - x$.

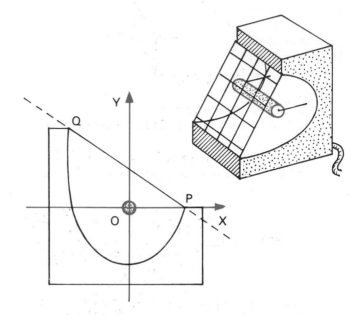

a Make an equation, and solve it to find points P and Q (units are centimetres).

b Use Pythagoras' Theorem to find the length of PQ, to the nearest cm.

QUADRATIC EQUATIONS AS MATHEMATICAL MODELS

EXERCISE 9

1 The length of this roll of carpet is 3 metres more than its breadth. Its area is 18 m².

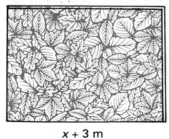

x m

$x + 3$ m

Area = 18 m²

a Show that $x^2 + 3x - 18 = 0$.

b Find the length and breadth of the carpet.

2 Another roll has an area of 60 m², and its length is 4 metres more than its breadth, x m.

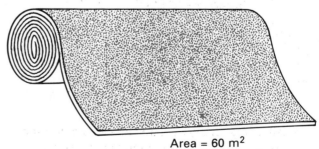

Area = 60 m²

a Show that $x^2 + 4x - 60 = 0$.

b Find the length and breadth of the carpet.

3 The volume of this metal box is 20 cm³.

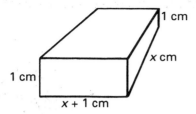

1 cm

x cm

1 cm

x + 1 cm

a Show that $x^2 + x - 20 = 0$.
b Calculate the length and breadth of the box.

4 When a clay pigeon is fired upwards, its height h metres after t seconds is given by the formula $h = 18t - 5t^2$.

a To find t when $h = 9$, make an equation and solve it.
b Why are there two answers?

5 Up goes the flare to mark the start of a balloon flight. After t seconds the height of the flare is $50t - t^2$ metres, and the height of the balloon is $11t$ metres.

a After how many seconds are they at the same height? (Make an equation and solve it.)
b How can you tell that they start at the same height?

6 Calculate the length and breadth of this goods container, given that its volume is 80 m³.

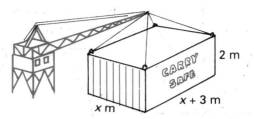

2 m

CARRY SAFE

x + 3 m

x m

7 a Apply Pythagoras' Theorem to this triangle to find the quadratic equation $x^2 + 2x - 48 = 0$.

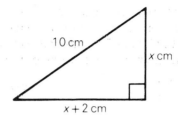

10 cm

x cm

x + 2 cm

b Use the equation to calculate the lengths of the two sides about the right angle.

8 a Look at this wedge, then form a quadratic equation, and solve it to find x.

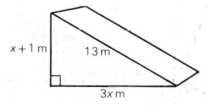

x + 1 m   13 m

3x m

b Write down the lengths of the sides about the right angle.
c If the wedge is 2 cm thick, calculate its volume.

9 The sum, S, of n terms of $1 + 2 + 3 + \ldots + n$ is given by the formula $S = \frac{1}{2}n(n+1)$.
a Check the formula for $n = 1, 2$ and 3.
b Find n when $S = 55$:
   (i) by adding terms
   (ii) using a quadratic equation.
c Repeat **b** for $S = 210$.

10 An aluminium strip 16 cm wide is bent to form a gutter. The area of the rectangular end is 32 cm².

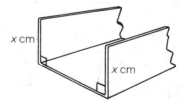

x cm

x cm

a Express the width of the end in terms of x.
b Form a quadratic equation, and calculate the height and width of the gutter.

TRIAL AND IMPROVEMENT

Give a computer an approximate root of an equation, and in a flash it will give you as accurate a value as you wish. Here is one of the methods it uses.

From the graph, approximate roots of the equation $x^2 + x - 4 = 0$ at A and B lie between -2 and -3, and between 1 and 2.
Find a better approximation for the root at B.

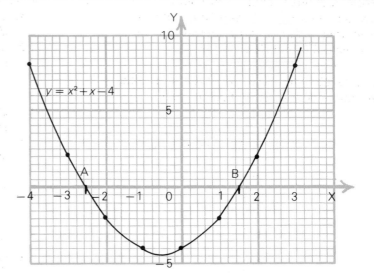

Step-by-step

If f is the function defined by $f(x) = x^2 + x - 4$, then
$f(1) = 1^2 + 1 - 4 = -2$ (curve below x-axis)
$f(2) = 2^2 + 2 - 4 = 2$ (curve above x-axis)
the root lies between 1 and 2.

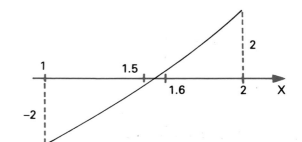

$f(1.5) = 1.5^2 + 1.5 - 4 = -0.25$ (below x-axis)
$f(1.6) = 1.6^2 + 1.6 - 4 = 0.16$ (above x-axis)
the root lies between 1.5 and 1.6

$f(1.55) = 1.55^2 + 1.55 - 4 \doteqdot -0.05$ (below)
$f(1.56) = 1.56^2 + 1.56 - 4 \doteqdot -0.01$ (below)
$f(1.57) = 1.57^2 + 1.57 - 4 \doteqdot 0.03$ (above)
the root lies between 1.56 and 1.57 → 1.6, correct to 1 decimal place

$f(1.565) = 1.565^2 + 1.565 - 4 \doteqdot 0.014$ (above the x-axis)
the root lies between 1.56 and 1.565 → 1.56, correct to 2 decimal places

From the symmetry of the graph about $x = -0.5$, the other root is -2.56, correct to 2 decimal places.

This trial and improvement is an example of **iteration**. An iterative process produces approximations which become more and more accurate.

EXERCISE 10

1 Prove that one root of the equation $x^2 + x - 3 = 0$ lies between 1 and 2; then find it, correct to 1 decimal place. (Let $f(x) = x^2 + x - 3$, and calculate $f(1)$ and $f(2)$, etc.).

2 Use iteration to find the positive root of each equation, correct to 1 decimal place.

a

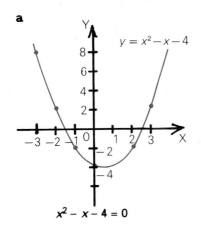

$y = x^2 - x - 4$

$x^2 - x - 4 = 0$

b

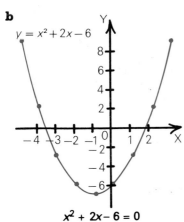

$y = x^2 + 2x - 6$

$x^2 + 2x - 6 = 0$

3 Use iteration to find the root of $x^3 - 3x + 1 = 0$ (correct to 1 decimal place) that lies between:
  a 1 and 2
  b 0 and 1
  c -2 and -1

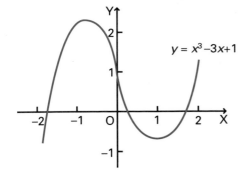

$y = x^3 - 3x + 1$

4 Show that:
  a $x = 1$ is a solution of the equation $x^3 - 3x^2 + 2 = 0$
  b there is another solution of the equation between $x = 2$ and $x = 3$, and find it, correct to 1 decimal place.

5 a Show that the equation $x^3 - x^2 + x + 1 = 0$ has a root between -1 and 0.
  b Use iteration to find the root, correct to 3 significant figures.

6 a Find, in standard form, a quadratic equation whose solution is the x-coordinates of the points of intersection of the line $y = 2x$ and the parabola $y = x^2 - 6x + 11$.
  b One root of the equation lies between 6 and 7. Find it, correct to 3 significant figures, using iteration.

7 The height, h metres, of a toy space rocket t seconds after firing, is given by the function $h(t) = 3t - t^3$.

Show that the rocket reaches a height of 1 metre between $t = 0.3$ and $t = 0.4$, and use iteration to find this time, correct to 2 decimal places.

8 Find, correct to 3 significant figures, the solution of the equation $x^3 - 2x + 3 = 0$ which lies between -1 and -2.

CHECK-UP ON QUADRATIC EQUATIONS

1 Use the graph $h = 6t - t^2$ to solve these equations:
a $6t - t^2 = 0$ **b** $6t - t^2 = 5$
c $6t - t^2 = 9$ **d** $6t - t^2 = 8$
e $6t - t^2 = 7$, correct to 1 decimal place.

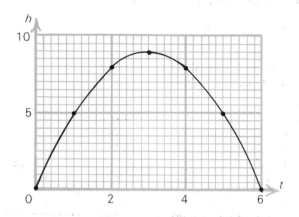

2 Solve:
a $(x-1)(x+5) = 0$ **b** $y(y+1) = 0$
c $x^2 - 3x = 0$ **d** $y^2 - 25 = 0$
e $(x+9)(2x+1) = 0$ **f** $x^2 - x - 6 = 0$
g $4y^2 - 4y + 1 = 0$ **h** $2y^2 - 7y - 4 = 0$.

3 Arrange the following equations in standard form, then solve them.
a $x^2 - 2x = 3$ **b** $y(y-4) = 21$
c $6(x^2 + 1) = 13x$ **d** $(3x-1)^2 = 4$

4 Make a quadratic equation for each diagram below, and find x.

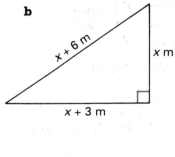

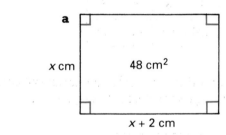

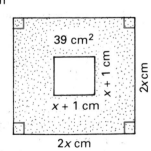

5 Find the coordinates of the points of intersection of these straight lines and parabolas.

a

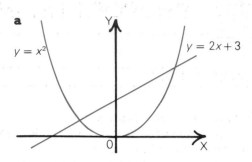

b

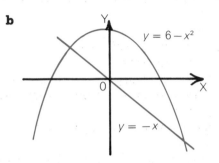

c $y = x^2 + 3x - 4$

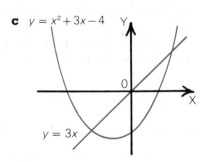

6 Solve these equations, giving the solutions correct to 1 decimal place.
a $x^2 - 6x - 6 = 0$ **b** $x^2 - 8 = x$
c $(x+1)^2 = 3$ **d** $9x^2 + 6x - 4 = 0$

7 *Sketch* these parabolas:
a $y = x^2 - 8x + 12$ **b** $y = 5 - 4x - x^2$

8 The parabola with equation $y = 2x^2 + 3x - 7$ cuts the x-axis between $x = 1$ and 2, and between $x = -2$ and -3.
Use iteration to find the roots of $2x^2 + 3x - 7 = 0$ correct to 1 decimal place.

9 An electronic probe travels into the depths of the ocean. Its depth, d km, after time t hours, is given by the formula $d(t) = t^3 + 2t^2 - 7t - 3$.
a Show that the probe surfaces after 2.0 to 2.2 hours.
b Use iteration to find the time it surfaces, to the nearest: (i) $\frac{1}{100}$ hour   (ii) minute.

7 PROPORTION IN PRACTICE

LOOKING BACK

1 Which of the following illustrate:
  a direct proportion (for example, 'double one quantity, double the other')
  b inverse proportion ('double one, halve the other')
  c neither?
  (i) the radius of a circle and its circumference
  (ii) the number of painters on the Forth Bridge and the number of days needed to paint it
  (iii) the speed in running a mile and the time taken
  (iv) the heights of people and their weights
  (v) the number of steps climbed and the increase in height
  (vi) the price of a litre of milk and the number of litres that can be bought for £5.

2 List the entries in the second row of each table.

  a Direct proportion: TV rental £8 a month.

Number of months	3	6	9	12	15
Total cost (£)					

  b Inverse proportion: Total cost of party £50.

Number at party	1	2	5	10	25
Cost per person (£)					

3 Solve these equations for k:
  a $20 = 5k$ **b** $4 = 8k$ **c** $4 = \dfrac{k}{3}$ **d** $5 = \dfrac{k}{0.2}$.

4 $y = x^2$. Calculate:
  a y, when $x = 9$
  b x, when $y = 16$, given $x > 0$.

5 $s = \dfrac{32}{t}$. Calculate:
  a s, when $t = 8$ **b** t, when $s = 2$.

6 Sketch the graphs, for $x > 0$, of:
  a $y = x$ **b** $y = \dfrac{1}{x}$.

7 Write down the gradients and equations of: **a** OA **b** OB.

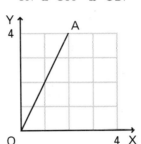
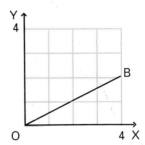

8 $q = 3$ and $r = 4$. Calculate p, if:
  a $p = \dfrac{5qr}{6}$ **b** $p = q\sqrt{r}$ **c** $p = \dfrac{8q}{r}$.

9 Which table has quantities in direct proportion, and which in inverse proportion?

  a

x	1	2	3	4	5
y	1.5	3	4.5	6	7.5

  b

x	1	2	3	4	5
y	240	120	80	60	48

10 An electric amplifier multiplies the input voltage v to produce a greater output voltage V, i.e. $V = kv$.

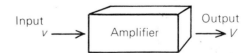

An experiment provides this data:

Input (v volts)	1	2	3	4	5	6
Output (V volts)	5	9	16	20	24	30

  a Plot the points, and draw the best-fitting straight line through the origin.
  b Write down:
    (i) the gradient (ii) the equation, of the line.

EXPERIMENT AND THEORY

In science, medicine, economics, business and many kinds of research it is often necessary to find whether or not two quantities are related. A theory is put forward, and then tested by experiment. Mathematical models in the form of graphs and equations are used to test the relationship between the quantities. Here are three famous examples from science.

a In the nineteenth century, George Ohm, a German scientist, investigated the relationship between the **current** I and **voltage** V in an electrical circuit.

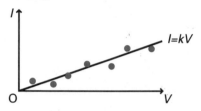

b In the seventeenth century, Isaac Newton studied the connection between the **force** F on a body and the **acceleration** a it produced.

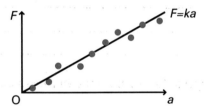

c Another seventeenth-century scientist, Robert Hooke, looked at the relationship between the **tension** T in a spring and its **extension** E.

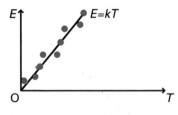

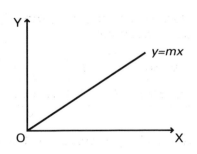

The work of all three scientists is summed up in the graph on the right. The quantities they studied are connected by straight line graphs which pass through the origin.

From Chapter 1, you know that the equation of a straight line is $y = mx + c$. Here $c = 0$, so all these graphs have equations of the form $y = mx$, for example $y = 2x$, $y = \frac{1}{2}x$, $y = -x$ and so on.

x and y behave in the same way—if you double one, you double the other; halve one, halve the other, etc.

y is directly proportional to x, or y varies directly as x.
$y \propto x$, or $y = kx$, where k is a constant.

DIRECT PROPORTION (OR VARIATION)

There are many other situations where one quantity is directly proportional to another. Here is an example.

Number of packets (N)	1	2	3	4
Cost (C p)	30	60	90	120

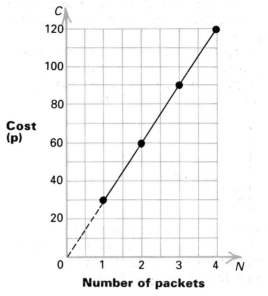

The points lie on a straight line through O.
So the cost is directly proportional to the number of packets.
$C \propto N$, or $C = kN$, where k is a constant.
The gradient of the line $= \frac{30}{1} = \frac{60}{2} = \frac{90}{3} = \ldots = 30$.
So the equation is $C = 30N$. (Compare $y = mx$.)
Direct proportion, or direct variation, can be checked by:
 (i) **drawing a graph**
(ii) **calculating gradient ratios.**

EXERCISE 1

1 Is the cost of these books proportional to the number purchased?

Number of books (N)	5	10	15	20	25
Cost (£C)	35	70	105	140	175

  a Check by calculating values of the ratio $\dfrac{C}{N}$.

  b $C \propto N$, or $C = kN$. What is:
    (i) the value of k
    (ii) the equation connecting C and N?

2 Do these earnings vary directly as the number of hours worked?

Hours (H)	7	14	28	35	40
Earnings (£E)	35	70	140	175	200

  a Check by calculating values of $\dfrac{E}{H}$.

  b $E \propto H$, or $E = kH$. What is:
    (i) the value of k
    (ii) the equation connecting E and H?

3 a Use the graph to list the interest entries in this table.

Principal (£P)	0	100	200	300	400
Interest (£I)		5			

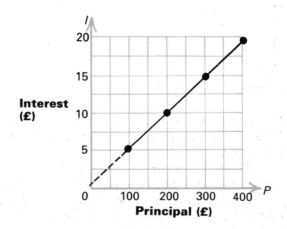

  b How does the graph show that the interest is directly proportional to the principal?

  c Copy and complete: $I = \ldots P$.

4 Instead of the usual Christmas tree price list, Jeff Jones of the Forestry Commission put this graph in the sales shed.

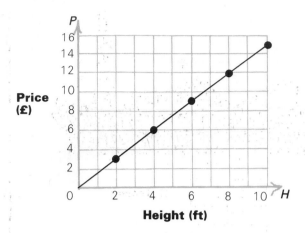

Height (ft)

a Jeff claims that his price (£P) is proportional to the height (H feet) of a tree. Do you agree? Give a reason.
b Find a formula for P in terms of H.
c Calculate:
   (i) the cost of a tree 30 ft high
   (ii) the height of a tree which costs £30.

5 Which of these are examples of direct variation?
   a 1 cassette costs £4, 2 cassettes cost £7.
   b 2 bus fares cost 80p, 3 fares for the same journey cost 120p.
   c 1 raffle ticket costs 10p, a book of 10 tickets cost 50p.
   d 3 periods last 165 minutes, 5 periods last 275 minutes.

6 Does the angle through which the minute hand of a clock turns vary directly with the time?

   a Copy and complete this table:

Time passed (T minutes)	15	30	45	60
Angle turned ($A°$)				

   b Answer the question by:
   (i) using a graph   (ii) calculating ratios.
   c Find a formula for A in terms of T.

7 The results of an experiment to verify Robert Hooke's law are:

Tension (T newtons)	0	1	2	3	4	5	6
Extension (E mm)	0	6	10	14	20	26	30

   a Plot the points, using these axes and scales.

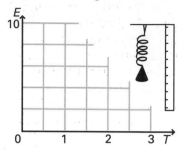

   b Draw the best-fitting line through the origin.
   c Write down the relation between E and T which best fits the data:
   (i) as an equation, $E = \ldots T$ (ii) in words.

8 The results of an experiment to verify one of Newton's 'laws of motion' are:

Acceleration (a m/s²)	0	5	10	15	20	25	30
Force (F newtons)	0	0.4	0.8	1.1	1.6	2.1	2.4

   a Plot the points, using these axes and scales.

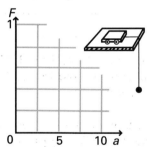

   b Draw the best-fitting line through the origin.
   c Write down the relation between F and a which best fits the data:
   (i) as an equation, $F = \ldots a$ (ii) in words.

9 The results of an experiment which verifies 'Ohm's law' are:

Voltage (V volts)	0	2	4	6	8	10
Current (I amps)	0	0.7	1.3	2.2	2.8	3.5

   a Plot the points on squared paper.
   b Draw the best-fitting straight line.
   c Write down the relation between the current and the voltage:
   (i) as an equation   (ii) in words.

MAKING AND USING PROPORTION MODELS

Example
The *Silver Star* leaves for the fishing grounds at 02 00, and by 02 50 she has sailed 15 km. Her skipper knows that the distance from port (D km) is proportional to the sailing time (T minutes).
a Find a formula connecting T and D.
b Use the formula to estimate how long the boat will take to reach the fishing grounds, which are 84 km distant.

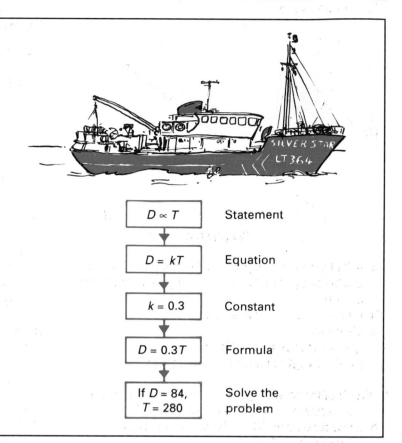

a D is proportional to T, so $D = kT$.
  When $T = 50$, $D = 15$, so $15 = 50k$
$$k = \frac{15}{50} = 0.3$$
  and $\boldsymbol{D = 0.3T}$.

b When $D = 84$, $84 = 0.3T$
$$T = \frac{84}{0.3} = 280.$$

The estimated time to reach the fishing grounds is 4 hours 40 minutes.

$D \propto T$	Statement
$D = kT$	Equation
$k = 0.3$	Constant
$D = 0.3T$	Formula
If $D = 84$, $T = 280$	Solve the problem

EXERCISE 2A

---

1 W is proportional to I. When $W = 1000$, $I = 4$.
  a Find a formula connecting W and I.
  b Calculate W when $I = 3$.

2 The time (T minutes) to serve school lunches varies as the number (N) of pupils taking lunch. When $T = 40$, $N = 200$.
  a Find a formula connecting T and N.
  b Calculate T when $N = 260$.

3 The cost of plate glass for shop windows (£C) varies directly as the area (A m^2). The cost of 2 m^2 is £12.
  a Find a formula connecting C and A.
  b Calculate the cost of 5 m^2 of glass.

4 Electricians know that for copper wire of given cross-section the electrical resistance (R ohms) is proportional to the length of the wire (L metres). For example, 100 m of a certain wire has a resistance of 10 ohms.
  a Find a formula connecting R and L.
  b Calculate the resistance of 88 m of wire.

5 Jennifer Lawson travels for a fabric firm. She notices that the cost of petrol she uses (£P) is proportional to the distance (D km) she travels.

On Monday 12th October she clocked up 300 km, and spent £12 on petrol.
a Construct a formula connecting P and D.
b Calculate the cost of petrol for a journey of 450 km.

6 In silver plating, the number of grams (N) of silver deposited is proportional to the number of minutes (M) the current flows. 3 g of silver are deposited in 45 minutes.
a Find the formula connecting N and M.
b Calculate the time required for a deposit of 5 g.

7 The manageress of the local supermarket guesses that the weekly takings (£T) vary directly as the number of customers (N). During one week, 550 customers spent £4950. Assuming her 'model' is a good one:
a construct a formula connecting T and N
b estimate the takings in a week when the supermarket had 720 customers
c how many customers were there in a week when £11 700 was spent?

EXERCISE 2B

Example
A new car is being tested. The distance (d metres) it travels is proportional to the square of the time (t seconds) taken. In 3 seconds it travels 18 metres.

(i) Find a formula connecting d and t.

  d is proportional to t^2, so $d = kt^2$.
  When $t = 3$, $d = 18$, so $18 = k \times 9$
  $$k = \tfrac{18}{9} = 2$$
  $$\text{and } d = 2t^2$$

(ii) How far will the car travel in 5 seconds?

  When $t = 5$, $d = 2 \times 25 = 50$.
  In 5 seconds the car will travel 50 m.

---

1 Use the symbol $\propto$ to express the relationships in **a–d**, and then write down an equation for each.
a The profit (£P) is proportional to the number (N) of articles sold.
b The distance travelled down a slide (d metres) is proportional to the square of the time (t seconds) in motion.
c The volume (V cm³) of a sphere varies directly as the cube of its radius (r cm).
d Over a ten-day period the height of a plant (h cm) varied as the square root of the number of days' growth (d days).

2 A stone falls D metres in T seconds, and it is known that D varies directly as T^2. After 3 seconds the stone has fallen 45 m.
a Find the formula for D in terms of T.
b How far will the stone fall in 6 seconds?
c How long will it take to fall 125 m?

3

If the train travels round the curve too quickly it will leave the rails. But how quickly should it go? A working model is:
'safe speed (V m/s) is proportional to the square root of the radius (R m) of the curve.'
a Construct a formula connecting V and R, given that for a radius of 400 m the safe speed is 40 m/s.
b Calculate the safe speed for a radius of 80 m (to the nearest m/s).

4 Is there a connection between the length of a pendulum and the time of its swing?
Alison and Tina set up an experiment.

Length (L cm)	0	9	16	25	36
Time of swing (T s)	0	0.6	0.8	1.0	1.2

'The ratios are not equal' said Alison, 'so T is not proportional to L. What about T against L^2?' Tina shook her head 'Looks more like T against $\sqrt{L}$'.

a Make a new table, with values of $\sqrt{L}$ in the top row, and $T(0, 0.6, \ldots, 1.2)$ in the second row.

b Draw the graph of T against $\sqrt{L}$. ($\sqrt{L}$ on the horizontal axis.)

c Find a formula connecting T and $\sqrt{L}$, and calculate T for $L = 100$.

5 a

N	2	3	4	5	6
M	12				

$$M \propto N^2$$

(i) Find a formula connecting M and N.
(ii) Copy and complete the table.

b

Q	0	1	4	9	16
P		1			

$$P \propto \sqrt{Q}$$

(i) Find a formula connecting P and Q.
(ii) Copy and complete the table.

6 In the engineering laboratory Tessa and Peter are testing different materials. They measure the sag (S mm) for different lengths (L m).

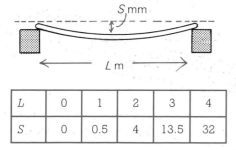

L	0	1	2	3	4
S	0	0.5	4	13.5	32

a Draw the graphs of:
(i) S against L (ii) S against L^2
(iii) S against L^3.

b Which gives a straight line through O? Find a formula connecting S and L.

c Calculate S when $L = 5$.

7 a This working shows that when the radius of a circle is doubled, the circumference is also doubled: $C_1 = 2\pi r$, $C_2 = 2\pi(2r) = 4\pi r$, so $C_2 = 2C_1$.
In a similar way show that when the radius is doubled, the area is multiplied by 4.

b The volume V cm^3 of a sphere varies directly as the cube of its radius, r cm.
Write down a relationship between V and r, and show that when the radius is doubled, the volume is eight times as great.

CHALLENGE

Eastern Gas Board charges 8p per unit used. Western Gas Board has a standing charge of £10, plus 6p per unit used. Make a table of values for accounts from each Board for cost in pence of 0, 100, 200, . . . , 600 units, and draw two graphs. Which Board has charges that are directly proportional to the number of units used? Give reasons for your answer. Discuss which Board would send the lower bills, according to the number of units likely to be used.

PRACTICAL PROJECT

*Set up an experiment involving a pendulum (for example, a variable length of string and a weight), and see whether you agree with Alison and Tina's conclusions in question **4**.*

BRAINSTORMERS

1 *Jacobini, the Swiss diamond cutter, knows that the value of a diamond is directly proportional to the square of its weight. He has to cut a diamond weighing 6 g into two parts in the ratio 2:1. Express the value of the diamond after cutting as a fraction of the value before cutting.*

2 *A famous scientist, Kepler, studied the motion of the planets in their orbits round the sun. One of Kepler's 'Laws' is that the square of the time a planet takes to circle the sun varies directly as the cube of its distance from the sun. The Earth takes 1 year, at a distance of 1.5 million km. Calculate a 'year' on Mars, which is at a distance of 2.25 million km from the sun.*

INVERSE PROPORTION (OR VARIATION)

The sponsors of Bluebell Rovers' 'Spot the Ball' competition are considering how to divide up the £1200 prize-money.

Number of prizes (N)	1	2	3	4	5
Value of each (£V)	1200	600	400	300	240

Is V proportional to N? How can you tell?
From the table, as N increases, V decreases.
Perhaps N and V are in inverse proportion?

This graph looks like the hyperbola $y = \dfrac{a}{x}$ you saw in Chapter 2.

This suggests $V = \dfrac{k}{N} = k \times \dfrac{1}{N}$. Is $V \propto \dfrac{1}{N}$?

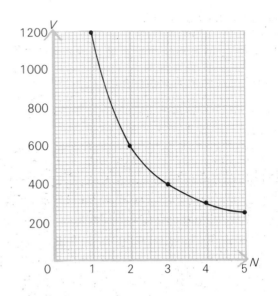

$\dfrac{1}{N}$	1	0.5	0.33	0.25	0.2
V	1200	600	400	300	240

The graph of V against $\dfrac{1}{N}$ is a straight line

through O, so $V \propto \dfrac{1}{N}$, i.e. $V = \dfrac{k}{N}$, or $VN = k$.

From the table, or the gradient of the graph,

$k = 1200$, so the relation is $V = \dfrac{1200}{N}$.

V is **inversely proportional** to N, or V **varies inversely** as N.

$$V \propto \frac{1}{N}, \text{ so } V = \frac{k}{N}, \text{ or } VN = k.$$

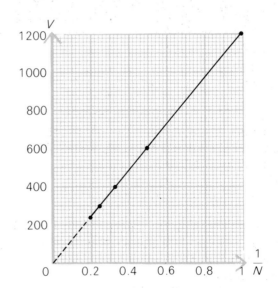

Example
Two electrical charges attract one another with a force (F units) which varies inversely as the square of the distance (d units) between them. $F = 4$ when $d = 6$. Find F when $d = 10$.

$F \propto \dfrac{1}{d^2}$, so $F = \dfrac{k}{d^2}$

Then $4 = \dfrac{k}{36}$, and $k = 4 \times 36 = 144$

The formula is $F = \dfrac{144}{d^2}$.

When $d = 10$, $F = \dfrac{144}{d^2}$

$= \dfrac{144}{10^2}$

$= 1.44$

EXERCISE 3

1 y varies inversely as x, i.e. $y \propto \dfrac{1}{x}$, so $y = \dfrac{k}{x}$ or $xy = k$. If $y = 6$ when $x = 2$:
  a find a formula for y.
  b calculate: (i) y when $x = 6$ (ii) x when $y = 3$.

2 The time (H hours) taken to deliver a batch of leaflets in the town centre varies inversely as the number (N) of people delivering them. For one job 60 people take 8 hours.

  a Find a formula for H.
  b Calculate:
    (i) H when $N = 80$ (ii) N when $H = 12$.

3 The current (I amps) in a circuit is inversely proportional to the resistance (R ohms). The current is 2 amps when the resistance is 250 ohms.
  a Find a formula for I.
  b Calculate:
    (i) I when $R = 200$ (ii) R when $I = 4$.

4 On a railway curve of radius R m, the outer rail is H cm higher than the inner rail. Also, H varies inversely as R, and when $R = 500$, $H = 12$.
  a Find a formula for H.
  b Calculate H when $R = 400$.

5 The pressure P of a given mass of gas varies inversely as its volume, V, at constant temperature. When $P = 600$, $V = 2$.
  a Find a formula for P.
  b Calculate:
    (i) P when $V = 3$ (ii) V when $P = 800$.

6 The resistance (R ohms) to the current passing through a copper wire is inversely proportional to the square of the diameter (d mm) of the wire. For a wire of diameter 0.3 mm the resistance is 0.2 ohm. Find the formula connecting R and d.

7 The intensity of illumination (I lumens per m²) on a screen varies inversely as the square of the distance (d m) of the light from the screen. When $d = 5$, $I = 1$.
  a Find a formula for I.
  b Calculate:
    (i) I when $d = 2.5$ (ii) d when $I = 4$.

8 The weight (W kg) of a body varies inversely as the square of its distance (d km) from the centre of the Earth. Peter weighs 100 kg, and the radius of the Earth is 6400 km.
  a Find a formula for W.
  b Calculate Peter's weight 1600 km *above* the Earth's surface.

9

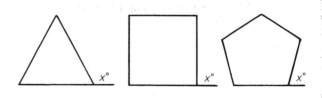

  a Katie has a slow puncture in her front tyre! The pressure is P after T minutes. Which of these models would you reject?
    (i) $P \propto T$ (ii) $P \propto T^2$ (iii) $P \propto \dfrac{1}{T}$ (iv) $P \propto \dfrac{1}{\sqrt{T}}$
  b In fact after 9 minutes $P = 12$, and after a *further* 16 minutes $P = 7.2$. Now choose the best model, and find the formula for P.

CHALLENGE

  a *Copy and complete this table for the sequence of regular polygons:*

Number of sides (n)	3	4	5	6
Number of degrees in each exterior angle (x)				

  b *Find a formula for x in terms of n.*
  c *Write out your formula like this:*
    The number of degrees in an exterior angle of a regular polygon is ... proportional to ....

JOINT VARIATION

How long will Viv take to type the manuscript?
 (i) The greater the number of pages, the longer she will take.
    The time (T minutes) varies directly as the number of pages (N). So $T \propto N$.
(ii) The greater her typing speed, the shorter the time she will take.
    The time varies inversely as the speed (S words/minute).
    So $T \propto \dfrac{1}{S}$.

T varies directly as N and inversely as S, or T varies _jointly_ as N and $\dfrac{1}{S}$.

$$T \propto \frac{N}{S}, \text{ or } T = \frac{kN}{S}.$$

Example
Viv types a 24-page manuscript in 2 hours 24 minutes at a speed of 50 words per minute.
a Find a formula for T.
b How long would she take for 30 pages at 40 words per minute?

(i) $\quad T = \dfrac{kN}{S}$

$\quad 144 = \dfrac{k \times 24}{50}$

$\quad k = \dfrac{50 \times 144}{24} = 300$

So $T = \dfrac{300N}{S}$

(ii) $\quad T = \dfrac{300N}{S}$

$\quad = \dfrac{300 \times 30}{40}$

$\quad = 225$

She would take 3 hours 45 minutes.

EXERCISE 4A

1 Write down an equation for each of these, including a constant k. For example, if u varies directly as v and inversely as w^2; then $u = \dfrac{kv}{w^2}$.

 a y varies directly as x and inversely as z.
 b p varies directly as q and as r.
 c a varies directly as b and as c, and inversely as d.
 d s varies directly as t and inversely as the square root of u.

2 A varies directly as r and as h. So $A \propto rh$, or $A = krh$. $A = 30$ when $r = 2$ and $h = 5$.
 a Find a formula for A in terms of r and h.
 b Calculate A when $r = 4$ and $h = 3$.

3 p varies directly as q and as r.
    $p = 12$ when $q = 2$ and $r = 3$.
 a Find a formula for p in terms of q and r.
 b Calculate p when $q = 1$ and $r = 5$.

4 V varies directly as x, y and z. $V = 80$ when $x = 2$, $y = 4$ and $z = 5$. Find a formula for V in terms of x, y and z.

5 I varies directly as m and as the square of r. $I = 100$ when $m = 5$ and $r = 2$.
 a Find a formula for I in terms of m and r.
 b Calculate I when $m = 8$ and $r = 3$.

6 y varies directly as x and inversely as z. So $y \propto \dfrac{x}{z}$, or $y = \dfrac{kx}{z}$.
    $y = 3$ when $x = 2$ and $z = 4$.
 a Find a formula for y in terms of x and z.
 b Calculate y when $x = 5$ and $z = 10$.

7 F varies directly as m and inversely as n. $F = 50$ when $m = 25$ and $n = 8$.
    Find a formula for F in terms of m and n.

8 A varies directly as s and inversely as t^2.
$A = 60$ when $s = 20$ and $t = 5$.
a Find a formula for A in terms of s and t.
b Calculate A when $s = 9$ and $t = 9$.

9 T varies directly as x and inversely as the
square root of y. $T = 12$ when $x = 6$ and $y = 4$.
a Find a formula for T in terms of x and y.
b Calculate T when $x = 15$ and $y = 9$.

10 y varies directly as x and as z, and inversely as
t^2. $y = 100$ when $x = 25$, $z = 2$ and $t = 1$.
a Find a formula for y in terms of x, z and t.
b Calculate y when $x = 12$, $z = 5$ and $t = 4$.

11 Write these formulae in words, using some of
the following phrases:
directly proportional, inversely proportional,
varies directly, varies inversely, varies jointly:

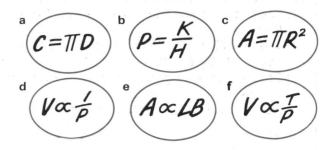

a $C = \pi D$ b $P = \dfrac{K}{H}$ c $A = \pi R^2$

d $V \propto \dfrac{1}{P}$ e $A \propto LB$ f $V \propto \dfrac{T}{P}$

EXERCISE 4B

1 Write an equation for each of these three
sentences.
a The power (E) in a circuit is directly
proportional to the square of the current (C)
and the length (L). (Remember the constant.)
b The stopping distance (D) of a train is directly
proportional to the square of its speed (S), and
inversely proportional to the resistance (R) to
its motion.
c The distance (D) possible on a full tank of
petrol varies directly as the capacity (C) of the
tank and inversely as the square root of the
speed (S).

2 Overton's Wednesday market attracts a lot of
shoppers. Joe has a fruit stall, and reckons that
his profit (£P) is directly proportional to the
number of hours (H) he works, and inversely
proportional to the number of fruit stalls (N) in
the market.
For a 7-hour day, with four fruit stalls, his profit is
£175.
a Find a formula connecting P, H and N.
b Calculate his profit in a 6-hour day when there
are five fruit stalls.

3 The time (T minutes) Aisha takes to type a page
of a manuscript varies jointly as the number of
lines on the page (N) and the average number of
words per line (A). She takes 6 minutes to type a
page which has 24 lines with an average of 15
words per line.
a Find a formula connecting T, N and A.
b Calculate the time she takes to type a page
which has 20 lines with an average of 18
words per line.

4 The number of gallons of petrol (n) used by the
new Super Sports Saloon is in direct proportion
to the distance travelled (d miles) and to the
square root of the average speed (s mph).

a If 12 gallons are required for a journey of 360
miles travelled at an average speed of
64 mph, find a formula expressing n in terms
of d and s.
b Calculate n when $d = 480$ miles and
$s = 49$ mph.

5 Safe and Secure Insurance Company provides
pensions (£P) for its employees which are
directly proportional to their length of service
(Y years) and to their final salary (£S). Mrs
Jackson had 20 years' service and a final salary
of £15 000. Her pension is £3000.
a Calculate the formula for P.
b Calculate the pension for 30 years' service
and a salary of £18 000.

6 The simple interest (£I) in a bank account varies
directly as the principal (£P), the time (T years)
and the rate of interest p.a. (R%). The interest on
£800 for 6 months (0.5 year) at 5% p.a. is £20.
a Find the formula for I.
b Calculate the interest on £1600 for 9 months at
7% p.a.

7 The volume ($V\,\text{cm}^3$) of a certain mass of gas varies directly as the temperature (T°) and inversely as the pressure ($P\,\text{mm Hg}$).
$V = 200$ when $T = 250$ and $P = 750$.
   a Find a formula for V in terms of T and P.
   b Calculate V when $T = 350$ and $P = 1000$.

8

As the Daredevil drum at the fairground speeds up you're held against the side. The force on you (F newtons) varies directly as the square of your speed ($S\,\text{m/s}$) and as your mass ($M\,\text{kg}$), and inversely as the radius of the drum ($R\,\text{m}$).
   a Given that $F = 20$ when $S = 10$, $R = 5$ and $M = 75$, find the formula for F.
   b Calculate the force on Craig, whose mass is 50 kg, when the speed of the drum is 15 m/s.

9 The area $A\,\text{cm}^2$ of the ellipse varies directly as a and as b.

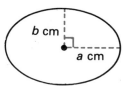

   a Write down an equation for A.
   b What happens to the area if:
      (i) a is doubled (ii) b is doubled
      (iii) a and b are doubled?

10 The volume ($V\,\text{cm}^3$) of a cone varies directly as the square of its radius ($r\,\text{cm}$) and its height ($h\,\text{cm}$). For radius 10 cm and height 30 cm the volume is $3142\,\text{cm}^3$, to the nearest cm^3.
   a Find a formula for V, and calculate V when $r = 5$ and $h = 12$.
   b What happens to the volume when:
      (i) h is doubled (ii) r is doubled
      (iii) h and r are both doubled?

INVESTIGATIONS

1 *The electrical power in a circuit (P watts) is directly proportional to the current (I amperes) and the voltage (V volts). For 1200 watts the current is 5 amps and the voltage is 240. Find the formula for P. Investigate the current, and hence the size of fuse required in a plug, for different household items such as a hair-dryer (500 W), iron (1000 W), fire (3 kW), etc.*

2

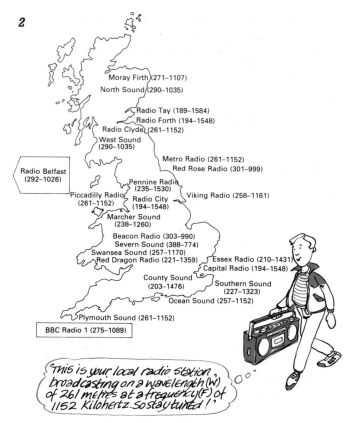

"This is your local radio station, broadcasting on a wavelength (W) of 261 metres at a frequency (F) of 1152 kilohertz. So stay tuned!"

Investigate the relationship between the wavelengths (W) and the frequencies (F) of all these local radio stations.
Include a graph and a formula in your investigation.

Conundrum:
What is the connection between the speed of light (300 000 km/s) and your investigation?

CHALLENGE

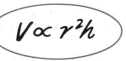

$$V \propto r^2 h$$

a *Find the effect on V if r is trebled and h is halved.*
b *Calculate the percentage change in V if r is increased by 20% and h is decreased by 25%.*

CHECK-UP ON PROPORTION IN PRACTICE

1 Frances kept a record of the petrol she used, to the nearest 10 miles and $\frac{1}{2}$ gallon.

Distance (D miles)	80	120	40	160	180	200
Petrol (P gallons)	2	3	1	4	4.5	5

a Plot the points, and draw the best-fitting straight line through the origin.
b Write down the relation between P and D:
(i) as an equation (ii) in words.

2 p is proportional to q^2.
a Use the table to find a formula connecting p and q.
b Copy and complete the table.

q	2	4	
p	20		500

3 M varies inversely as N. $M = 12$ when $N = 6$. Find:
a a formula for M **b** M when $N = 3$
c N when $M = 16$.

4 Sketch graphs which illustrate:
a $y \propto x$ **b** $y \propto \dfrac{1}{x}$.

5 The weekly bonus (£B) for each worker at Sparks' factory is directly proportional to the weekly profit (£P). For the week ending 22nd June, £16 bonus was paid for a £20 000 profit.
a Find a formula for B in terms of P.
b Calculate:
(i) the bonus for a profit of £18 750
(ii) the profit for an £18 bonus.

6 The number of rectangular slabs (N) required to pave a patio varies inversely as the area of each slab (A cm²). 192 slabs, each 90 cm by 60 cm, can cover the patio.
a Find a formula for N in terms of A.
b How many 60 cm by 60 cm slabs would be needed?
c If A is doubled, what happens to N?

7 a Write $F \propto \dfrac{v^2}{r}$:
(i) in words   (ii) as an equation.
b $F = 32$ when $v = 4$ and $r = 2$. Calculate F when $v = 3$ and $r = 6$.

8 A current I produces a deflection $\theta°$ in an electrical measuring instrument such that I varies as $\tan \theta°$.
a When $I = 0.5$, $\theta = 18.5$. Show that $I \doteqdot 1.5 \tan \theta°$.
b Calculate I, correct to 3 significant figures, when $\theta = 37$.
c What is the deflection, to the nearest degree, when $I = 2$?

9 Kirkfield Youth Club are going by coach to a pop concert. The cost for each member (£C) varies directly as the number of hours (H) of hire, and inversely as the number of members going (N). $C = 5$ when $H = 5$ and $N = 40$.
a Find a formula for C.
b Calculate the cost per member if 50 travel, and the coach is hired for six hours.

10 a Copy and complete this table, using the graph.

Mass of model train (M kg)	1	2	3	4	5
Acceleration (a cm/s²)					

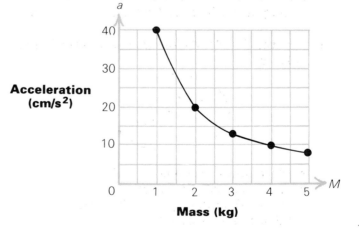

b Find a formula for a in terms of M.
c Graph a against $\dfrac{1}{M}$. What do you find?
d Copy and complete: 'The acceleration is . . .'

8 HANDLING DATA

1 The Happy Hen Free Range Farm records the weights of eggs laid daily, to the nearest gram.

Size	Weight (g)	Frequency
7	40–44	10
6	45–49	35
5	50–54	75
4	55–59	90
3	60–64	100
2	65–69	125
1	70–74	65

a Calculate the mean weight of an egg, to the nearest gram.
b In which class interval is the median weight?
c Draw a frequency diagram.

2 a Use the data in question **1** to draw a cumulative frequency curve.
b Use the curve to find:
  (i) the median weight
  (ii) the interquartile range of the weights.

3 Again using the data in question **1**, calculate:
a the probability that an egg chosen at random is size: (i) 3 (ii) 2 or 3
b the number of size 1 eggs that could be expected in a batch of 2800.

4 The piechart shows the proportion of cars travelling at various speeds on a 30 mph road. 24 cars travelled at 26–30 mph.
a How many cars were:
  (i) in the survey
  (ii) travelling at 36–40 mph?

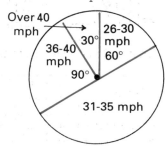

b What is the probability that one of the cars chosen at random was exceeding the speed limit of 30 mph?
c In a sample of 50 of the cars, how many would you expect to be travelling at over 40 mph?

5 A card is chosen at random from this set of five cards:

The card is replaced, and a card is again chosen at random.
a Copy and complete this table of outcomes.

Second card

	10	J	Q	K	A
10	(10, 10)	(10, J)			
J	(J, 10)				
Q					
K					
A					

First card

b Write down:
  (i) P(Ace, Ace)
  (ii) P(choosing the same card twice)
  (iii) P(at least one Ace).

6 A coin is tossed three times.
a Copy and complete this tree diagram.

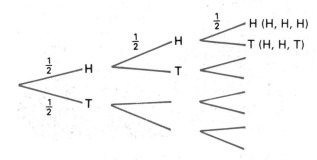

b How many equally likely outcomes are there?
c Calculate:
  (i) P(T, T, T) (ii) P(at least 2 Hs)
  (iii) P(fewer than 2 Hs).

HISTOGRAMS AND FREQUENCY POLYGONS

The frequency diagram on the right shows the distribution of weights in a batch of 37 melons. **A diagram like this, in which the areas of the columns are proportional to the frequencies, is called a histogram.**

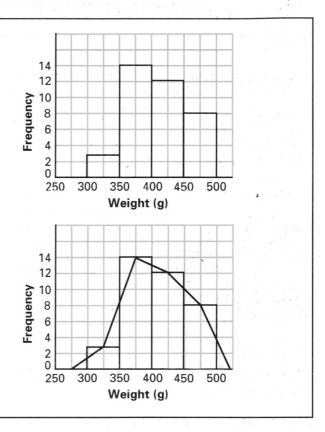

The second diagram shows the **frequency polygon formed by joining the midpoints of the tops of the rectangles and the 'zero rectangles' on either side.** The polygon formed with the horizontal axis has the same area as the histogram.

EXERCISE 1A

1 As his statistics project, Keith surveys and analyses the times taken by 150 students in his year to travel from home to school.

Time (t min)	Frequency
$0 \leqslant t < 10$	21
$10 \leqslant t < 20$	25
$20 \leqslant t < 30$	30
$30 \leqslant t < 40$	40
$40 \leqslant t < 50$	24
$50 \leqslant t < 60$	10

a Draw a histogram of Keith's data.
b Draw a frequency polygon on your histogram.
c In which class interval is the median time?
d Use mid-interval times 5, 15, 25, . . . to calculate the mean time of travel, to the nearest second.

2 The spring medal competition at Greenvale Golf Club is always popular.

This table shows a distribution of the scores.

Score	66 –70	71 –75	76 –80	81 –85	86 –90	91 –95	96 –100
Frequency	4	23	38	34	20	16	5

a Draw a histogram and a frequency polygon.
b In which class interval is the median score?
c Construct a cumulative frequency table, and draw a cumulative frequency curve. Use the curve to find the median score.

3

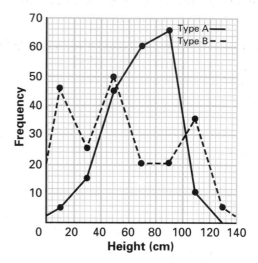

TOUGH TYRES
TIRELESS TYRES

Tough Tyres and Tireless Tyres check their manufacturing processes by testing 100 tyres to see how long they last.

Distance (d 1000 km)	$0 \leqslant d < 10$	$10 \leqslant d < 20$
Tough Tyres' frequency	0	15
Tireless Tyres' frequency	10	24

$20 \leqslant d < 30$	$30 \leqslant d < 40$	$40 \leqslant d < 50$	$50 \leqslant d < 60$
32	46	7	0
14	22	18	12

a Draw a frequency polygon for each sample on the same diagram.
b Which type of tyre would you recommend? Justify your choice statistically.

4 An agricultural research centre tests the growth of two types of grain, and displays the results in these frequency polygons.

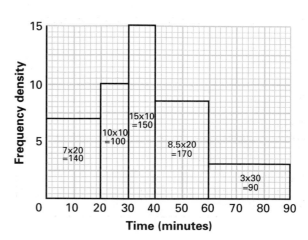

a How many seeds were in each sample?
b Make cumulative frequency tables, and draw two cumulative frequency curves.
c Calculate the interquartile range of each distribution.
d Comment on the growth rates of the two types of grain.

HISTOGRAMS WITH UNEQUAL CLASS INTERVALS

Patricia is also studying the times taken by students to travel to school. However, she has grouped her data in unequal class intervals of 20, 10, 10, 20 and 30 minutes. To keep areas proportional to frequencies in her histogram she has to calculate the frequency density of the times, i.e. the frequency per minute.

Time (t min)	Frequency	Frequency density
$0 \leqslant t < 20$	140	$140 \div 20 = 7$
$20 \leqslant t < 30$	100	$100 \div 10 = 10$
$30 \leqslant t < 40$	150	$150 \div 10 = 15$
$40 \leqslant t < 60$	170	$170 \div 20 = 8.5$
$60 \leqslant t < 90$	90	$90 \div 30 = 3$

Notice that the areas of the columns in the histogram, $7 \times 20 = 140$, etc., are the same as the frequencies in the table.

EXERCISE 1B

1 Joanne has kept a record of her overtime earnings during the past year.

Overtime income (£A)	Frequency	Frequency density
$0 \leqslant A < 10$	12	$12 \div 10 = 1.2$
$10 \leqslant A < 20$	14	
$20 \leqslant A < 30$	8	
$30 \leqslant A < 50$	10	
$50 \leqslant A < 80$	6	
$80 \leqslant A < 120$	4	

a Calculate all the frequency densities.
b Draw a histogram of the data.

2 Ken works in a supermarket, part-time. This histogram shows how his hours of work, per week, have varied over the past year.

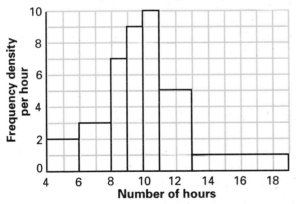

a Copy and complete this table:

Hours worked (h)	Frequency density	Frequency
$4 \leqslant h < 6$	2	$2 \times 2 = 4$
$6 \leqslant h < 8$	3	$3 \times 2 = 6$
$8 \leqslant h < 9$	7	$7 \times 1 = 7$
$9 \leqslant h < 10$		
$10 \leqslant h < 11$		
$11 \leqslant h < 13$		
$13 \leqslant h < 19$		
Total		

b Check that the area of each column gives the corresponding frequency.
c In how many weeks did Ken work fewer than 10 hours?

3

Superstyle Hair Salon kept a record of daily takings to the nearest £.

Takings (£)	0–150	151–250	251–350
Frequency	18	30	44

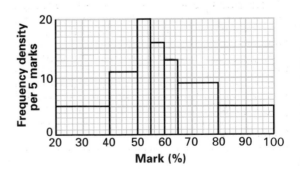

351–400	401–450	451–500	501–600	601–800
48	65	52	30	12

a Calculate the frequency density per £50, for example $18 \div 3 = 6$.
b Draw a histogram of the data with frequency density per £50.

4 This histogram shows the exam marks of a group of students.

a Make a table which shows the number of students in each class interval
($20 \leqslant N < 40$, $40 \leqslant N < 50$, etc.).
b How many students scored at least 50%?

SAMPLING

In carrying out statistical research or investigations it is often necessary to select a sample of the population for study. It is important that this sample is made up of a fair, unbiased selection from the population.

For example, Langton High School student council has decided to investigate students' views on the length of the lunch interval. There are 1000 students in the school, and the council wants to select a sample of 50. They can choose:

(i) **a random selection**
Choose 50 students at random—put names in a hat, or allocate numbers and use the random key on the calculator.

(ii) **a systematic selection**
List all the students alphabetically, and select every 20th name.

(iii) **a stratified selection**
Choose a random sample for each year in proportion to the number in that year.
There are 200 students in Year 1, so the number needed would be $\frac{200}{1000} \times 50 = 10$, and the ten students would then be chosen by methods (i) or (ii). Similarly for the other years.

EXERCISE 2

1 Here are the students in Mr Wallace's maths class.

a Choose five students to represent the class, using each of the three methods listed above. In (iii), girls and boys have to be represented proportionally.

b Did all three methods give you three girls and two boys in the sample?

2 The Short Fuse factory produces 20 000 electrical fuses per day. It claims that a fuse will 'blow' if a current greater than 13 amps goes through it. Explain how you might select a 2% sample to test this claim.

3 On the payroll of Chips Computers are 10 managers, 30 clerical staff and 80 production workers. To assess opinions of working conditions a stratified sample of 12 is to be chosen. How many from each group would be in the sample?

4 Students and staff at Western Academy agree to set up a school council with 30 members, using a stratified sample. How many students should be selected from each year?

Year	1st	2nd	3rd	4th	5th	6th
Number of students	186	143	214	225	286	80

5 A sample of 25% of students in Miss Kerr's class is selected by the Examination Board in order to check her marking standard. The marks are out of 30.

Student's number	Mark	Student's number	Mark
01	21	13	20
02	9	14	15
03	27	15	23
04	18	16	17
05	15	17	12
06	25	18	28
07	10	19	19
08	30	20	22
09	14	21	18
10	19	22	12
11	22	23	28
12	8	24	19

a Would you choose the sample using the students' numbers or the marks?

b List the marks the Board might choose, along with the students' numbers.

CHALLENGE

Students in Sally's class have been asked to collect data about possible voting patterns in their local constituency at the next General Election. Here are some of their ideas.

I'll choose names from the telephone book

I'll ask all the people who live in South Street

I'll ask passers-by in Main Square at 9am.

I'll ask parents at tonight's parents' meeting

a Write down a reason in each case why the sample might not give a true picture of the voting pattern of the constituency.

b How would you go about choosing a sample, making it as fair and accurate as possible?

INVESTIGATION

A 'Head of Year' Election

The Fifth Year at City High are going to vote for a pupil to be their Head of the Year. There are two candidates, Oliver and Belinda.

The week before the election Jane decides to carry out an opinion poll by asking 10 students how they intend to vote. There are six forms in the fifth year, each with 30 students, and she will take the poll while the students are in their form rooms. This diagram shows the students' voting intentions, O for Oliver and B for Belinda.

5A	5B
B B B B B B	B B B B B B
O B B B B B	B O B O B B
B B B B O B	B B O O O O
B B B B B B	B B O O O O
B B B O B B	O O O B O B

5C	5D
B B B B B B	B B B B B B
O O O O O O	B O O O B B
O B O O O B	B B B B B B
O O O O B B	B B B B B B
B O O B O B	B B B B B B

5E	5F
B B B B B B	B B B B B B
B B B B B B	B O B B B B
B O B B B B	B B O B B B
B B O B B B	B O O O B B
B B B O B B	B O B O B B

Use each of the following methods to choose and list 10 students, giving their class and the rows and columns of their desks:
(i) random   (ii) systematic
(iii) stratified, based on classes.
Explain fully how you would make your selection, then write your prediction of the result of the voting, and compare it with the actual result by counting all the votes.

PRACTICAL PROJECT

Design a questionnaire to collect data about school meals. Decide which aspects you want to investigate, carry out a survey and write a report which includes the results and your conclusions.

Value for money — Variety — Quality — Healthy eating — Choice — Time available

MORE PROBABILITY

EXERCISE 3 (REVISION)

1 L-O-N-G-L-I-F-E Lights test a sample of 50 bulbs.

This table shows the results.

Number of hours	< 100	100 –199	200 –299	300 –399	⩾ 400
Number of bulbs	3	12	18	11	6

a Based on this sample, estimate the probability that a bulb will last:
(i) less than 200 hours   (ii) 200 hours or more.

b In March the factory produced 12 000 bulbs. How many could be expected to have a life of:
(i) less than 200 hours   (ii) 200 hours or more?

2 The two spinners are spun, and the scores are added.

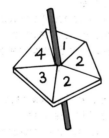 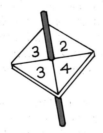

a Copy and complete the table.

```
              2nd spinner
        +  |  2  3  3  4
        1  |  3  4
        2  |
  1st   2  |
spinner 3  |
        4  |
```

b Calculate:
(i) P(total of 4)   (ii) P(total of 4 or 5)
(iii) P(total of 4, 5 or 6)

c In 400 pairs of spins how many totals of 6 would you expect?

3 Autospares have a production target each week. The probability of just meeting the target is 0.2, and the probability of exceeding it is 0.35.

a Calculate the probability of:
(i) meeting or exceeding the target
(ii) failing to meet the target.

b Estimate the number of weeks in a working year of 50 weeks when the factory will fail to meet its target.

4 a Assuming that births are equally likely to take place in summer (Su), autumn (A), winter (W) or spring (Sp), and that they are equally likely to be male (M) or female (F), copy and complete this tree diagram:

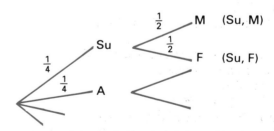

b A student is chosen at random. Calculate:
(i) P(born in autumn)
(ii) P(a male, born in spring)
(iii) P(female, born in summer or winter).

P(*A* AND *B*)

Look at the table of outcomes when these two spinners are spun.

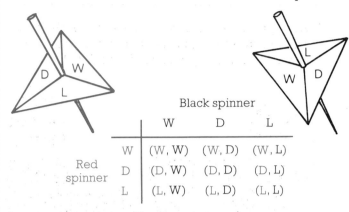

For the red spinner, $P(W) = \frac{1}{3}$.

For the black spinner, $P(W) = \frac{1}{3}$.

From the table, $P(W, W) = \frac{1}{9}$.

Notice that $P(W, W) = \frac{1}{9} = \frac{1}{3} \times \frac{1}{3}$
$= P(W) \times P(W)$.

Check that $P(W, D) = P(W) \times P(D)$.

	Black spinner		
	W	D	L
Red spinner W	(W, W)	(W, D)	(W, L)
D	(D, W)	(D, D)	(D, L)
L	(L, W)	(L, D)	(L, L)

It seems that $P(A$ and $B) = P(A) \times P(B)$. Obtaining a win with the first spinner does not affect the outcome on the second spinner. The two events are **independent**.

For two **independent** events A and B, $P(A$ and $B) = P(A) \times P(B)$.

EXERCISE 4A

1 A 2p coin and a 5p coin are tossed.
   a List all the possible outcomes.
   b Write down:
      (i) P(H) for the 2p   (ii) P(H) for the 5p
      (iii) P(H, H).
   c Check that $P(H, H) = P(H) \times P(H)$.

2 Two dice are rolled.
   a List all the outcomes.
   b Write down:
      (i) P(6) for the first dice
      (ii) P(6) for the second dice
      (iii) P(6, 6).
   c Check that $P(6, 6) = P(6) \times P(6)$.

3 A coin is tossed and a dice is rolled.
   a List all the outcomes.
   b Write down:
      (i) P(H)   (ii) P(6)
      (iii) P(H, 6), that is Head, then 6.
      (iv) An equation connecting P(H), P(6) and P(H, 6).

4 In the Sunshine Maternity Unit, P(boy) = 0.48.
   a Write down P(girl).
   b Calculate, correct to 2 decimal places, for the next two births:
      (i) P(B, B)
      (ii) P(Boy and Girl)—in any order.

5 In a large batch of silicon chips, 10% are known to be defective.
   a Write down in decimal form the probability of choosing at random a chip which is:
      (i) defective   (ii) not defective.
   b A sample of five chips is taken at random from the batch, and tested. Calculate, correct to 2 decimal places, the probability that none of the chips is defective.

6 Robin is a member of the Bullseye Archery Club. On average, 80% of his shots hit the target. Calculate the probability that in three successive shots he will hit the target each time.

7 In a traffic survey on an east–west stretch of road it was discovered that only one car in six travelled west.

What is the probability that:
a the next car to pass is heading west
b the next two cars are heading west
c the next car is heading west, followed by one heading east?

8 The probability that an aircraft will fail to return from a mission is 0.1. Calculate the probability that it *will* return from:
a one mission
b ten missions, correct to 2 decimal places.

9 In a TV game show, contestants have a chance of winning prizes by spinning two wheels.

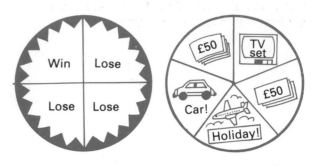

Calculate the probability of winning, in one attempt:
a a car, i.e. P(Win and Car) **b** £50 **c** £100.

10 These bags contain red and white buttons. A button is taken at random from each bag.

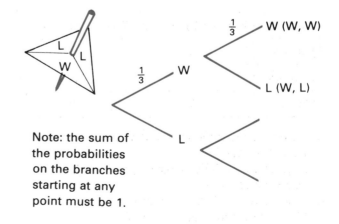

Calculate:
a P(W, W) **b** P(R, R)
c P(both have the same colour).

EXERCISE 4B

1 Three coins are tossed.
a List all the outcomes of the tree diagram.
b Write down: (i) P(H) for any coin
                   (ii) P(H, H, H).
c Copy and complete:
P(H, H, H) = ... × ... × ... = ...
d Calculate: (i) P(H, H, T), in order
                  (ii) P(T, H, T), in order.

2 The spinner is equally likely to land on any one of the three sectors.
a Copy and complete the tree diagram for two spins.
b Calculate: (i) P(W, W) (ii) P(W, L)
                  (iii) P(L, W) (iv) P(L, L).
c Check that the sum of your answers in **b** is 1.

Note: the sum of the probabilities on the branches starting at any point must be 1.

3 A bag contains four red beads and six blue beads. A bead is drawn and replaced. A second bead is then drawn from the bag at random.
  a Copy and complete the tree diagram.

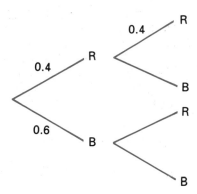

  b Calculate:
   (i) P(R, R) (ii) P(R, B) (iii) P(B, R) (iv) P(B, B).
  c What was done to make sure that the events were independent?
  d Calculate the probability of drawing a red and blue bead in any order.

4 There are 11 boys and 9 girls in Megan's class, and 10 boys and 15 girls in Katie's class. A student is chosen at random from each class.
  a Draw a tree diagram which shows the probabilities of choosing a boy or girl.
  b Calculate: (i) P(both girls)
   (ii) P(both boys) (iii) P(a boy and a girl).

5 Brian buys tickets in the monthly prize draw at his workplace.

Month	Number he bought	Total number sold
January	12	150
February	20	200
March	9	180

  a Calculate the probability that one of his tickets wins the prize in:
   (i) January (ii) February (iii) March.
  b Draw a tree diagram.
  c Calculate: (i) P(three wins)
   (ii) P(two wins) (iii) P(one win)

At the fairground

Marie throws darts, and each one has an equal chance of landing anywhere on the large board. Each card is 6 cm × 9 cm. Darts which miss the board can be thrown again.

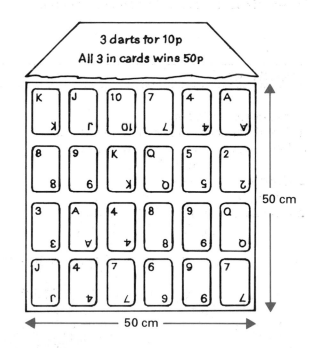

  a *Calculate, correct to 2 decimal places, the probability that:*
   (i) one dart will hit a card
   (ii) all three darts will hit cards.
  b *For each £10 taken, how much should the stall-holder expect to pay out in winnings? How could this be altered?*

CONDITIONAL PROBABILITY

a Dan has three 50p coins (F) and two 10p coins (T) in his pocket. He takes out one coin at random, and puts it back. He then takes out a second one. What is the probability that he gets a 50p coin both times?

From the tree diagram, $P(F, F) = \dfrac{9}{25}$ or 36%.

b Suppose Dan **does not replace the first coin**, before taking out the second one. What is the probability that he gets two 50p coins this time?
The choice for his second coin is from **two** 50p and two 10p coins, so the new tree diagram

shows that $P(F, F) = \dfrac{3}{10}$, or 30%.

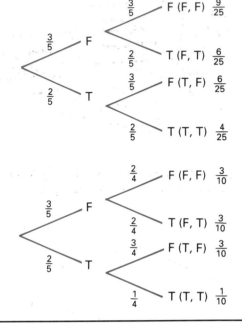

$\frac{3}{5}$ F
  $\frac{3}{5}$ F (F, F) $\frac{9}{25}$
  $\frac{2}{5}$ T (F, T) $\frac{6}{25}$
$\frac{2}{5}$ T
  $\frac{3}{5}$ F (T, F) $\frac{6}{25}$
  $\frac{2}{5}$ T (T, T) $\frac{4}{25}$

$\frac{3}{5}$ F
  $\frac{2}{4}$ F (F, F) $\frac{3}{10}$
  $\frac{2}{4}$ T (F, T) $\frac{3}{10}$
$\frac{2}{5}$ T
  $\frac{3}{4}$ F (T, F) $\frac{3}{10}$
  $\frac{1}{4}$ T (T, T) $\frac{1}{10}$

EXERCISE 5

1 A drawer contains 3 black and 2 white socks, in a muddle as usual! Brendan takes one out at random. He doesn't replace it, but takes out another.
  a Copy and complete the tree diagram.

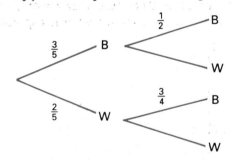

$\frac{3}{5}$ B
  $\frac{1}{2}$ B
  W
$\frac{2}{5}$ W
  $\frac{3}{4}$ B
  W

  b Calculate the probability that he gets a pair of:
    (i) black socks (ii) white socks
    (iii) socks of the same colour
    (iv) socks of different colours,
      $P(B, W) + P(W, B)$.

2 A bag contains 5 red and 5 white discs.
  a What is the probability that the first disc taken out is red?
  b The first disc *is* red, and is not replaced. How many discs:
    (i) are left in the bag (ii) are red?
  c What is the probability that a second disc taken out is red?
  d Draw a tree diagram of events.
  e What is P(R, R)?

3 Marjory buys 5 tickets in a raffle: 100 tickets are sold, and there are 2 prizes. In the draw the first ticket is not replaced, naturally.

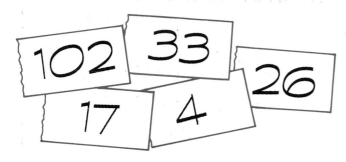

a Copy and complete the diagram of probabilities for Marjory winning (W) or losing (L).

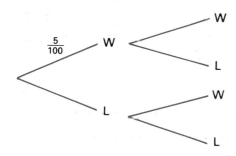

b Calculate, correct to 3 decimal places, the probability that Marjory will win:
(i) 2 prizes   (ii) only one prize   (iii) no prize.

4 An operation has a 60% chance of success first time, and, if repeated, has a 30% chance of success the second time.
a Draw a tree diagram, noting that if the operation is successful first time, there are no further branches in the diagram for this outcome.
b Calculate the probability of:
(i) success after two operations
(ii) failure after both.

5 Cards are drawn at random, one at a time, from a pack of 52, and not replaced. Calculate the probability that the first:
a card is an ace   **b** 2 cards are aces
c 3 cards are aces   **d** 4 cards are aces
e 5 cards are aces.

INVESTIGATION

Ibo has 10 blue and 10 red discs. He is planning a game where he puts 10 of these discs into a bag, and asks his friends to pick 2 out at random, one after the other without replacement. If they get two of the same colour they win, otherwise he wins. How many of each colour should he put in the bag to give him the best chance of winning?
For example, he could put in 8 blue and 2 red discs.

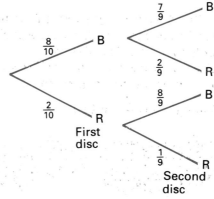

$$P(B, B) = \frac{8}{10} \times \frac{7}{9} = \frac{56}{90} = \frac{28}{45}$$

$$P(R, R) = \frac{2}{10} \times \frac{1}{9} = \frac{2}{90} = \frac{1}{45}$$

$$P(\text{same colours}) = \frac{56}{90} + \frac{2}{90} = \frac{58}{90} \doteqdot 0.64$$

a *Investigate all possible combinations of colours for his 10 discs, and show the results in a graph.*

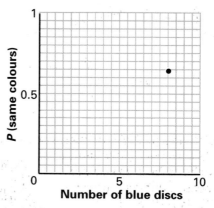

b *Which combination gives Ibo the best chance of winning? Which gives him a 'better than even' chance?*
c *Investigate different numbers of discs in the bag, including odd numbers. Can you make any general rules?*
d *Investigate the situation if Ibo decides to choose from 3 colours.*

CHECK-UP ON HANDLING DATA

1 In a darts competition, each person throws three darts. Here is a table of scores:

Score (s)	$0 \leqslant s < 40$	$40 \leqslant s < 50$	$50 \leqslant s < 60$
Frequency	60	38	52

$60 \leqslant s < 80$	$80 \leqslant s < 100$	$100 \leqslant s < 130$	$130 \leqslant s < 180$
74	64	72	40

a Draw a histogram of the scores with frequency density per 10 marks.

b Taking the midpoints of the class intervals as 20, 45, 55, 70, 90, 115 and 155, calculate the mean score, to the nearest whole number.

2 Jeff McLean is a forester with Uplands Forestry Commission. He manages a woodland of mixed trees.

Type	Oak	Ash	Birch	Pine	Sycamore
Number	250	150	200	800	100

To measure the effects of pollution he decides to take a stratified sample of 100 trees. How many of each type should he include?

3 Mr Jaffrey is concerned about the cost of his electricity. On the first day of each month for a year he recorded the maximum temperature and the cost of units used that day.

Month	Jan	Feb	Mar	Apr	May
Temperature (°C)	−1	3	10	13	24
Cost (p)	230	220	210	150	90

Jun	Jul	Aug	Sep	Oct	Nov	Dec
26	30	27	17	9	5	−6
100	40	70	140	180	220	280

a Draw a scatter diagram, and a best-fitting straight line.

b Estimate the cost of electricity on a day when the maximum temperature is 20°C.

4 The probability that a car driver will have a puncture in a given week is 0.01.

a Calculate the probability that he or she will have four punctures in the same week.

b What should the driver tell friends about this, if it happens?

5 This bag contains three white discs and five black discs. One is taken out at random, and replaced. Then another is taken out at random.

a Draw a tree diagram of the probabilities of taking out black or white each time.

b Calculate:
(i) P(W, W) (ii) P(B, B) (iii) P(W, B) (iv) P(B, W)

c Are two of the same colour more likely to be selected than one of each colour?

6 The scoring probabilities on this game are:
P(5) = 0.1, P(3) = 0.4 and P(1) = 0.5.

a Draw a tree diagram for rolling two balls, one after another.

b Calculate the probability of scoring:
(i) 10 (ii) 8 (iii) 6.

c Continue the diagram for three balls, then calculate the probability of scoring a total of:
(i) 9 (ii) 11.

7 The Fergusons hope to have three children.

a Assuming equal probabilities for boy or girl, what is the probability that all three will be girls?

b In fact the first two are girls. What is the probability now that they will have three girls?

8 A skin-graft operation has an 80% success rate first time, but if a second operation is needed the success rate this time is only 40%. Find the probability that the operation will fail twice. Include a tree diagram in your answer.

9 INDICES AND SURDS

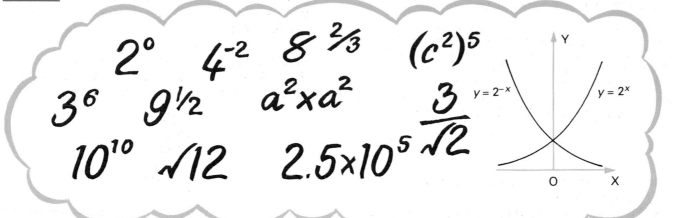

LOOKING BACK

1 Calculate mentally:

 a $2-1$ **b** $-2+1$ **c** $-2-1$
 d $2+(-1)$ **e** $2-(-1)$ **f** $-2-(-1)$

2 Write these in a shorter form:

 a $a \times a$ **b** $b \times b \times b$ **c** $5 \times c \times c \times c \times c$

3 Write down three more terms in the sequence
 $1000, 100, 10, \ldots$

4 Calculate mentally:

 a $\frac{1}{2}+\frac{1}{2}$ **b** $\frac{3}{2}-\frac{1}{2}$ **c** $\frac{2}{3}+\frac{2}{3}$ **d** $\frac{1}{4}-\frac{3}{4}$

5 Find the value of:

 a x^2 when $x = -3$ **b** $3y^2$ when $y = -1$

6 Write in standard form $a \times 10^n$:

 a $300\,000$ **b** 0.007 **c** 1800

7 Calculate mentally:

 a $5 \times (-2)$ **b** -1×3 **c** $-2 \times (-3)$ **d** -2×0

8 Solve these equations:

 a $2x-5 = 1$ **b** $2x+5 = 1$ **c** $2x+1 = 4$

9 Use the $\boxed{y^x}$ key on your calculator to find the
 value of:

 a 2^5 **b** 2^{10} **c** 2^{50} in standard form, correct to
 1 decimal place.

10 Calculate mentally:

 a $2 \times \frac{1}{2}$ **b** $2 \times (-\frac{1}{2})$ **c** $3 \times \frac{2}{3}$ **d** $4 \times (-\frac{3}{4})$

11 Calculate:

 a the length of the altitude
  AD of $\triangle$ABC
 b the area of $\triangle$ABC.

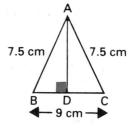

12 List the numbers in this collection which are:

 a positive **b** negative **c** negative fractions.

$$-3 \quad 5 \quad \tfrac{1}{3} \quad 0 \quad -\tfrac{1}{2} \quad 7 \quad -1 \quad \tfrac{3}{4} \quad -\tfrac{2}{5} \quad 10$$

13 The edge of this cube is e cm long.
 Write down formulae for:
 a its volume V cm³
 b its total surface area A cm².

e cm

14 Calculate V and A in question **13**, correct to 3
 significant figures, when $e = 8.75$.

15 Find the square numbers in the list below, and
 write them out, like this: $100 = 10^2$
 $4, 6, 9, 12, 16, 20, 25, 30, 36, 45, 49$

16 Calculate:

 a $f(3)$, if $f(x) = x^2-1$ **b** $f(4)$, if $f(x) = \dfrac{1}{\sqrt{x}}$

17 Multiply out:

 a $3(2x+1)$ **b** $(x-y)^2$ **c** $(a+b)(c+d)$

18 $f(t) = a+bt$. $f(3) = 5$ and $f(1) = 3$. Use these
 values of f to make two equations in a and b.
 Solve the equations, and hence write down a
 formula for f.

SAVING SPACE AND TIME

In 1750, the mathematician Euler discovered the largest prime number known at that time:

$2 \times 2 - 1.$

This number can be written $2^{31} - 1$, '2 to the power 31, minus 1.' Why 31? 31 is called the **index** of the power.

2... 3... 5... 7... 11... 13... 17... ...59... 61... 101... 103... 1007... ... 2607... 5301413...

EXERCISE 1

1 Use your calculator to calculate:

  a $9 \times 9 \times 9 \times 9$, with the $\boxed{\times}$ key

  b 9^4, with the $\boxed{y^x}$ key.

2 Calculate the following using the same keys as in question **1**:

  a (i) $10 \times 10 \times 10$ (ii) 10^3

  b (i) $3 \times 3 \times 3 \times 3 \times 3$ (ii) 3^5

  c (i) $7 \times 7 \times 7 \times 7 \times 7 \times 7 \times 7 \times 7$ (ii) 7^8

Do you agree that indices save time and space?

3 Write these in index form. For example, $2 \times 2 \times 2 = 2^3$, and $a \times a \times a \times a = a^4$.

  a $2 \times 2 \times 2 \times 2$ **b** $5 \times 5 \times 5$ **c** $6 \times 6 \times 6 \times 6 \times 6$

  d $a \times a$ **e** $b \times b \times b$ **f** $c \times c \times c \times c \times c$

4 Write these in full. For example, $4^2 = 4 \times 4$, and $t^5 = t \times t \times t \times t \times t$.

  a 3^4 **b** 9^2 **c** 10^3 **d** 2^5

  e a^3 **f** c^2 **g** k^4 **h** n^5

5 a Copy and complete:

    (i) $2^3 \times 2^2 = 2 \times 2 \times \ldots \ldots = 2^{\cdots}$

    (ii) $3^2 \times 3^4 = 3 \times 3 \times \ldots \ldots = 3^{\cdots}$

    (iii) $a^3 \times a^3 = a \times a \times \ldots \ldots = a^{\cdots}$

    (iv) $b^4 \times b = b \times b \times \ldots \ldots = b^{\cdots}$

  b Can you see a quick way to write down answers to the questions in **a**, using the indices?

Rule 1

To multiply powers of the same number, add their indices.

$$a^m \times a^n = a^{m+n}$$

6 Copy this: $8^2 \times 8^3 = 8^{2+3} = 8^5$.

Check that $8^2 \times 8^3 = 8^5$ with your calculator.

7 a Use your calculator to check that $10^2 \times 10^4 = 10^6$.

  b Write $10^3 \times 10^4$ as a power of 10.

8 Simplify these by adding indices. For example, $a^4 \times a^3 = a^{4+3} = a^7$.

  a $t^3 \times t^2$ **b** $y^4 \times y^4$ **c** $n^2 \times n^5$ **d** $p^3 \times p^3$

  e $x^2 \times x^3$ **f** $y^6 \times y^6$ **g** $z^4 \times z^2$ **h** $k^7 \times k$

9 Write in index form, as in question **8**.

  a $2^3 \times 2^2$ **b** $3^4 \times 3^4$ **c** $9^5 \times 9^2$ **d** $10^8 \times 10$

  e $a^5 \times a^2$ **f** $b^6 \times b^6$ **g** $c^2 \times c^7$ **h** $d \times d^4$

10 Write each of these as a power of 10:

  a $10^2 \times 10^3$ **b** $10^6 \times 10^2$ **c** $10^4 \times 10$ **d** $10^5 \times 10^5$

11 Write in standard form, $a' \times 10^n$, where $1 \leqslant a < 10$.

  a $3 \times 10^4 \times 10^2$ **b** $8 \times 10 \times 10^7$ **c** $7.5 \times 10^2 \times 10^3$

12 Write in standard form, $a \times 10^n$, with a correct to 2 significant figures:

  a 2^{31} **b** 5^{20} **c** 123^{10} **d** 3^{100}

EXERCISE 2

1 a Copy and complete:

(i) $2^5 \div 2^3 = \dfrac{\cancel{2} \times \cancel{2} \times \cancel{2} \times 2 \times 2}{\cancel{2} \times \cancel{2} \times \cancel{2}} = 2^2$

(ii) $3^6 \div 3 = \dfrac{3 \times 3 \times \cdots}{3} = 3^{\cdots}$

(iii) $a^4 \div a^2 = \dfrac{a \times a \times \cdots}{a \times \cdots} = a^{\cdots}$

(iv) $b^3 \div b^2 = \dfrac{b \times b \times \cdots}{b \times \cdots} = b^{\cdots}$

b Can you see a quick way to write down the answers, using the indices?

> ### Rule 2
>
> To divide powers of the same number, subtract their indices.
>
> $$a^m \div a^n = a^{m-n}$$

2 a Copy this: $2^8 \div 2 = 2^{8-1} = 2^7$.

b Check that $2^8 \div 2 = 2^7$ with your calculator.

3 Write each of these as a power of 2:

a $2^6 \div 2^2$ **b** $2^7 \div 2^5$ **c** $2^3 \div 2$ **d** $2^9 \div 2^6$

4 Simplify these by subtracting indices. For example, $a^7 \div a^2 = a^{7-2} = a^5$.

a $t^4 \div t^2$ **b** $u^5 \div u^2$ **c** $v^8 \div v^3$ **d** $w^6 \div w$

e $p^3 \div p^2$ **f** $k^7 \div k^3$ **g** $c^9 \div c^7$ **h** $d^5 \div d^4$

5 Simplify:

a $\dfrac{m^6}{m^2}$ **b** $\dfrac{n^5}{n^4}$ **c** $\dfrac{a^3}{a^2}$ **d** $\dfrac{c^4}{c}$ **e** $\dfrac{v^8}{v^3}$

6 Simplify, writing answers in index form:

a $3^4 \div 3^2$ **b** $7^7 \div 7^4$ **c** $9^6 \div 9^2$ **d** $10^8 \div 10^5$

e $x^4 \div x^2$ **f** $y^5 \div y$ **g** $z^6 \div z^3$ **h** $n^{10} \div n^4$

EXERCISE 3

1 a Copy and complete:

(i) $(2^4)^2 = 2^4 \times 2^4 = 2^{4+4} = 2^{\cdots}$

(ii) $(5^2)^3 = 5^2 \times 5^2 \times \cdots = 5^{2+2+\cdots} = 5^{\cdots}$

(iii) $(a^3)^4 = a^3 \times a^3 \times \cdots = a^{3+3+\cdots} = a^{\cdots}$

b Can you see a quick way to write down the answers to (i)–(iii) in part **a**, using the indices?

> ### Rule 3
>
> To find a power of a power, multiply the indices.
>
> $$(a^m)^n = a^{mn}$$

2 a Copy this: $(3^2)^3 = 3^{2 \times 3} = 3^6$

b Check that $(3^2)^3 = 3^6$ with your calculator.

3 Write each of the following as a power of 3:

a $(3^2)^4$ **b** $(3^5)^2$ **c** $(3^3)^3$ **d** $(3^4)^{10}$ **e** $(3^6)^6$

4 Simplify these. For example, $(a^4)^3 = a^{12}$.

a $(p^3)^2$ **b** $(q^4)^2$ **c** $(r^5)^2$ **d** $(s^2)^3$ **e** $(t^6)^5$

5 Simplify, writing answers in index form:

a $(2^6)^2$ **b** $(7^5)^3$ **c** $(8^4)^5$ **d** $(10^3)^4$ **e** $(3^9)^9$

f $(u^2)^7$ **g** $(v^7)^2$ **h** $(w^3)^6$ **i** $(m^5)^5$ **j** $(n^8)^7$

6 Say whether each of these is true (T) or false (F).

a $2^5 = 32$ **b** $3^2 = 6$ **c** $10^3 = 1000$ **d** $2^3 = 3^2$

e $5^5 \times 5^5 = 5^{10}$ **f** $10^{10} \div 10^5 = 10^5$

g $(2^{10})^{10} = 2^{100}$ **h** $(2^3)^4 = (2^6)^2$

i $2^{10} > 1000$ **j** $5^{10} < 10$ million

7 Copy and complete:

a $(ab)^2 = ab \times ab = a^2 b^{\cdots}$

b $(mn)^3 = mn \times \cdots \times \cdots = m^3 n^{\cdots}$

8 In general, $(ab)^m = a^m b^m$. Use this result to simplify:

a $(ab)^4$ **b** $(cd)^5$ **c** $(xy)^{10}$ **d** $(pq)^{20}$

EXERCISE 4B (ON CONTENT OF EXERCISES 1–3)

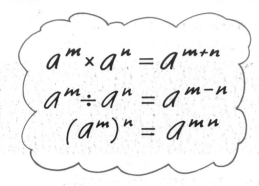

$$a^m \times a^n = a^{m+n}$$
$$a^m \div a^n = a^{m-n}$$
$$(a^m)^n = a^{mn}$$

1 Simplify:

  a $n^2 \times n^3$ **b** $p^4 \times p^4$ **c** $t^3 \times t$ **d** $u^5 \times u^2$

  e $k^5 \div k^2$ **f** $s^4 \div s^3$ **g** $v^6 \div v^4$ **h** $w^2 \div w$

  i $(a^2)^3$ **j** $(b^4)^2$ **k** $(c^5)^2$ **l** $(d^2)^6$

2 Simplify. For example, $3a^2 \times 4a^3 = 12a^5$.

  a $2a^2 \times a^3$ **b** $x^2 \times 3x^4$ **c** $2y^2 \times 3y^2$

  d $8x^2 \div 2x$ **e** $10y^3 \div 2y^2$ **f** $6z^4 \div 3z^2$

3 Express in standard form, $a \times 10^n$:

  a 5000 **b** $230\,000$ **c** $1\,470\,000$

  d $3 \times 10^4 \times 4 \times 10^2$ **e** $2.5 \times 10 \times 1.4 \times 10^9$

4 Multiply out the brackets:

  a $x^3(x^2 + x^4)$ **b** $y^2(y^3 - y)$ **c** $z^2(z^4 - 1)$

5 Simplify these, using $(ab)^n = a^n b^n$.

  a $(uv)^8$ **b** $(2x)^3$ **c** $(3y)^4$ **d** $(mn^2)^5$

6 Express as powers of 2 or 5:

  a $\dfrac{2^5 \times 2^4}{2^3}$ **b** $\dfrac{2^2 \times 2^6}{2^4}$ **c** $\dfrac{5^3 \times 5^4}{5^2}$ **d** $\dfrac{5 \times 5^9}{5^3}$

7 Simplify:

  a $\dfrac{x^3 \times x^4}{x^2}$ **b** $\dfrac{y^5 \times y^2}{y}$ **c** $\dfrac{z^2 \times z^8}{z^3}$ **d** $\dfrac{t^3 \times t^6}{t^4}$

8 Find n. For example, if $2^n = 16 = 2^4$, $n = 4$.

  a $2^n = 8$ **b** $3^n = 81$ **c** $4^n = 4$ **d** $5^n = 625$

9 Make equations, and solve them. For example, if $a^x \times a^2 = a^5$, then $x + 2 = 5$, and $x = 3$.

  a $a^x \times a^3 = a^8$ **b** $a^x \times a^4 = a^7$ **c** $a^3 \times a^x = a^6$

10 1 parsec $= 2.06 \times 10^5$ astronomical units, and 1 astronomical unit $= 1.5 \times 10^8$ km. How many km are there in 1 parsec?

11

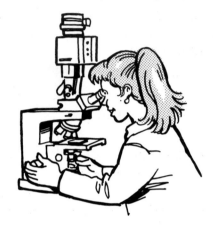

Sandra works in a Health and Safety laboratory. She is analysing a batch of bacteria which contained 100 at first, but increased by 8% every hour.

  a Explain why there are 100×1.08 after one hour.

  b Calculate the number of bacteria after:
    (i) one hour (ii) two hours (iii) three hours.

  c Use trial and improvement to find the number of hours needed for the original number of bacteria to double.

ZERO AND NEGATIVE INDICES

Assuming that the rule $a^m \times a^n = a^{m+n}$ holds for $n = 0$ and n negative:

(i) $a^m \times a^0 = a^{m+0} = a^m$

So $\boxed{a^0 = 1}$ **Rule 4**

(ii) $a^m \times a^{-m} = a^{m-m} = a^0 = 1$

So $\boxed{a^{-m} = \dfrac{1}{a^m}}$ **Rule 5**

EXERCISE 5A

1 Use your calculator to check that:
a $2^0 = 1$ **b** $3^0 = 1$ **c** $100^0 = 1$ **d** $999^0 = 1$

2 Using your calculator, copy and complete:
a $2^{-1} = 0. \ldots = \dfrac{1}{2}$ **b** $2^{-2} = \ldots = \dfrac{1}{2^2}$

c $10^{-1} = \ldots = \dfrac{1}{10}$ **d** $10^{-2} = \ldots = \dfrac{1}{10^2}$

3 Copy and complete these two sequences, without using your calculator:

a 10^3 10^2 10^1 $10^{\cdots}$ $10^{\cdots}$ $10^{\cdots}$ $10^{\cdots}$
    1000   100   10   1 $\dfrac{1}{10}$ $\ldots$ $\ldots$

b $10^0 = \ldots, \ 10^{-1} = \ldots, \ 10^{-2} = \ldots, \ 10^{-3} = \ldots$

> Note: $10^0 = 1$, $10^{-1} = \frac{1}{10}$

4 Write down the value of:
a 5^0 **b** 7^0 **c** a^0 **d** x^0 **e** t^0

5 Write with positive indices. For example, $x^{-3} = \dfrac{1}{x^3}$
a x^{-2} **b** y^{-3} **c** z^{-4} **d** u^{-6} **e** v^{-1}

6 Write these with positive indices:
a 9^{-1} **b** 3^{-2} **c** 5^{-2} **d** 2^{-3} **e** 10^{-2}

> **REMEMBER RULES 1, 2 & 3**
> $a^m \times a^n = a^{m+n}$
> $a^m \div a^n = a^{m-n}$
> $(a^m)^n = a^{mn}$

7 Simplify the following. For example, $y^{-2} \div y^2 = y^{-2-2} = y^{-4}$.
a $a^3 \times a^{-2}$ **b** $t^5 \times t^{-3}$ **c** $m^{-1} \times m^{-1}$
d $n^2 \times n^{-2}$ **e** $x^2 \div x^{-1}$ **f** $y^4 \div y^{-2}$
g $t^{-3} \div t^3$ **h** $t^{-3} \div t^{-3}$ **i** $(u^{-2})^3$
j $(v^4)^{-1}$ **k** $(w^{-2})^{-2}$ **l** $(k^{-1})^0$

8 Which is the larger number in each pair?
a 2^{-2} or 3^{-2} **b** 5^0 or 5^{-1} **c** 3^{-1} or $(-1)^3$

9 Find the value of:
a $(5^2)^0$ **b** $3^5 \times 3^{-4}$ **c** $2^2 \div 2^{-1}$ **d** $(7^0)^{-9}$
e $5^6 \times 5^{-5}$ **f** $4^3 \div 4^4$ **g** $10^{-3} \times 10^3$ **h** $(2^{-2})^{-2}$

10 $f(x) = 2^x$. Calculate the value of:
a $f(3)$ **b** $f(0)$ **c** $f(-2)$ **d** $f(1)$ **e** $f(-1)$

EXERCISE 5B

1 Express in standard form:
a 0.0025 **b** 0.03 **c** 0.000 001 9
d $3.14 \times 10^2 \times 10^{-5}$ **e** $7.5 \times 10^{-1} \times 1.2 \times 10^{-3}$

2 Simplify, and express with positive indices:
a $p^2 \times p^{-4}$ **b** $q^3 \times q^{-4}$ **c** $r^2 \times r^{-2}$ **d** $s^{-5} \times s^{-5}$
e $t^4 \div t^{-2}$ **f** $t^{-4} \div t^{-2}$ **g** $t^{-4} \div t^2$ **h** $t^{-4} \div t^{-4}$
i $(u^3)^{-1}$ **j** $(v^{-4})^2$ **k** $(w^{-5})^{-5}$ **l** $(x^{-1})^{10}$

3 Simplify, and express with positive indices.
For example, $2x^{-1} = 2 \times x^{-1} = 2 \times \dfrac{1}{x} = \dfrac{2}{x}$.

a $3x^{-1}$ **b** $5y^{-3}$ **c** $8m^{-2}$ **d** $10t^{-1}$
e $\dfrac{1}{2}x^{-1}$ **f** $\dfrac{1}{3}t^{-2}$ **g** $\dfrac{3}{4}u^{-3}$ **h** $\dfrac{2}{3}v^{-4}$

4 Multiply out:
a $y^4(y^2 + y^{-2})$ **b** $k^3(k - k^{-1})$ **c** $n^{-2}(n^3 + n)$
d $m^{-1}(m + m^2)$ **e** $u(u^2 - u^{-2})$ **f** $v^{-2}(1 - v^2)$

5 The course for a yacht race is a rectangle 8.5×10^5 m long and 4.5×10^3 m wide. Calculate the area of the rectangle, in standard form.

6 The mass of an electron is 9.11×10^{-28} g. Calculate, in standard form, to 1 decimal place:
a the mass of 6×10^{17} electrons
b the number of electrons that have a total mass of 1.09×10^{48} g.

FRACTIONAL INDICES

The mystery of $a^{\frac{1}{2}}$

I know what a^2, a^{100}, a^0, a^{-1}, a^{-10} mean, but what does $a^{\frac{1}{2}}$ mean?

Assuming that the rule $(a^m)^n = a^{mn}$ is true for fractional indices:

(i) $(a^{1/2})^2 = a$, so $a^{1/2} = \sqrt{a}$ (ii) $(a^{1/3})^3 = a$, so $a^{1/3} = \sqrt[3]{a}$ (iii) $(a^{2/3})^3 = a^2$, so $a^{2/3} = \sqrt[3]{a^2}$.

These illustrate **Rule 6**. $\boxed{a^{m/n} = \sqrt[n]{a^m}}$ a^m is the power on each side, n is the root.

Examples
a $x^{3/4} = \sqrt[4]{x^3}$ (x^3 is the power, 4 is the root.) **b** $y^{1/2} = \sqrt{y}$ $(\sqrt[2]{y^1})$

EXERCISE 6A

1 Write these in root form (see the examples above).

a $m^{3/4}$ **b** $n^{4/5}$ **c** $k^{2/3}$ **d** $x^{1/2}$ **e** $y^{1/3}$

2 Write these in index form. For example, $\sqrt[3]{x^5} = x^{5/3}$ (x^5 is the power, 3 is the root).

a $\sqrt[3]{y^5}$ **b** $\sqrt[3]{z^4}$ **c** $\sqrt[3]{y^2}$ **d** $\sqrt[3]{t}$ **e** $\sqrt{u}$

3 Use your calculator to check that:
a $\sqrt{10} = 10^{1/2}$ $(10^{0.5})$ **b** $\sqrt{2} = 2^{1/2}$

4 Express these as powers of 2, 3 or 5; for example, $81 = 3^4$.

a 4 **b** 9 **c** 25 **d** 8 **e** 16
f 27 **g** 32 **h** 125 **i** 64 **j** 243

5 Evaluate these; for example, $36^{1/2} = (6^2)^{1/2} = 6$.
a $9^{1/2}$ **b** $4^{1/2}$ **c** $100^{1/2}$ **d** $25^{1/2}$ **e** $81^{1/2}$
f $8^{1/3}$ **g** $27^{1/3}$ **h** $64^{1/3}$ **i** $1000^{1/3}$

6 Evaluate these; for example, $16^{3/4} = (2^4)^{3/4} = 2^3 = 8$.
a $8^{2/3}$ **b** $27^{2/3}$ **c** $4^{3/2}$ **d** $25^{3/2}$

7 a Evaluate: (i) $100^{3/2}$ (ii) $81^{3/4}$.
b Check your answers to **a** with a calculator, using:
(i) $100^{1.5}$ (ii) $81^{0.75}$.

8 Which is greater in each pair?
a $16^{1/2}$ or $8^{1/3}$ **b** $32^{1/5}$ or $27^{1/3}$

9 $x = 4$, $y = 9$ and $z = 16$. Evaluate:
a $x^{1/2} + y^{1/2} + z^{1/2}$ **b** $x^{1/2} + (y + z)^{1/2}$

10 Calculate the lengths of the edges of the square and the cube, correct to 2 significant figures.

a

Area
12 cm²

b

Volume
20 cm³

11 Given $f(x) = 25^x$, calculate:
a $f(\frac{1}{2})$ **b** $f(0)$ **c** $f(\frac{3}{2})$

EXERCISE 6B

$$a^m \times a^n = a^{m+n}$$
$$a^m \div a^n = a^{m-n}$$
$$(a^m)^n = a^{mn} \qquad a^0 = 1$$
$$a^{-m} = \frac{1}{a^m}$$
$$a^{m/n} = \sqrt[n]{a^m}$$

1 Simplify:

a $u^{3/2} \times u^{1/2}$ **b** $v^{4/3} \times v^{-1/3}$ **c** $w^{1/2} \times w^{-1/2}$

d $x^{3/2} \div x^{1/2}$ **e** $y^{3/4} \div y^{1/4}$ **f** $y^{3/4} \div y^{-1/4}$

g $(t^{1/2})^2$ **h** $(p^{-1/2})^2$ **i** $(q^{1/4})^0$ **j** $(r^3)^{1/3}$

2 Multiply out the brackets:

a $x^{1/2}(x^{1/2} + x^{-1/2})$ **b** $y^{2/3}(y^{4/3} - y^{1/3})$

c $m^{-3/4}(m^{7/4} - m^{-1/4})$ **d** $n^{-1/2}(n^{3/2} - n^{-1/2})$

3 Find these values; for example, when $x = 8$,
$2x^{-1/3} = 2 \times 8^{-1/3} = 2 \times (2^3)^{-1/3} = 2 \times 2^{-1}$
$= 2^0 = 1$.

a $6x^{-1/2}$ when $x = 9$ **b** $3y^{-2/3}$ when $y = 27$

c $5z^{-1/2}$ when $z = 25$ **d** $4t^{-3/4}$ when $t = 16$

4 Given $x = 36$, $y = 27$ and $z = 16$, find the value of
$6x^{-1/2} + 3y^{-1/3} + 2z^{-1/4}$.

5 Simplify:

a $\dfrac{a^3 \times a^{-2}}{a}$ **b** $\dfrac{b^{-1} \times b^4}{b^{-2}}$ **c** $\dfrac{c^2 \times c^{-2}}{c^{-1}}$

6 Simplify:

a $\dfrac{x^{1/2} \times x^{-3/2}}{x^2}$ **b** $\dfrac{y^{-1/3} \times y^{4/3}}{y}$ **c** $\dfrac{z^{3/4} \times z^{-3/4}}{z^{-1}}$

7 Multiply out:

a $(a^2 + 1)(a^{-2} + 1)$ **b** $(b^{-1} + 1)(b^{-1} - 1)$

8 Multiply out:

a $(x^{1/2} + 1)(x^{1/2} + 1)$ **b** $(y^{1/2} + 1)(y^{1/2} - 1)$

c $(u^{1/2} + 1)(u^{-1/2} + 1)$ **d** $(v^{1/2} + 1)(v^{-1/2} - 1)$

/ **CHALLENGE**

Many formulae contain powers and roots. Here are a few to use in calculations. Give answers correct to 3 significant figures.

	Formula	Used for	Calculate	Given
a	$A = \pi r^2$	area of circle	A	$r = 12.5$
b	$V = x^3$	volume of cube	V	$x = 75$
c	$T = 2\pi\sqrt{\dfrac{l}{g}}$	time of pendulum	T	$l = 39,$ $g = 9.8$
d	$A = PR^n$	compound interest	A	$P = 80,$ $R = 1.07,$ $n = 15$
e	$T = k\sqrt{R^3}$	planet's 'year'	T	$k = 1.2,$ $R = 5.9$
f	$r = \sqrt[3]{\dfrac{3V}{4\pi}}$	radius of sphere	r	$V = 147$

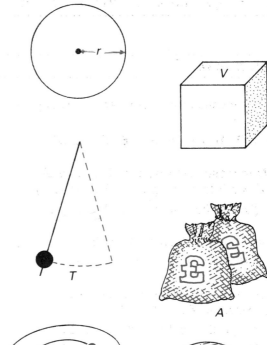

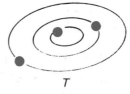

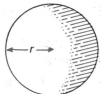

GROWTH AND DECAY

Growth and decay are all around you—you can see them in plants, in populations, even in life itself. Sometimes they can be described mathematically.

Examples

a Leave £1 in the bank at 10% p.a. compound interest.
After 1 year you'll have £1 + £0.1 = £1.1.
After 2 years you'll have £1.1 + £0.11 = £1.21 = £1.1².
After 3 years, you'll have £1.21 + £0.121 = £1.331 = £1.1³.
The formula for the amount £A after n years is $A = 1.1^n$.

b A profit of £1 is doubled every year.
The formula for the profit £P after n years is $P = 2^n$.

c A loss of £1 is halved every year.
The formula for the loss £P after n years is

$$P = \frac{1}{2^n} = 2^{-n}.$$

d The unit mass of a radioactive mineral decays after t years according to
the formula $m = e^{-0.05t}$, where $e \doteqdot 2.718$.

These four formulae describe **exponential** growth or decay, which have a characteristic equation $y = a^x$, and a graph like the one shown below when $a > 1$.

EXERCISE 7

1 a Copy and complete this table.

x	-3	-2	-1	0	1	2	3
2^x	0.13	0.25					

b Draw the graph of $y = 2^x$, for $-3 \leqslant x \leqslant 3$, and compare it with the one opposite.

2 a Copy and complete:

x	-3	-2	-1	0	1	2	3
2^{-x}	8						

b Draw the graph of $y = 2^{-x}$, for $-3 \leqslant x \leqslant 3$ on the same diagram as question **1**.

c Which line is an axis of symmetry for the combined graphs?

d Which curve illustrates:
(i) growth (ii) decay?

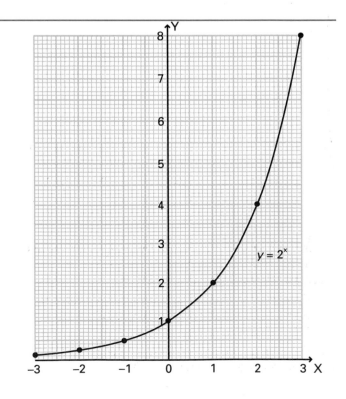

$y = 2^x$

3 a Copy and complete this table, correct to 1 decimal place where necessary.

x	0	0.5	1	1.5	2
10^x		3.2			

b Draw the graph of $y = 10^x$ for $0 \leqslant x \leqslant 2$.

c Estimate, correct to 2 significant figures:
(i) $10^{1.2}$ (ii) x, when $10^x = 40$.

4 a Draw the graph of the compound interest formula $A = 1.1^n$ using $n = 0, 10, 20, 30$ and 40.

b From your graph, estimate A after:
(i) 25 years   (ii) 35 years.

c Check your answers to **b** by calculator.

5 The mass–time formula for radioactive mineral decay is $m = e^{-0.05t}$.

a Calculate m, correct to 2 decimal places for $e = 2.718$ and $t = 0, 10, 20, 30$ and 40, and draw the graph.

b 'Half-life' is the time at which half the mass remains. Check that this is about 14 years.

6 In 1970 there were 320 000 students in secondary schools in Scotland. A year later the number was 328 000.

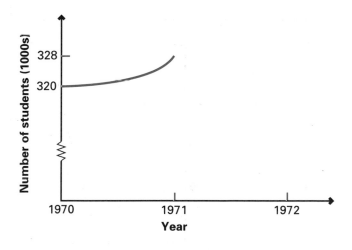

Assume that the number of thousands of students, S, after t years is given by $S(t) = a \times b^t$.
Then $S(0) = 320$ and $S(1) = 328$.

a Use these two values of S to find the values of a and b, and show that the formula is $S(t) = 320 \times 1.025^t$.

b Use the formula to estimate the number of thousands of students in 1980.

7 At the start of an experiment ($t = 0$), there were 100 bacteria in a dish. After 2 hours ($t = 2$), there were 625. Assume that the number of bacteria, N, after t hours is given by $N(t) = a \times b^t$.

a Find the values of a and b, and write down a formula for $N(t)$.

b Calculate the number of bacteria after 12 hours (rounded in a sensible way).

/ **BRAINSTORMER**   /

In Barundia the population is increasing at the rate of 2% every year. The Minister of Planning, Major Diawara, said in a speech that the population would double in 35 years. Was he right?

/ **CHALLENGE**   /

On one diagram draw the graphs of $y = 2^x$ and $y = x + 2$, for $-1 \leqslant x \leqslant 3$. Write down one value of x for which $2^x = x + 2$. Then find the other solution of this equation, correct to 2 decimal places, using an iterative (step-by-step) method.

/ **PRACTICAL PROJECT**   /

Newton's law of cooling

Heat a beaker or pan of water, until it has nearly reached the boiling point. Put a thermometer in the water, and measure the temperature every minute until it is nearly constant. Put your readings in a table, and plot the points. Join them by a 'best-fitting' smooth curve.

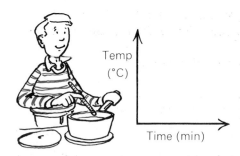

The equation of the curve is $T = a^{-kt}$, where T is the temperature difference between the water and the room, a and k are positive constants, and t is the time in minutes from the start. Find the equation of your curve.

SOME SPECIAL KINDS OF NUMBERS: SURDS

CLASS DISCUSSION

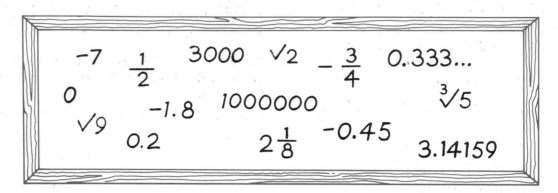

In mathematics you have worked with different kinds of numbers.

Whole numbers: 0, 1, 2, 3, 4, 5, . . .

Integers: . . . , $-3, -2, -1, 0, 1, 2, 3,$ . . .

Rational numbers: for example, $7, -4, \frac{1}{2}, -\frac{3}{2}$ (numbers which can be put in ratio form, $\frac{p}{q}$, where p and q are integers, but $q \neq 0$).

There are other kinds of numbers you have not yet met. Solve these equations to find one of these.

(i) $2x - 3 = 1$. The solution is a whole number. Which one?

(ii) $2x + 3 = 1$. The solution is an integer, but not a whole number. Which one?

(iii) $2x - 2 = 1$. The solution is a rational number. Which one?

(iv) $2x^2 - 3 = 1$. The solutions are not whole numbers, integers or rational numbers.

$x^2 = 2$, so $x = \sqrt{2}$ or $-\sqrt{2}$, and these cannot be written in the form $\frac{p}{q}$. They are **irrational** numbers. π is another irrational number, $3.14159265 \ldots$

Every point on this number line represents a **rational** or an **irrational** number.

Which numbers above the line are irrational?

Together, the rational numbers and the irrational numbers make up the set of **real** numbers, represented by *all* the points on the number line.

A **surd** is a special kind of irrational number. It is a square root, cube root, etc., which cannot be expressed as a rational number (so 'cannot work out exactly').
For example, $\sqrt{2}, \sqrt{10}, \sqrt[3]{5}$ are all surds, but $\sqrt{16}$ and $\sqrt[3]{27}$ are *not* surds, since $\sqrt{16} = 4$ and $\sqrt[3]{27} = 3$.

EXERCISE 8A

1 Which of these are surds (ones which do not 'work out exactly')?

a $\sqrt{4}$ **b** $\sqrt{5}$ **c** $\sqrt{6}$ **d** $\sqrt{9}$ **e** $\sqrt{10}$

f $\sqrt{25}$ **g** $\sqrt{30}$ **h** $\sqrt{36}$ **i** $\sqrt{40}$ **j** $\sqrt{49}$

k $\sqrt[3]{1}$ **l** $\sqrt[3]{5}$ **m** $\sqrt[3]{8}$ **n** $\sqrt[3]{100}$ **o** $\sqrt[3]{1000}$

2 Use your calculator to check that:

a $\sqrt{6} = \sqrt{2} \times \sqrt{3}$ **b** $\sqrt{10} = \sqrt{2} \times \sqrt{5}$ **c** $\sqrt{\dfrac{6}{5}} = \dfrac{\sqrt{6}}{\sqrt{5}}$

Rules for surds

Assuming that $(ab)^n = a^n b^n$ is true for fractional indices, $(ab)^{1/2} = a^{1/2}b^{1/2}$, or $\sqrt{(ab)} = \sqrt{a}\sqrt{b}$;

and $\sqrt{\dfrac{a}{b}} = \dfrac{\sqrt{a}}{\sqrt{b}}$.

Example   Simplify $\sqrt{75}$.
$\sqrt{75} = \sqrt{(25 \times 3)} = \sqrt{25} \times \sqrt{3} = 5\sqrt{3}$.

Hint   Look for factors, like 25, that are square numbers.

---

3 Write down the value of:

a $\sqrt{16}$ **b** $\sqrt{100}$ **c** $\sqrt{25}$ **d** $\sqrt{1}$ **e** $\sqrt{81}$

4 Simplify. For example, $\sqrt{40} = \sqrt{(4 \times 10)} = 2\sqrt{10}$.

a $\sqrt{12}$ **b** $\sqrt{20}$ **c** $\sqrt{18}$ **d** $\sqrt{27}$ **e** $\sqrt{8}$

f $\sqrt{24}$ **g** $\sqrt{28}$ **h** $\sqrt{32}$ **i** $\sqrt{45}$ **j** $\sqrt{48}$

k $\sqrt{44}$ **l** $\sqrt{63}$ **m** $\sqrt{50}$ **n** $\sqrt{54}$ **o** $\sqrt{200}$

5 Use Pythagoras' Theorem to calculate the length of the third side of $\triangle ABC$, as a surd in its simplest form, when:

a $b = 2, c = 2$ **b** $b = 4, c = 6$ **c** $b = 4, c = 8$

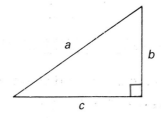

6 Add or subtract these surds. For example:
$8\sqrt{3} - 2\sqrt{3} = 6\sqrt{3}$ (compare $8x - 2x = 6x$).

a $4\sqrt{2} + 3\sqrt{2}$ **b** $5\sqrt{2} - 3\sqrt{2}$ **c** $6\sqrt{3} + 2\sqrt{3}$

d $6\sqrt{3} - 2\sqrt{3}$ **e** $\sqrt{5} + \sqrt{5}$ **f** $\sqrt{5} - \sqrt{5}$

g $8\sqrt{2} + 2\sqrt{2}$ **h** $2\sqrt{3} - \sqrt{3}$ **i** $3\sqrt{3} + 3\sqrt{3}$

7 The grid consists of cm squares. Calculate the perimeter of each shape, in simplest surd form.

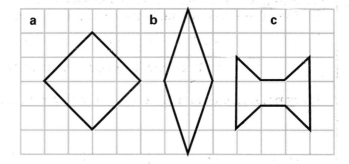

EXERCISE 8B

1 Calculate, in simplest surd form, the length of this cube's:

   a face diagonal

   b space diagonal.

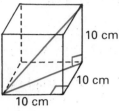

10 cm
10 cm
10 cm

2 Simplify these; for example,
$\sqrt{50}-3\sqrt{2}=5\sqrt{2}-3\sqrt{2}=2\sqrt{2}.$

   a $\sqrt{8}+\sqrt{2}$ **b** $\sqrt{18}+\sqrt{2}$ **c** $\sqrt{125}-5\sqrt{5}$

   d $\sqrt{48}-\sqrt{12}$ **e** $\sqrt{45}-\sqrt{20}$ **f** $\sqrt{63}+\sqrt{28}$

3 Simplify these; for example,
$\sqrt{2}\times\sqrt{6}=\sqrt{12}=\sqrt{4\times3}=2\sqrt{3}.$

   a $\sqrt{2}\times\sqrt{2}$ **b** $\sqrt{6}\times\sqrt{6}$ **c** $\sqrt{2}\times\sqrt{50}$

   d $\sqrt{3}\times\sqrt{12}$ **e** $\sqrt{3}\times\sqrt{27}$ **f** $\sqrt{10}\times\sqrt{2}$

   g $\sqrt{3}\times\sqrt{15}$ **h** $\sqrt{5}\times\sqrt{10}$ **i** $\sqrt{5}\times\sqrt{15}$

4 a Calculate the lengths of AC and AD as surds in their simplest form.

   b Write down the length of the hypotenuse of the:
   (i) 3rd   (ii) 4th   (iii) nth
   triangle in the sequence of right-angled triangles constructed as shown.

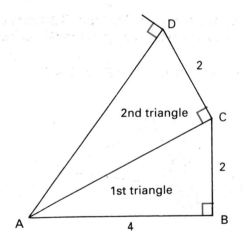

D

2nd triangle

C

2

1st triangle

2

A   4   B

5 Multiply out the brackets. For example:
$(\sqrt{3}+2)(\sqrt{3}-1)=\sqrt{3}(\sqrt{3}-1)+2(\sqrt{3}-1)$
$=3-\sqrt{3}+2\sqrt{3}-2=1+\sqrt{3}.$

   a $(2+\sqrt{2})(3+\sqrt{2})$ **b** $(2+\sqrt{2})(3-\sqrt{2})$

   c $(\sqrt{5}-\sqrt{3})(\sqrt{5}+\sqrt{3})$ **d** $(\sqrt{3}-\sqrt{2})^2$

6 Simplify: (i) $x+y$ (ii) $x-y$ (iii) xy,   when:

   a $x=\sqrt{3}+1, y=\sqrt{3}-1$ **b** $x=1+\sqrt{2}, y=1-\sqrt{2}$

   c $x=\sqrt{3}, y=\sqrt{2}-\sqrt{3}$ **d** $x=\sqrt{5}-\sqrt{2}, y=\sqrt{2}$

   Which answers are rational?

7 Calculate, as surds in their simplest form, the lengths of this cuboid's:

   a face diagonals

   b space diagonals.

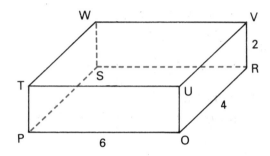

W   V
                      2
        S   R
T   U
            U   4
P   6   O

Rationalising a surd denominator

$\dfrac{1}{\sqrt{2}}=\dfrac{1}{\sqrt{2}}\times\dfrac{\sqrt{2}}{\sqrt{2}}=\dfrac{\sqrt{2}}{2}$. Given $\sqrt{2}\doteqdot1.414$, which form is easier to calculate, $\dfrac{1}{\sqrt{2}}$ or $\dfrac{\sqrt{2}}{2}$?

Example

Rationalise the denominator of $\dfrac{8}{\sqrt{6}}$

$\dfrac{8}{\sqrt{6}}=\dfrac{8}{\sqrt{6}}\times\dfrac{\sqrt{6}}{\sqrt{6}}=\dfrac{8\sqrt{6}}{6}=\dfrac{4\sqrt{6}}{3}$

8 Rationalise the denominators, and simplify where possible:

   a $\dfrac{1}{\sqrt{6}}$ **b** $\dfrac{1}{\sqrt{7}}$ **c** $\dfrac{2}{\sqrt{6}}$ **d** $\dfrac{3}{\sqrt{3}}$ **e** $\dfrac{5}{\sqrt{10}}$

   f $\dfrac{1}{\sqrt{11}}$ **g** $\dfrac{4}{\sqrt{2}}$ **h** $\dfrac{20}{\sqrt{5}}$ **i** $\dfrac{6}{\sqrt{3}}$ **j** $\dfrac{12}{\sqrt{6}}$

9 Simplify:

   a $\dfrac{1}{2+\sqrt{3}}\times\dfrac{2-\sqrt{3}}{2-\sqrt{3}}$ **b** $\dfrac{1}{\sqrt{5}-1}\times\dfrac{\sqrt{5}+1}{\sqrt{5}+1}$

   c $\dfrac{1}{\sqrt{2}+1}\times\dfrac{\sqrt{2}-1}{\sqrt{2}-1}$ **d** $\dfrac{1}{2+\sqrt{2}}$ **e** $\dfrac{1}{\sqrt{2}-1}$

   f $\dfrac{1}{\sqrt{3}+1}$ **g** $\dfrac{4}{\sqrt{5}-1}$

CHECK-UP ON INDICES AND SURDS

1 Simplify:

  a $a^3 \times a^2$ **b** $a^3 \div a^2$ **c** $(a^3)^2$ **d** $(a^3)^0$

2 Simplify:

  a $b^3 \times b^{-1}$ **b** $b^3 \div b^{-1}$ **c** $(b^3)^{-1}$ **d** $(b^{-3})^{-1}$

3 Express with positive indices:

  a u^{-1} **b** v^{-2} **c** w^{-3} **d** $2x^{-1}$

4 Express in index form:

  a $\sqrt{5}$ **b** $\sqrt{x}$ **c** $\sqrt[3]{p}$ **d** $\sqrt[3]{p^2}$

5 Simplify:

  a $x^{1/2} \times x^{3/2}$ **b** $y^{2/3} \div y^{1/3}$ **c** $(z^{3/2})^2$

6 Find the value of:

  a $4^{1/2}$ **b** $27^{1/3}$ **c** $9^{3/2}$ **d** 5^{-1} **e** $16^{-1/2}$

7 Simplify:

  a $x^7 \times x^3$ **b** $x^{12} \div x^{10}$ **c** $x^{1/2} \times x^{3/2}$ **d** $x^{4/3} \div x^{1/3}$

8 Given $x = 9$ and $y = 4$, find the value of:

  a $x^{1/2} + y^{1/2}$ **b** $x^{3/2} - y^{3/2}$

  c $x^{-1/2} + y^{-1/2}$ **d** $(xy)^{1/2}$

9 Copy and complete this diagram, putting the answer for each calculation in the next circle.

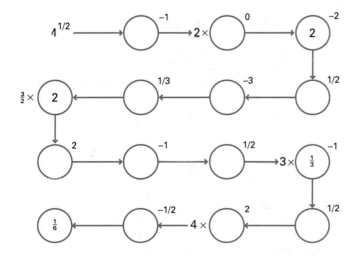

10 Express these in standard form, $a \times 10^n$.

  a $15 \times 8 \times 1000$ **b** $2.5 \times 3 \times 0.001$

  c $2 \times 10^4 \times 3 \times 10^8$ **d** $8 \times 10^2 \div (4 \times 10^6)$

11 $f(x) = 8^x$. Calculate the value of f when $x =$:

  a 0 **b** -1 **c** $\tfrac{1}{3}$ **d** $\tfrac{2}{3}$

12 Find the value of x if:

  a $2^x = 8$ **b** $3^x = 1$ **c** $2^x = \tfrac{1}{2}$ **d** $3^x = \tfrac{1}{27}$

13 Multiply out:

  a $x^2(x^3 + x^4)$ **b** $y^3(y^3 + y^{-6})$ **c** $z^{1/2}(z^{1/2} - z^{-1/2})$

14 a Draw the graphs of $y = 5^x$ and $y = 5^{-x}$ for $-2 \leqslant x \leqslant 2$.

  b Write down:

    (i) the coordinates of the point where the graphs cross the y-axis

    (ii) the equation of the axis of symmetry.

15 In an experiment, 10 fruit flies were placed in a jar. Two days later there were 40. The number N after t days is given by $N(t) = a \times b^t$.

  a Find the values of a and b, and write down a formula for N.

  b Predict the number of flies in the jar after a week.

16 Which of these are surds?

  $\sqrt{1}, \sqrt{2}, \sqrt{3}, \sqrt{4}, \sqrt{5}, \sqrt{6}, \sqrt{7}, \sqrt{8}, \sqrt{9}, \sqrt{10}$

17 Simplify:

  a $\sqrt{100}$ **b** $\sqrt{300}$ **c** $\sqrt{20}$ **d** $\sqrt{80}$ **e** $\sqrt{150}$

18 Simplify:

  a $\sqrt{3} + 4\sqrt{3}$ **b** $5\sqrt{7} - 2\sqrt{7}$ **c** $\sqrt{8} - \sqrt{2}$

19 Each square has sides 1 km long. Calculate, in simplest surd form, the length of the TV cable lines:

  a $A \to B \to C$ **b** $C \to D \to E$ **c** $E \to A$

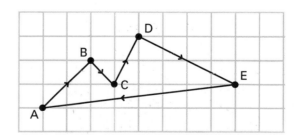

20 Rationalise the denominators of:

  a $\dfrac{1}{\sqrt{5}}$ **b** $\dfrac{2}{\sqrt{6}}$ **c** $\dfrac{4}{\sqrt{2}}$ **d** $\dfrac{9}{\sqrt{3}}$ **e** $\dfrac{5}{2\sqrt{10}}$

10 TRIGONOMETRY – TRIANGLE CALCULATIONS

Note In this chapter give answers correct to
1 decimal place, unless there are other instructions.

LOOKING BACK

1 Write down ratios for sin A, cos A and tan A in
each triangle:

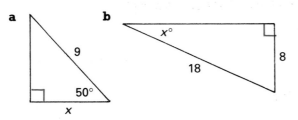

Reminder
SOH - CAH - TOA

2 Calculate *x* in each triangle:

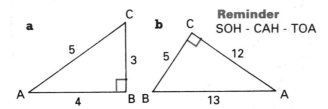

3 Write down the bearings of A, B and C from the
point O.

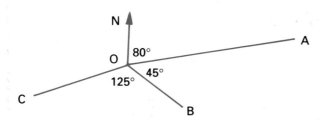

4 Calculate the width of the river, *w* metres.

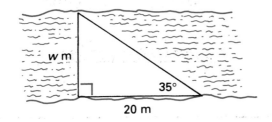

5 What is the bearing of:
a Q from P **b** P from Q?

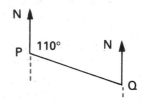

6 Calculate the angle of depression, *y*°, of the boat
from the cliff-top.

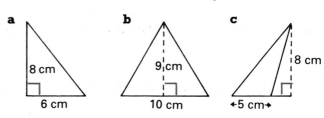

7 Calculate the area of each triangle below:

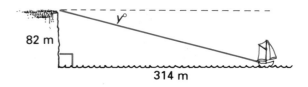

8 Copy and complete this table:

A	50°	134°	(A < 90°)	(A < 90°)
sin A			0.5	
cos A				0.5

9 Solve each equation for A, where $0° \leqslant A \leqslant 180°$:
a $\cos A = 0.1$ **b** $\cos A = -0.2$
c $\sin A = 0.8$ (two solutions)

10 The Northern Star sails 800 m on a bearing of
072° from A to B, then for 500 m on a bearing of
147° to C. Make a scale drawing, and find the
distance and bearing of C from A.

11 Make *x* the subject in each of these:

a $\dfrac{x}{a} = b$ **b** $\dfrac{x}{a} = \dfrac{b}{c}$ **c** $\sin A = \dfrac{x}{d}$

d $\dfrac{a}{x} = b$ **e** $\dfrac{a}{x} = \dfrac{b}{c}$ **f** $\sin A = \dfrac{d}{x}$

THE SINE RULE

CLASS DISCUSSION

Tracking stations at A and B observe the ascent of the Space Shuttle, now at C. From A its angle of elevation is 50° and its distance is 100 km. From B its angle of elevation is 60°. How can they find its distance from B?

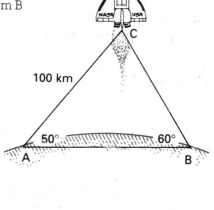

a Is there enough information above for a scale drawing?
b Sketch △ABC, and draw CD perpendicular to AB.
   Can you now use trigonometry to calculate: (i) CD   (ii) BC?
   Using the Sine Rule would give a quicker method.

(i) ∠A acute

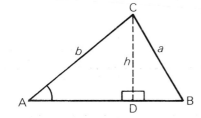

(ii) ∠A obtuse

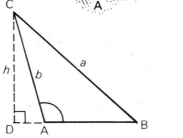

Draw altitude CD to make two right-angled triangles, ADC and BDC. Let CD = h units.

In △ACD,

$$\sin A = \frac{h}{b} \left(\text{In (ii), } \sin A = \sin(180° - A) = \frac{h}{b} \right)$$

So $h = b \sin A$

In △BCD,

$$\sin B = \frac{h}{a}$$

So $h = a \sin B$

Hence $b \sin A = a \sin B$

$$\frac{b \sin A}{\sin A \sin B} = \frac{a \sin B}{\sin A \sin B} \text{ (dividing each side by } \sin A \sin B).$$

So $\dfrac{a}{\sin A} = \dfrac{b}{\sin B}$.   In the same way, $\dfrac{a}{\sin A} = \dfrac{c}{\sin C}$.

The Sine Rule: in any △ABC, $\dfrac{a}{\sin A} = \dfrac{b}{\sin B} = \dfrac{c}{\sin C}$.

Example
Calculate the distance from tracking station B to Shuttle C.

$\dfrac{\textcircled{a}}{\sin A \checkmark} = \dfrac{b \checkmark}{\sin B \checkmark} = \dfrac{c}{\sin C}$ (Circle the part you want, and tick the parts you're given.)

$$\frac{a}{\sin 50°} = \frac{100}{\sin 60°}$$

$$a = \frac{100 \sin 50°}{\sin 60°} = 88.5, \text{ correct to 1 decimal place.}$$

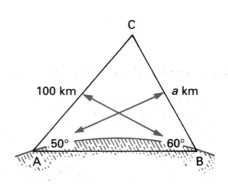

The distance is 88.5 km.

EXERCISE 1

1 Write down two equal 'Sine Rule' ratios for each of these triangles.

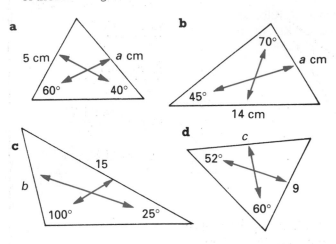

a

5 cm   *a* cm
60°   40°

b

70°   *a* cm
45°
14 cm

c

15
b
100°   25°

d

c
52°
9
60°

2 Calculate *a* in each triangle below.

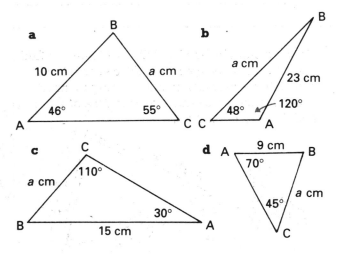

a

B
10 cm   *a* cm
46°   55°
A   C

b

B
a cm   23 cm
48°   120°
C   A

c

C
110°
a cm
30°
B   15 cm   A

d

A   9 cm   B
70°
45°   *a* cm
C

3 In △PQR, calculate:
a ∠QPR   **b** *p*.

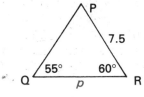

P
7.5
55°   60°
Q   *p*   R

4 In △XYZ, calculate:
a ∠YXZ   **b** *x*.

X
15
110°   30°
Y   *x*   Z

5 A tunnel is to be made along the line AB. To help in planning, a point C is chosen, from where A and B can both be seen.

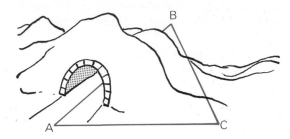

a Sketch △ABC, marking ∠A = 46°, ∠C = 68° and AC = 400 m.
b Calculate, to the nearest metre:
(i) BC   (ii) AB.

6 Meena sets sail at a point 25 m from the lighthouse. Her course is at an angle of 33° to the shoreline. Calculate, to the nearest metre:
a PR   **b** QR.

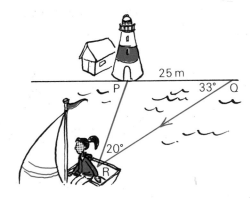

7 A laser beam is sent out from A. It bounces off the building at B and is picked up at C. Calculate, to the nearest metre:
a BA   **b** BC.

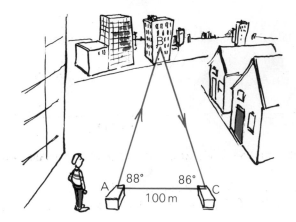

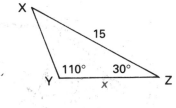

CALCULATING AN ANGLE

Example
Calculate $\angle A$ and $\angle B$ in $\triangle ABC$.

$$\frac{a\,✓}{\boxed{\sin A}} = \frac{c\,✓}{\sin C\,✓}$$

$$\frac{3}{\sin A} = \frac{9}{\sin 120°}$$

$$9\sin A = 3\sin 120°$$

$$\sin A = \frac{3\sin 120°}{9}$$

$\angle A = 16.8°$, correct to 1 decimal place

$\angle B = 180° - 120° - 16.8° = 43.2°$.

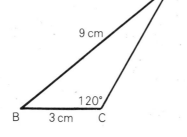

An alternative setting

$$\frac{\sin A}{a} = \frac{\sin C}{c}$$

$$\frac{\sin A}{3} = \frac{\sin 120°}{9}$$

$$\sin A = \frac{3\sin 120°}{9}$$

$\angle A = 16.8°$, etc.

Note: $\sin A = \sin(180° - A)$, so $\angle A$ *could* be $180° - 16.8° = 163.2°$, by calculation.
From the given data in the triangle, $\angle A$ must be acute, i.e. 16.8°. Why?

EXERCISE 2

1 Calculate angle A in each of these triangles.

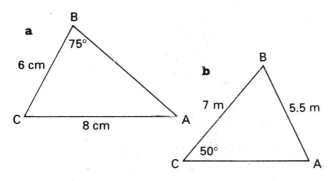

a

b

2 Calculate the remaining two angles in each triangle below.

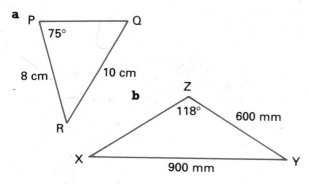

a

b

3 Sketch these triangles, and in each case calculate $\angle A$:
  a $\angle C = 68°$, $a = 28$ and $c = 35$
  b $\angle B = 140°$, $b = 106$ and $c = 46$.

4 Underground in the Blackhill Coal Mine, the Red and White Roadways run at 40° to each other. A new 500 metre roadway link is being planned. Calculate the acute angle between the new link and the White Roadway.

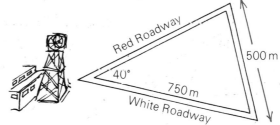

5 Habib measures his new bicycle:
AB = 40 cm, AD = 45 cm, DC = 64 cm,
$\angle ABD = 62°$ and $\angle DBC = 66°$.
  a Make a sketch of the bicycle frame.
  b Calculate: (i) $\angle ADB$ (ii) DB   (iii) $\angle DCB$.

EXERCISE 3B

1 A tree, T, stands on an island in the pond. Calculate the distance AT.

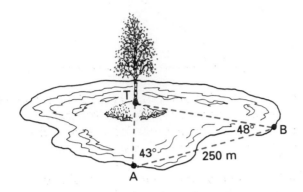

2 a Sketch △ABC, with BC = 10 cm, AC = 12 cm and ∠ABC = 50°.
b Find the size of the largest angle in the triangle.

3 Observations of a hilltop, T, are made from points A and B, 100 m apart. The angles of elevation are 20° and 30°. Calculate:
a TB **b** the height of the hill (TH).

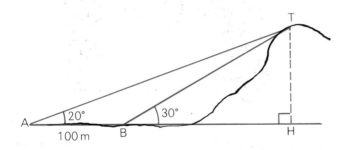

4 This diagram shows the positions of three ships at S, T and U.

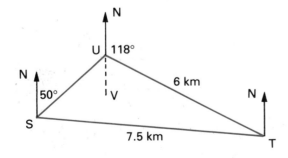

a Write down the size of:
  (i) ∠SUV (ii) ∠VUT (iii) ∠SUT.
b Calculate the size of ∠TSU, using the Sine Rule.
c What is the bearing of T from S?

5 There are reports of a UFO sighting. Adam says its angle of elevation is 40°. Bethan, who lives 3 km from Adam, measures the angle of elevation as 55°. Calculate:
a the distance from Adam to the UFO
b the height of the UFO above the ground.

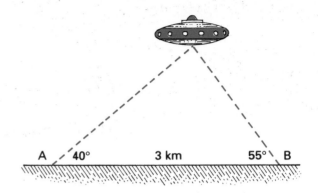

6 On this crane, calculate:
a ∠RPQ **b** ∠RQP **c** PR.

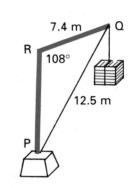

7 The tolls, A and B, at either end of the Tay Road Bridge are 2.5 km apart. The bridge runs on a bearing of 120° between the tolls. Woodhaven is due South of A, and is 3 km from B.

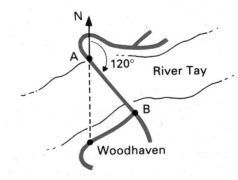

a Draw the triangle formed by Woodhaven and the two tolls.
b Calculate the bearing of B from Woodhaven.

INVESTIGATION

Jane is a surveyor. She makes a map of the country by measuring one distance and lots of angles, and then calculating distances using the Sine Rule. Her method is called triangulation.

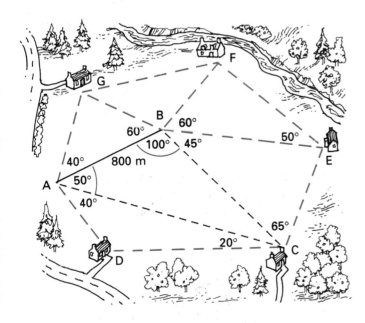

a She chooses a base line AB, and measures its length, 800 m. Starting with △ABC, she measures the angles at A(50°) and B(100°), and makes a scale drawing of △ABC. Do this.

b She moves to △ACD, and measures the angles at A(40°) and C(20°), and adds △ACD to her scale drawing. Do this, then add △s ABG, BCE and BEF to your drawing.

c Use the Sine Rule to calculate, to the nearest metre, the distances AC, BC, BE, BF and BG.

d Measure FG. How many metres long is FG?

BRAINSTORMERS

1

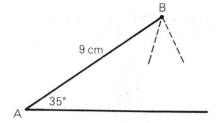

Given ∠A = 35°, AB = 9 cm and BC = 6 cm, make an accurate construction for two different positions of C on the base-line. Measure, then calculate, ∠ACB in each case.

2 A heavy swinging weight is being used to demolish this building. Calculate:

a the angle of swing C_1BC_2.

b the length of the arc of swing from C_1 to C_2.

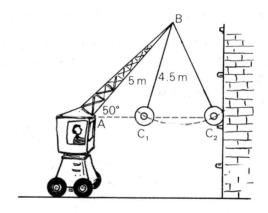

CHALLENGE

To find the height h metres of the pyramid, a surveyor measures the distance d metres and angles α° ('alpha') and β° ('beta').

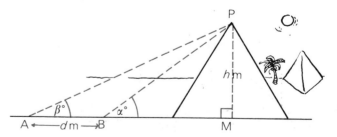

By investigating triangles ABP and PBM, can you find a formula involving h, d, α, β that he could use? Use your formula to calculate h, taking d = 200, α = 30 and β = 20.

Use your formula to calculate the height of a local landmark.

THE COSINE RULE

CLASS DISCUSSION

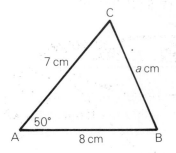

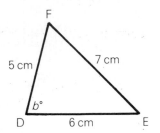

Look at these triangles.
You *could* find *a* and *b* by making scale drawings.
What about trigonometry?
Any right-angled triangles?
The Sine Rule? No?
We're back to *making* right-angled triangles . . . and Pythagoras' Theorem!

(i) ∠A acute

(ii) ∠A obtuse

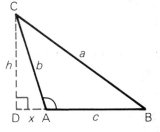

Draw altitude CD to make two right-angled triangles ADC and BDC.
Let CD = h units, and AD = x units.
Using Pythagoras' Theorem in △BCD:

(i) $a^2 = h^2 + (c-x)^2$
$= h^2 + c^2 + x^2 - 2cx$
$= (h^2 + x^2) + c^2 - 2cx$
$= b^2 + c^2 - 2bc \cos A,$

$\left(\text{since } \dfrac{x}{b} = \cos A, \; x = b \cos A \right)$

(ii) $a^2 = h^2 + (c+x)^2$
$= h^2 + c^2 + x^2 + 2cx$
$= (h^2 + x^2) + c^2 + 2cx$
$= b^2 + c^2 - 2bc \cos A$

$\left(\text{since } \dfrac{x}{b} = \cos(180° - A) = -\cos A, \; x = -b \cos A \right).$

The Cosine Rule: in any △ABC, $a^2 = b^2 + c^2 - 2bc \cos A$.

In the same way, $b^2 = c^2 + a^2 - 2ca \cos B$
$c^2 = a^2 + b^2 - 2ab \cos C.$

Note: (i) a and A in $a^2 = b^2 + c^2 - 2bc \cos A$
(ii) the 'cyclic symmetry' of the letters and angles from one formula to the next. (See circular diagram.)

Example
In △ABC, $b = 3$, $c = 5$ and ∠A = 35°. Calculate a.
$a^2 = b^2 + c^2 - 2bc \cos A$
$= 3^2 + 5^2 - 2 \times 3 \times 5 \times \cos 35°$
$(= 9.43)$
$a = 3.1$, correct to 1 decimal place.

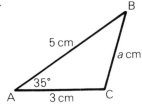

EXERCISE 4

1 To calculate a, copy and complete:
$a^2 = b^2 + \ldots - 2bc \cos \ldots$
$\quad = 4^2 + \ldots - 2 \times 4 \times 7 \ldots$
$\quad = \ldots$
$a = \ldots$, correct to 1 decimal place.

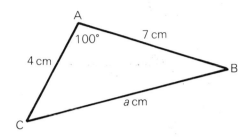

2 Use the Cosine Rule to find a in each of the following:

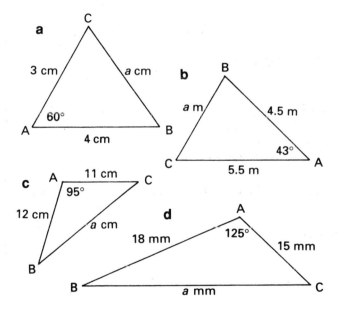

3 a For $\triangle$PQR, write down the Cosine Rule for:
   (i) p^2 (ii) q^2 (iii) r^2.
  b Calculate the length of the third side, given:
   (i) $q = 10$, $r = 7$ and $\angle P = 48°$
   (ii) $p = 4.5$, $q = 5.2$, $\angle R = 118°$.
  c What does the formula for p^2 become when $\angle P = 90°$?

4 Clare, an apprentice surveyor, sketches the boating pond, and marks in these measurements. Calculate the width of the pond (AB).

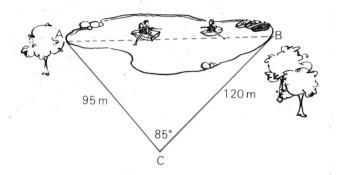

5 This window is held open by the strut BC. Calculate the length of BC when the window is open at an angle of 40° (AB = 45 cm and AC = 50 cm).

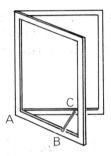

6 Calculate x for each wing position of this 'swing-wing' aircraft. Lengths are in metres.

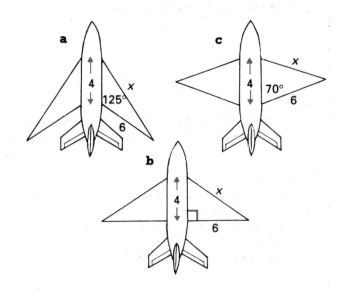

CALCULATING AN ANGLE OF A TRIANGLE, GIVEN THE LENGTHS OF THE SIDES

Example
Calculate the largest angle in $\triangle$ABC.

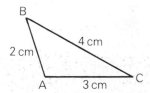

$$a^2 = b^2 + c^2 - 2bc \cos A$$

$$2bc \cos A = b^2 + c^2 - a^2$$

$$\cos A = \frac{b^2 + c^2 - a^2}{2bc}$$

The largest angle is opposite the largest side, so it is $\angle$A.

$$\cos A = \frac{b^2 + c^2 - a^2}{2bc} = \frac{3^2 + 2^2 - 4^2}{2 \times 3 \times 2} \ (= -0.25); \ \angle A = 104.5°$$

EXERCISE 5

1 Write down formulae for cos A, cos B and cos C in terms of a, b and c. (Remember the 'cyclic symmetry' $a \rightarrow b \rightarrow c \rightarrow a \dots$.)

2 In $\triangle$ABC, calculate:
  a $\angle$A when $a = 4$, $b = 5$, $c = 6$
  b $\angle$B when $a = 31$, $b = 42$, $c = 53$
  c $\angle$C when $a = 2.5$, $b = 4.5$, $c = 3.5$.

3 In $\triangle$PQR, $p = 8$, $q = 12$ and $r = 10$.
  a Write down formulae for cos P, cos Q and cos R.
  b In the triangle find, and calculate the size of:
    (i) the largest angle   (ii) the smallest angle.

4 Stuart's ladder has legs 150 cm and 146 cm long. When the ladder is fully open, the feet are 86 cm apart.

  a Calculate the angles of the triangle formed when the ladder is fully open.
  b In a narrow space, Stuart can only get the feet 80 cm apart. Calculate the angle between the legs of the ladder then.

5 Calculate angle X in each diagram:

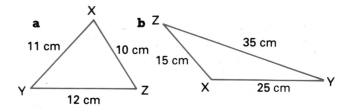

6 Use the Cosine Rule to calculate the sizes of the smallest and largest angles of $\triangle$XYZ, in which $x = 105$, $y = 125$ and $z = 205$.

7 Aimee is measuring the floor of her lounge for a fitted carpet. Calculate:
  a the sizes of the angles at the corners of the room
  b the length of the other diagonal.

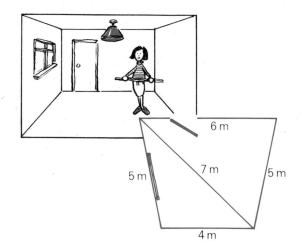

EXERCISE 6B

1 Sketch parallelogram ABCD in which AB = 10 cm, AD = 8 cm and ∠BAD = 60°. Calculate the lengths of its diagonals.

2 The planet Mars (M) has two moons. Phobos (P) is 5900 miles and Deimos (D) is 14 600 miles from the planet's centre, to the nearest 100 miles. How far apart are the moons, to the nearest 100 miles, when:
a ∠PMD = 70° **b** ∠PMD = 140°?

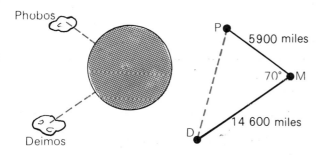

3 Hilbre Point is 9 km from Point of Ayr, on a bearing of 070°. Flint is 15.2 km from Hilbre Point and 17.8 km from Point of Ayr.
a Make a sketch, and mark the given distances and bearing.
b Calculate the bearing of Flint from Point of Ayr.

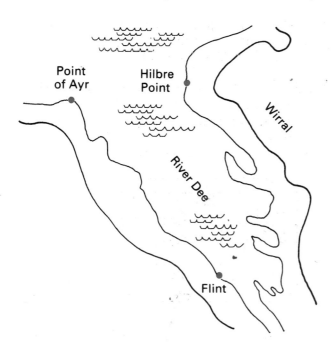

4 A ship leaves H and sails to B on a course bearing 040°. From B, the lighthouse L bears 250°.

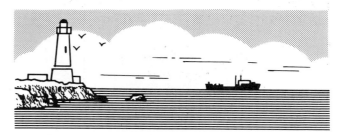

a Using the parallel lines, explain why ∠HLB = 110°.
b Calculate the distance HB.

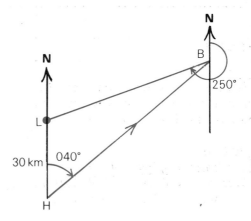

5 The vertical TV mast is 96 m tall. The angle of elevation of T from B is 18°. BC = 305 m and AC = 324 m. C is due west of A. Calculate:
a the distance AB, to the nearest metre
b the bearing of B from A.

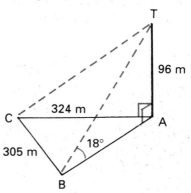

BRAINSTORMER

The hour hand of a clock is 6 cm long, and the minute hand is 10 cm long. Calculate:
a *the angle between the hands at ten to two*
b *the distance between their tips at that time.*

THE AREA OF A TRIANGLE

Reminder:

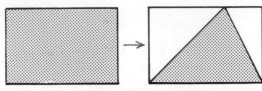

Area of rectangle
= base × height.

Area of triangle
= $\frac{1}{2}$ base × height.

Area = $\frac{1}{2}b \times h$.

A useful formula

(i) ∠C acute

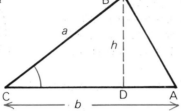

(ii) ∠C obtuse

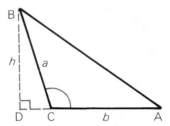

Draw altitude BD to make two right-angled triangles BDC and BDA. Let BD = h units.
The area of △ABC = $\frac{1}{2}bh$

$$= \frac{1}{2}b \times a \sin C \left(\text{In (ii)}, \frac{h}{a} = \sin(180° - C) = \sin C \right)$$

$$= \frac{1}{2}ab \sin C.$$

The area of △ABC = $\frac{1}{2}ab \sin$ C.

In the same way, the area of △ABC = $\frac{1}{2}bc \sin A = \frac{1}{2}ca \sin B$ = '$\frac{1}{2}$ product of two sides times sine of the included angle'.

Example
Calculate the area of △ABC in which $a = 3$, $b = 6$ and ∠C = 70°.
The lengths are in centimetres.

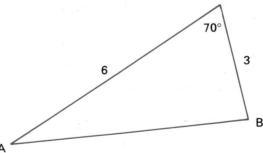

Area = $\frac{1}{2}ab \sin C$
= $\frac{1}{2} \times 3 \times 6 \times \sin 70°$
= 8.5, correct to 1 decimal place.

The area is 8.5 cm².

EXERCISE 7

1 Calculate the area of each triangle below.

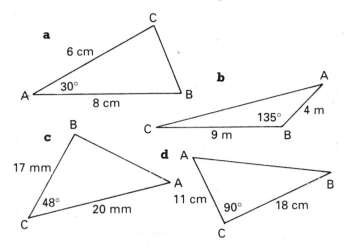

2 Calculate these triangular areas:

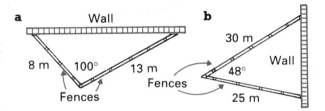

3 Choose the correct data to calculate the areas of these triangles.

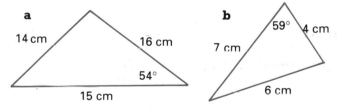

4 Calculate the area of △ABC, with:
   a $\angle A = 100°$, $b = 2.7$, and $c = 4$. The lengths are in centimetres.
   b $a = 7.1$, $b = 3.5$ and $\angle C = 21.5°$. The lengths are in metres.

5 Calculate the area of parallelogram PQRS.

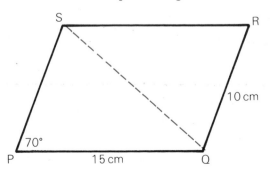

6 Calculate the area of rhombus STUV.

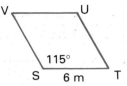

7 The area of △ABC is 12 cm². AC = 5 cm and BC = 6 cm.
   a Calculate two possible sizes of ∠C.
   b Sketch the two possible triangles.

8 A club badge consists of an equilateral triangle ABC inscribed in a circle with centre O and radius 13 cm. Calculate:
   a ∠BOC
   b the area of △OBC
   c the area of △ABC
   d the shaded area.

9 Calculate the area of this field, to the nearest m².

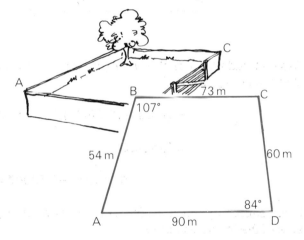

10 The body of Ryan's barrow is made from a sheet of aluminium. The front, base and back are rectangles. The two sides are congruent quadrilaterals. Calculate the area of aluminium sheet needed for the barrow. The lengths are in centimetres.

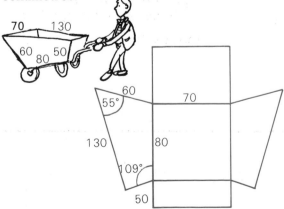

Every regular polygon can be divided into congruent isosceles triangles. For example:

a *Find a formula in terms of r for the area of each of the four polygons.*

b *Use a similar method to find a formula in terms of n and r for a regular n-sided polygon.*

c *(i) As n increases (more and more sides), the polygon's shape approaches a circle.*

Use this fact to prove that $\frac{n}{2} \sin\left(\frac{360°}{n}\right)$ is a good approximation for π.

(ii) What approximation does your calculator give for π?

d *Using your calculator, investigate how many sides a polygon must have before it gives an approximation as good as this.*

e *Construct a spreadsheet that calculates approximations for π for n = 50, 100, 150, 200, . . . , and their differences from π. Use your spreadsheet to draw a graph of the differences.*

The field is in the shape of an acute-angled triangle. Its area is 2580 m². Calculate its perimeter, correct to 3 significant figures.

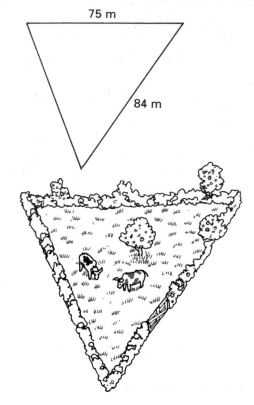

SELECTING A STRATEGY—WHICH FORMULA?

Given	Sketch	Use
3 sides		the Cosine Rule: $\cos A = \dfrac{b^2 + c^2 - a^2}{2bc}$
2 sides and the included angle		the Cosine Rule: $a^2 = b^2 + c^2 - 2bc \cos A$
Sides and opposite angle	or	the Sine Rule: $\dfrac{a}{\sin A} = \dfrac{b}{\sin B} = \dfrac{c}{\sin C}$
2 sides and the included angle		area of triangle $= \frac{1}{2}ab \sin C$

EXERCISE 8A

1 Which would you use—the Sine Rule or the Cosine Rule—to calculate x in each diagram? Do not make the calculations.

a
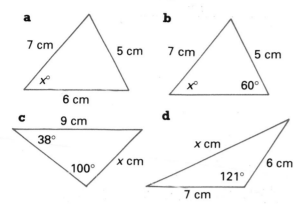
7 cm   5 cm $x°$ 6 cm

b
7 cm   5 cm $x°$ 60°

c
9 cm   38°   100° x cm

d
x cm   6 cm   121°   7 cm

2 Calculate AC in triangle ABC below.

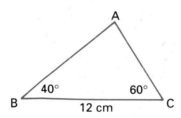
A   40°   60°   B   12 cm   C

3 Calculate QR in triangle PQR.

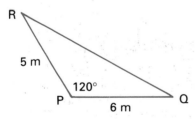
R   5 m   120°   P   6 m   Q

4 Calculate ∠UVW in triangle UVW below.

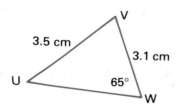
V   3.5 cm   3.1 cm   U   65°   W

5 In triangle ABC, calculate:
a BC   **b** the area of △ABC.

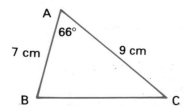
A   66°   7 cm   9 cm   B   C

6 Sketch a triangle with sides 5 cm, 6 cm and 10 cm long. Calculate the sizes of all the angles in the triangle.

7 P and Q are points on a river bank 30 m apart. T is a tree on the opposite bank.

Calculate:
a d
b the width of the river (copy the triangle, and draw TR perpendicular to PQ).

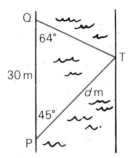
Q   64°   T   30 m d m   45°   P

8

Two tunnels LM and NM are drilled at angles of 24° and 36° to the horizontal. LM is 720 m long. Calculate:
a MN   **b** LN.

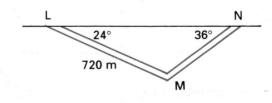
L   24°   N   36°   720 m   M

9 These triangles have the same area. Calculate the value of x.

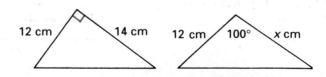
12 cm   14 cm   12 cm   100° x cm

10 Calculate x in each part of question **1**.

EXERCISE 8B

1 Fieldside High's playing fields are in the shape of a quadrilateral. Calculate:
 a GE
 b the area of the playing fields.

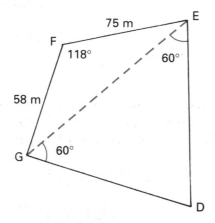

2 A plane flies 500 km from A to B on a bearing of 063°, then 350 km to C on a bearing of 137°. Calculate the distance and bearing of C from A.

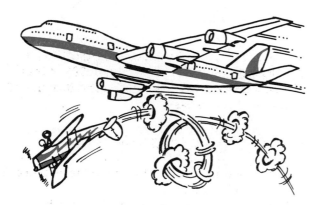

3 Hanif has used 26 m of rope to peg out a triangular plot in his garden. Calculate the area of the plot.

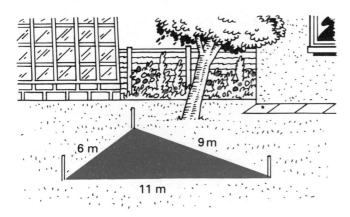

4 The vertical mast TU, 15 m tall, is supported by cables RU and SU. R, S and T are on horizontal ground. Calculate:
 a RT **b** TS **c** RS.

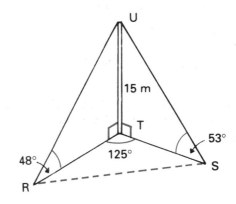

5 The fishing boats *Hopeful* and *Trusty* leave port at 10 am. *Hopeful* sails north at 12 km/h, and *Trusty* sails on a bearing of 075° at 21 km/h. Calculate:
 a the distance between the boats at 11.20 am
 b the bearing of *Trusty* from *Hopeful* then.

6 Calculate:
 a the total length of picture cord (P to Q to R)
 b ∠QPR when Q is in the middle of the cord (and the picture is horizontal).

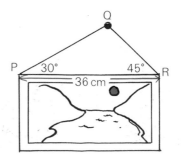

CHECK-UP ON TRIGONOMETRY— TRIANGLE CALCULATIONS

1 Copy and complete the following for $\triangle ABC$:

a $\dfrac{a}{\sin A} = \dfrac{\ldots}{\sin B} = \dfrac{c}{\ldots}$

b $a^2 = b^2 + \ldots$ (Cosine Rule)

c $\cos B = \dfrac{\ldots\ldots - b^2}{\ldots}$

d area of $\triangle ABC = \frac{1}{2} \ldots \sin C$.

2 Sine Rule, Cosine Rule, Pythagoras' Theorem— which would you use to calculate x in each triangle below?

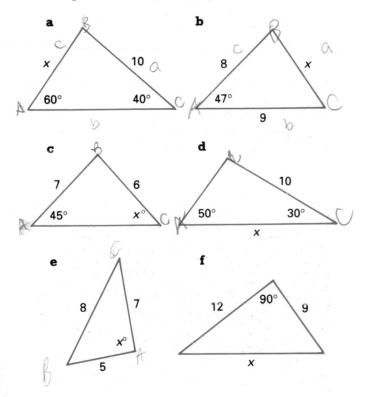

a x, 10, $60°$, $40°$

b 8, $47°$, x, 9

c 7, 6, $45°$, $x°$

d 10, $50°$, $30°$, x

e 8, 7, $x°$, 5

f 12, $90°$, 9, x

3 Calculate x in triangles **a**, **b** and **e** in question **2**.

4 A TV detector van picks up strong signals at A and B. Calculate the distance from each position to the TV set.

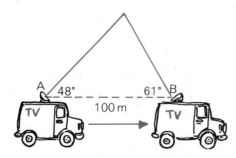

$48°$ $61°$ $100\,\text{m}$

5

$4\,\text{m}$ $5\,\text{m}$

Gareth pegs out a loop of rope 16 m long to form a triangle. Calculate:
a $\angle B$ **b** the area of $\triangle ABC$.

6 A ship radios its position A when it is 14 km from port P. It radios again at B, after sailing 16 km. At P, $\angle APB = 33°$. Calculate: **a** $\angle B$ **b** PB.

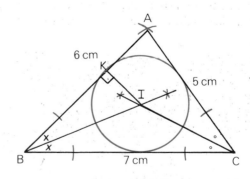

B   16 km   A

14 km

33°

P

7 A plane flies for 100 km on a bearing of 048°. It then flies for 60 km on a bearing of 159°. Make a sketch, and calculate the bearing and distance of its course back to base.

8 a   (i) Construct $\triangle ABC$ with BC = 7 cm, BA = 6 cm and CA = 5 cm.
   (ii) Construct the lines bisecting the angles at B and C, to meet at I.
   (iii) With centre I, and radius IK, draw the inscribed circle in $\triangle ABC$. Measure IK.

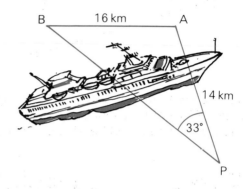

A   6 cm   K   5 cm   I   x   x   B   7 cm   C

b Calculate the length of IK. You'll need to use:
   (i) the Cosine Rule in $\triangle ABC$ for $\angle$s B and C
   (ii) the Sine Rule in $\triangle IBC$ for BI
   (iii) a 'trig' ratio in $\triangle BIK$ for IK.

11 FRACTIONS AND EQUATIONS

1 Solve these equations:

a $3x = -12$ **b** $2y - 9 = 0$ **c** $2(a-1) = 10$
d $5m + 14 = m - 2$ **e** $3n + 4 = 12 - n$

2 Multiply out, and simplify:

a $5(x+2)$ **b** $1 + 2(y-1)$ **c** $8 - 2(z-4)$

3 Factorise:

a $3x - 12$ **b** $y^2 - 2y$ **c** $u^2 - v^2$ **d** $1 - 4x^2$
e $m^2 + 8m + 16$ **f** $y^2 - 5y - 14$ **g** $2t^2 + 5t - 3$

4 a In the fraction $\dfrac{3}{4}$, which number is:

(i) the numerator (ii) the denominator?

b The reciprocal of $\dfrac{1}{2}$ is $\dfrac{2}{1}$.

Write down the reciprocal of $\dfrac{3}{4}$.

5 Write down the lcm (lowest common multiple) of:

a 3 and 4 **b** 5 and 10 **c** x and y **d** $2x$ and $3y$

6 a Simplify:

(i) $\dfrac{2}{6}$ (ii) $\dfrac{5}{10}$ (iii) $\dfrac{15}{20}$ (iv) $\dfrac{18}{24}$

b Calculate:

(i) $\dfrac{2}{3} \times \dfrac{1}{2}$ (ii) $\dfrac{3}{4} \times \dfrac{1}{3}$ (iii) $5 \times \dfrac{3}{5}$

7 Calculate the area and perimeter of each of these shapes:

a

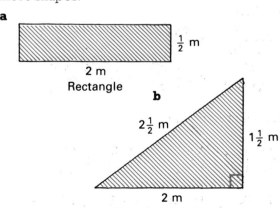

$\frac{1}{2}$ m

2 m
Rectangle

b

$2\frac{1}{2}$ m

$1\frac{1}{2}$ m

2 m
Right-angled triangle

8 The Chan family are off on a driving holiday. They travel d km in three hours. Write down an expression for the average speed of their car.

9 In each of the following, change the subject in the formula to the letter in brackets.

a

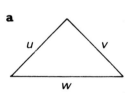

u v

w

$P = u + v + w \dots (u)$

b

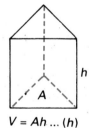

h

A

$V = Ah \dots (h)$

c

x

$P = 4x \dots (x);\ A = x^2 \dots (x)$

d

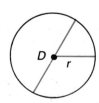

D r

$C = \pi d \dots (d);\ A = \pi r^2 \dots (r)$

e

D

S T

$D = ST \dots (T)$

f

C
F

$F \doteqdot 2C + 30 \dots (C)$

10 Solve these equations:

a $2(x-1) = -4$ **b** $3(t-4) + 6 = 15$
c $(n+2)(n+5) = (n+3)^2$ **d** $(y+5)^2 - (y-4)^2 = 9$

SIMPLIFYING FRACTIONS

Divide the numerator and denominator by any common factor

Examples

a $\dfrac{6}{8} = \dfrac{\overset{1}{\cancel{2}} \times 3}{\underset{1}{\cancel{2}} \times 4} = \dfrac{3}{4}$ **b** $\dfrac{5\overset{1}{\cancel{a}}}{6\underset{1}{\cancel{a}}} = \dfrac{5}{6}$ **c** $\dfrac{3u-6}{9} = \dfrac{\overset{1}{\cancel{3}}(u-2)}{\underset{3}{\cancel{9}}} = \dfrac{u-2}{3}$

(Factorise, *then* simplify)

EXERCISE 1A

Simplify the fractions in questions **1–6**:

1 a $\dfrac{8}{10}$ **b** $\dfrac{5}{15}$ **c** $\dfrac{14}{21}$ **d** $\dfrac{22}{33}$ **e** $\dfrac{100}{200}$

2 a $\dfrac{3a}{4a}$ **b** $\dfrac{2n}{3n}$ **c** $\dfrac{4b}{4c}$ **d** $\dfrac{u \times v}{a \times v}$

3 a $\dfrac{an}{bn}$ **b** $\dfrac{tx}{ty}$ **c** $\dfrac{p}{pq}$ **d** $\dfrac{y}{y \times y}$

4 a $\dfrac{x^2}{3x}$ **b** $\dfrac{2y}{y^2}$ **c** $\dfrac{z^2}{z}$ **d** $\dfrac{t}{t^2}$ **e** $\dfrac{2a^2}{3a}$

5 a $\dfrac{4x}{8y}$ **b** $\dfrac{6xy}{2x}$ **c** $\dfrac{a^2}{2ab}$ **d** $\dfrac{3cd}{6d}$ **e** $\dfrac{3k}{3k^2}$

6 a $\dfrac{abc}{ac}$ **b** $\dfrac{3xy}{5xy}$ **c** $\dfrac{5ab}{2ab^2}$ **d** $\dfrac{9u^2v}{3uv^2}$

Factorise (using common factors) in questions **7–9**:

7 a $2x+4$ **b** $3y-6$ **c** $5p+5$ **d** $7t-7$

8 a a^2+2a **b** k^2-3k **c** $2n^2+2$ **d** $3m^2-6$

9 a x^2+xy **b** $uv-v^2$ **c** y^2-3y **d** $5z-z^2$

10 Copy and complete:

a $\dfrac{3x-6}{9} = \dfrac{\overset{1}{\cancel{3}}(x-2)}{\underset{3}{\cancel{9}}} = \ldots$

b $\dfrac{u^2+uv}{2u} = \dfrac{\overset{1}{\cancel{u}}(u+v)}{2\underset{1}{\cancel{u}}} = \ldots$

Factorise, *then* simplify, in questions **11–13**:

11 a $\dfrac{2m+6}{4}$ **b** $\dfrac{3n+6}{9}$ **c** $\dfrac{2p-4}{2}$ **d** $\dfrac{5n-10}{15}$

12 a $\dfrac{2}{2x+4}$ **b** $\dfrac{4}{4t-8}$ **c** $\dfrac{6}{3u+9}$ **d** $\dfrac{10}{5v-5}$

13 a $\dfrac{x^2+xy}{x}$ **b** $\dfrac{xy-x}{x}$ **c** $\dfrac{m^2+m}{m}$ **d** $\dfrac{n-n^2}{n}$

14 Simplify:

a $\dfrac{2(x-3)}{x(x-3)}$ **b** $\dfrac{5(a+b)}{a+b}$ **c** $\dfrac{(x-y)(x+y)}{x-y}$

d $\dfrac{x^2}{x^2(x+y)}$ **e** $\dfrac{(a-b)^2}{(a-b)^3}$ **f** $\dfrac{(t-1)(t+2)}{(t+2)(t-3)}$

Factorise, then simplify:

15 a $\dfrac{2a+8}{a+4}$ **b** $\dfrac{3b+12}{b+4}$ **c** $\dfrac{c-2}{2c-4}$ **d** $\dfrac{d^2+d}{d+1}$

16 a $\dfrac{2t+2u}{3t+3u}$ **b** $\dfrac{5x+5y}{2x+2y}$ **c** $\dfrac{2-2v}{1-v}$ **d** $\dfrac{m^2-mn}{5m-5n}$

FACTORS AND FRACTIONS

Common	Difference of squares	Quadratic	Example
$ax+ay$ $= a(x+y)$	a^2-b^2 $= (a-b)(a+b)$	x^2+x-2 $= (x+2)(x-1)$	$\dfrac{y^2-6y+9}{y^2-9} = \dfrac{(y-3)(y-3)}{(y-3)(y+3)} = \dfrac{y-3}{y+3}$

EXERCISE 1B

1 Factorise:
  a x^2+4x **b** y^2-4 **c** n^2+6n+8
  d $10x-25$ **e** $9-a^2$ **f** $x^2-10x+25$
  g y^2-y-12 **h** $2m^2-32$ **i** $2p^2+4p+2$

Factorise, *then* simplify, in questions **2–11**.

2 a $\dfrac{2}{2x+6}$ **b** $\dfrac{5}{5a+5}$ **c** $\dfrac{2b-8}{2b+8}$

3 a $\dfrac{x^2-1}{x-1}$ **b** $\dfrac{x^2+2x+1}{x+1}$ **c** $\dfrac{m+3}{m^2-9}$

4 a $\dfrac{x-2}{3x-6}$ **b** $\dfrac{x-2}{x^2-2x}$ **c** $\dfrac{x-2}{x^2-x-2}$

5 a $\dfrac{y+4}{4y+16}$ **b** $\dfrac{y+4}{y^2-16}$ **c** $\dfrac{y+2}{y^2+4y+4}$

6 a $\dfrac{2b+10}{b^2-25}$ **b** $\dfrac{4x+4x^2}{4x}$ **c** $\dfrac{a^2+6a+9}{a^2+3a}$

7 a $\dfrac{u+3}{3u^2+3u-18}$ **b** $\dfrac{v^2-1}{v^2-5v+4}$ **c** $\dfrac{2p^2-2q^2}{p^2-2pq+q^2}$

8 a $\dfrac{x^2+2x+1}{2x+2}$ **b** $\dfrac{y^2-5y+6}{3y-9}$ **c** $\dfrac{2z^2+12z+10}{2z+2}$

9 a $\dfrac{d^2+d}{d^3+d^2}$ **b** $\dfrac{(c+1)^2}{(c+1)^3}$ **c** $\dfrac{u^2+2u+1}{(u+1)^2}$

10 a $\dfrac{c^2+c-6}{c^2-4c+4}$ **b** $\dfrac{d^2+7d-8}{d^2-2d+1}$ **c** $\dfrac{n^2-k^2}{an-ak}$

11 a $\dfrac{1-x^4}{1-x^2}$ **b** $\dfrac{y^4-1}{(y+1)(y^2+1)}$ **c** $\dfrac{x^4-y^4}{x^2-2xy+y^2}$

MULTIPLICATION AND DIVISION

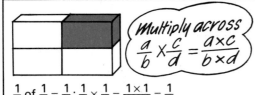

Multiply across $\dfrac{a}{b} \times \dfrac{c}{d} = \dfrac{a \times c}{b \times d}$

$\dfrac{1}{2}$ of $\dfrac{1}{2} = \dfrac{1}{4}$; $\dfrac{1}{2} \times \dfrac{1}{2} = \dfrac{1 \times 1}{2 \times 2} = \dfrac{1}{4}$

Examples

a $3 \times \dfrac{5}{6} = \dfrac{\overset{1}{\cancel{3}}}{1} \times \dfrac{5}{\underset{2}{\cancel{6}}} = \dfrac{5}{2}$ **b** $\dfrac{m^2}{n} \times \dfrac{n^2}{m} = \dfrac{\overset{m}{\cancel{m^2}} \times \overset{n}{\cancel{n^2}}}{\underset{1}{\cancel{n}} \times \underset{1}{\cancel{m}}} = mn$

EXERCISE 2

In questions **1–5** multiply, and simplify where possible:

1 a $\dfrac{3}{4} \times \dfrac{1}{3}$ **b** $\dfrac{2}{3} \times \dfrac{1}{4}$ **c** $\dfrac{5}{6} \times \dfrac{2}{5}$ **d** $\dfrac{3}{10} \times \dfrac{10}{3}$

2 a $\dfrac{3}{10} \times \dfrac{5}{1}$ **b** $6 \times \dfrac{2}{3}$ **c** $\dfrac{1}{5} \times 10$ **d** $\dfrac{7}{8} \times \dfrac{16}{7}$

3 a $\dfrac{m}{n} \times \dfrac{p}{q}$ **b** $\dfrac{x}{y} \times \dfrac{s}{t}$ **c** $\dfrac{a}{b} \times \dfrac{a}{b}$ **d** $\dfrac{u}{v} \times \dfrac{v}{u}$

4 a $\dfrac{x}{2} \times \dfrac{x}{3}$ **b** $y \times \dfrac{y}{5}$ **c** $\dfrac{z}{4} \times \dfrac{z}{4}$ **d** $\dfrac{a}{2} \times \dfrac{2}{a}$

5 a $\dfrac{k}{2} \times \dfrac{2}{n}$ **b** $a^2 \times \dfrac{1}{a}$ **c** $\dfrac{a^2}{b} \times \dfrac{b}{a}$ **d** $\dfrac{u^3}{4} \times \dfrac{4}{u}$

6 Calculate the area of each shape below in terms of x.

a

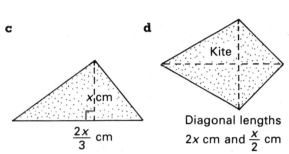

Square $\frac{x}{2}$ cm

$\frac{x}{2}$ cm

b

Rectangle $\frac{2y}{5}$ cm

$\frac{y}{2}$ cm

c

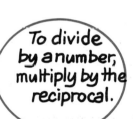

x cm

$\frac{2x}{3}$ cm

d

Kite

Diagonal lengths
$2x$ cm and $\frac{x}{2}$ cm

In questions **7–11** change these divisions to multiplications, and simplify:

7 **a** $\dfrac{3}{5} \div \dfrac{6}{5}$ **b** $\dfrac{2}{3} \div \dfrac{4}{3}$ **c** $\dfrac{3}{8} \div \dfrac{6}{4}$ **d** $\dfrac{7}{10} \div \dfrac{14}{5}$

8 **a** $\dfrac{a}{4} \div \dfrac{a}{3}$ **b** $\dfrac{n}{6} \div \dfrac{n}{3}$ **c** $\dfrac{t}{2} \div \dfrac{t}{4}$ **d** $\dfrac{u}{8} \div \dfrac{u}{2}$

9 **a** $\dfrac{b^2}{2} \div \dfrac{b}{2}$ **b** $\dfrac{x^2}{4} \div \dfrac{x}{2}$ **c** $\dfrac{y^4}{4} \div \dfrac{y^2}{2}$ **d** $\dfrac{c^3}{6} \div \dfrac{c}{3}$

10 **a** $\dfrac{u}{v} \div \dfrac{u}{v}$ **b** $\dfrac{a^2}{c} \div \dfrac{a}{c^2}$ **c** $\dfrac{1}{t^2} \div \dfrac{2}{t}$ **d** $\dfrac{1}{u^3} \div \dfrac{1}{u^2}$

11 **a** $\dfrac{a^2}{b} \div \dfrac{2a}{b}$ **b** $\dfrac{x^2}{y} \div \dfrac{x}{y}$ **c** $\dfrac{3x}{2y} \div \dfrac{3}{4}$ **d** $\dfrac{2a^2}{3b^2} \div \dfrac{a^2}{b^2}$

12 Find the length of each shape by dividing the area by the breadth:

a

Rectangle $\dfrac{x}{3}$ cm

Length

Area = $\dfrac{x^2}{6}$ cm²

b

Rectangle $\dfrac{a}{b}$ cm

Length

Area = $\dfrac{a^2}{b^2}$ cm²

Reminder!

The **reciprocal** of 3 is $\dfrac{1}{3}$, and of $\dfrac{1}{3}$ is 3, etc.

Do you agree that:

$3 \div 3 = 1$, and $3 \times \dfrac{1}{3} = 1$

$2 \div 2 = 1$, and $2 \times \dfrac{1}{2} = 1$

$\dfrac{1}{2} \div \dfrac{1}{2} = 1$, so $\dfrac{1}{2} \times \dfrac{2}{1} = 1$

$\dfrac{1}{3} \div \dfrac{1}{3} = 1$, so $\dfrac{1}{3} \times \dfrac{3}{1} = 1$?

To divide by a number, multiply by the reciprocal.

Examples

a $\dfrac{5}{6} \div \dfrac{2}{3} = \dfrac{5}{6} \times \dfrac{3}{2} = \dfrac{5}{4}$

b $\dfrac{3}{y} \div \dfrac{9}{y^2} = \dfrac{3}{y} \times \dfrac{y^2}{9} = \dfrac{y}{3}$

13 Copy and complete these tables:

a

$\times$	$\dfrac{a}{b}$	$\dfrac{c}{d}$
$\dfrac{a}{b}$		
$\dfrac{c}{d}$		

b

$\div$	$\dfrac{a}{b}$	$\dfrac{c}{d}$
$\dfrac{a}{b}$		
$\dfrac{c}{d}$		

143

ADDITION AND SUBTRACTION

Examples

a $\dfrac{2}{3}-\dfrac{1}{4}$

$=\dfrac{8}{12}-\dfrac{3}{12}$ (lcm of 3 and 4 is 12)

$=\dfrac{5}{12}$

b $\dfrac{3}{m}+\dfrac{2}{n}$

$=\dfrac{3n}{mn}+\dfrac{2m}{mn}$ (lcm of m and n is mn)

$=\dfrac{3n+2m}{mn}$

c $\dfrac{x}{a}-\dfrac{a}{x}$

$=\dfrac{x^2}{ax}-\dfrac{a^2}{ax}$ (lcm of a and x is ax)

$=\dfrac{x^2-a^2}{ax}$

EXERCISE 3A

1 Write down the lowest common multiple (lcm) of:
a 2 and 3 **b** 4 and 5 **c** 4 and 8 **d** 6 and 8
e x and y **f** m and n **g** x and x^2 **h** $3x$ and $4y$

2 Write down the lcm of the denominators, then add or subtract the fractions.
a $\dfrac{2}{3}+\dfrac{1}{4}$ **b** $\dfrac{3}{4}-\dfrac{1}{3}$ **c** $\dfrac{1}{5}+\dfrac{1}{3}$ **d** $\dfrac{4}{5}-\dfrac{1}{2}$
e $\dfrac{1}{2}-\dfrac{1}{6}$ **f** $\dfrac{1}{6}+\dfrac{1}{3}$ **g** $\dfrac{5}{8}-\dfrac{1}{4}$ **h** $\dfrac{3}{10}-\dfrac{1}{5}$

3 Copy and complete:
a $\dfrac{x}{2}+\dfrac{y}{3}$ (lcm 6) $=\dfrac{3x}{6}+\dfrac{2y}{6}=\dfrac{}{6}$

b $\dfrac{2u}{5}-\dfrac{3v}{10}$ (lcm 10) $=\dfrac{4u}{10}-\dfrac{3v}{10}=\dfrac{}{10}$

4 Add or subtract:
a $\dfrac{x}{5}+\dfrac{y}{2}$ **b** $\dfrac{a}{3}-\dfrac{b}{2}$ **c** $\dfrac{c}{4}+\dfrac{d}{3}$ **d** $\dfrac{m}{5}-\dfrac{n}{4}$
e $\dfrac{2u}{3}+\dfrac{v}{2}$ **f** $\dfrac{u}{2}-\dfrac{3v}{4}$ **g** $\dfrac{2s}{5}+\dfrac{t}{2}$ **h** $\dfrac{a}{3}-\dfrac{2b}{4}$

5 Copy and complete:
$\dfrac{3}{x}-\dfrac{4}{y}$ (lcm xy) $=\dfrac{3y}{xy}-\dfrac{4x}{xy}=\dfrac{}{xy}$

6 Add or subtract:
a $\dfrac{5}{x}+\dfrac{2}{y}$ **b** $\dfrac{4}{a}-\dfrac{2}{b}$ **c** $\dfrac{3}{u}+\dfrac{1}{v}$ **d** $\dfrac{1}{s}-\dfrac{2}{t}$
e $\dfrac{1}{x}+\dfrac{1}{y}$ **f** $\dfrac{1}{m}-\dfrac{1}{n}$ **g** $\dfrac{5}{c}+\dfrac{1}{d}$ **h** $\dfrac{1}{p}-\dfrac{4}{q}$

7 Copy and complete:
$\dfrac{a}{b}-\dfrac{c}{a}$ (lcm ab) $=\dfrac{a^2}{ab}-\dfrac{bc}{ab}=\dfrac{}{ab}$

8 Add or subtract:
a $\dfrac{m}{n}+\dfrac{n}{m}$ **b** $\dfrac{u}{v}-\dfrac{x}{y}$ **c** $\dfrac{u}{v}+\dfrac{v}{u}$ **d** $\dfrac{s}{t}-\dfrac{t}{s}$

Copy and complete these tables:

9 a

+	c	d
a	$a+c$	
b		

b

+	$\dfrac{1}{c}$	$\dfrac{1}{d}$
$\dfrac{1}{a}$	*	
$\dfrac{1}{b}$		

$*$ $\dfrac{1}{a}+\dfrac{1}{c}=\dfrac{c}{ac}+\dfrac{a}{ac}=\dfrac{c+a}{ac}$

10 a

−	c	d
a		
b		

b

−	$\dfrac{1}{c}$	$\dfrac{1}{d}$
$\dfrac{1}{a}$		
$\dfrac{1}{b}$		

11 a

+	$\dfrac{a}{b}$	$\dfrac{c}{d}$
$\dfrac{a}{b}$		
$\dfrac{c}{d}$		

b

−	$\dfrac{a}{b}$	$\dfrac{c}{d}$
$\dfrac{a}{b}$		
$\dfrac{c}{d}$		

EXERCISE 3B

1 Copy and complete:

$$\frac{2n-1}{2}-\frac{n-1}{3}\;(\text{lcm } 6)=\frac{3(2n-1)}{6}-\frac{2(n-1)}{6}$$

$$=\frac{3(2n-1)-2(n-1)}{6}=\frac{\ldots\ldots-2n+2}{6}=\frac{\ldots\ldots}{6}$$

2 Add these fractions:

a $\dfrac{x+1}{2}+\dfrac{x-1}{3}$ **b** $\dfrac{a+3}{4}+\dfrac{a-2}{6}$ **c** $\dfrac{v+3}{4}+\dfrac{v+1}{2}$

d $\dfrac{w-2}{5}+\dfrac{w+3}{2}$ **e** $\dfrac{x+3}{4}+\dfrac{x+1}{3}$ **f** $\dfrac{y-1}{2}+\dfrac{y-3}{3}$

3 Subtract or add:

a $\dfrac{x+3}{2}-\dfrac{x+2}{3}$ **b** $\dfrac{y+1}{2}-\dfrac{y-1}{5}$ **c** $\dfrac{z-2}{3}-\dfrac{z+1}{4}$

d $\dfrac{2a+3}{4}+\dfrac{a-1}{2}$ **e** $\dfrac{3u-1}{4}-\dfrac{2u-1}{5}$ **f** $\dfrac{v-3}{6}+\dfrac{v-1}{3}$

4 Copy and complete:

$$\frac{5}{x+1}-\frac{2}{x-3}\;(\text{lcm }(x+1)(x-3))$$

$$=\frac{5(x-3)}{(x+1)(x-3)}-\frac{2(x+1)}{(x+1)(x-3)}$$

$$=\frac{5(x-3)-2(x+1)}{(x+1)(x-3)}=\;\ldots\ldots$$

5 Add these fractions:

a $\dfrac{3}{x+2}+\dfrac{2}{x+1}$ **b** $\dfrac{4}{x-1}+\dfrac{3}{x-2}$ **c** $\dfrac{2}{x+4}+\dfrac{1}{x-2}$

6 Subtract these fractions:

a $\dfrac{5}{x+2}-\dfrac{3}{x+1}$ **b** $\dfrac{4}{x+1}-\dfrac{2}{x-1}$ **c** $\dfrac{1}{x-4}-\dfrac{2}{x-1}$

7 Add or subtract:

a $\dfrac{3}{x}+\dfrac{2}{x-1}$ **b** $\dfrac{2}{x}-\dfrac{1}{x-2}$ **c** $\dfrac{4}{x-3}-\dfrac{1}{x}$

8 When two electrical resistances are connected as shown, the overall resistance R is given by $\dfrac{1}{R}=\dfrac{1}{R_1}+\dfrac{1}{R_2}$.

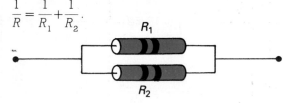

Find an expression for $\dfrac{1}{R}$ when $R_1=x+4$ and $R_2=x-3$.

9 The focal length, f, of a lens can be found from the formula $\dfrac{1}{f}=\dfrac{1}{u}+\dfrac{1}{v}$.

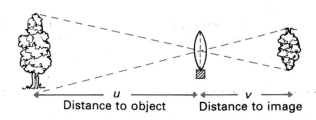

Distance to object   Distance to image

Find an expression for $\dfrac{1}{f}$ when $u=x$ and $v=x-2$.

10 Add or subtract:

a $\dfrac{2}{x}-\dfrac{3}{x^2}$ **b** $\dfrac{1}{x}+\dfrac{x-1}{x^2}$ **c** $\dfrac{3}{x}-\dfrac{1-x}{x^2}$

11 Prove that $\dfrac{x}{x-2}+\dfrac{x}{2-x}=0$

12 Show that:

a $\dfrac{1}{x+1}+\dfrac{x}{(x+1)(x+2)}=\dfrac{2}{x+2}$

b $\dfrac{3}{x-1}-\dfrac{2x+7}{(x-1)(x+2)}=\dfrac{1}{x+2}$

13 Simplify $\dfrac{4x-3}{(2x-1)(x-1)}-\dfrac{2}{2x-1}$, and check your answer for $x=3$.

⁣⁣/**INVESTIGATION**

The Egyptians only used fractions with unit numerators.

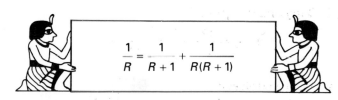

$$\frac{1}{R}=\frac{1}{R+1}+\frac{1}{R(R+1)}$$

a *Check that the formula works for $R=2,5$ and 10.*
b *Prove that the formula is true, by adding the fractions on the right-hand side.*
c *Investigate how the formula can help you to break a fraction into the sum of Egyptian fractions.*

CHALLENGE

Amaze your friends! Here's how you can tell them, in a split second, what the sum of

$$\frac{1}{1 \times 2} + \frac{1}{2 \times 3} + \frac{1}{3 \times 4} + \ldots \text{ is, to any number of terms.}$$

First, practise finding the sum of the first three terms using the reciprocal (1/x) key on your calculator for $\frac{1}{2}, \frac{1}{6}$ *and* $\frac{1}{12}$, *like this:*

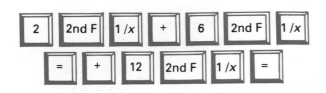

How long did the calculation take? Could you see that the answer would be $\frac{3}{4}$? *Why?*

Here is the secret:
$$S = \frac{1}{1 \times 2} + \frac{1}{2 \times 3} + \frac{1}{3 \times 4}$$
$$= \left(1 - \frac{1}{2}\right) + \left(\frac{1}{2} - \frac{1}{3}\right) + \left(\frac{1}{3} - \frac{1}{4}\right)$$
$$= 1 - \frac{1}{4} \quad \text{Why?}$$
$$= \frac{3}{4}$$

1 Write down the sum of $\dfrac{1}{1 \times 2} + \dfrac{1}{2 \times 3} + \cdots + \dfrac{1}{5 \times 6}$. Then write it out as above, to check.

2 Can you now write down the sum of
$$\frac{1}{1 \times 2} + \frac{1}{2 \times 3} + \cdots + \frac{1}{99 \times 100}?$$

3 a Simplify $\dfrac{1}{n} - \dfrac{1}{n+1}$

b Write down the sum of
$$\frac{1}{1 \times 2} + \frac{1}{2 \times 3} + \cdots + \frac{1}{n(n+1)}.$$

EQUATIONS WITH FRACTIONS

Good advice for solving equations

1 Remove fractions.
2 Remove brackets.
3 Use these rules:
  (i) add or subtract the same number on each side
  (ii) multiply or divide each side by the same number.

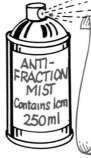

Instructions
Spray each side of equation. The active ingredient lcm (lowest common multiple) destroys all known fractions by quick-acting multiplication.

Examples
Look at how the rules are applied in solving these equations:

a
$$\frac{x}{3} = \frac{1}{2}$$
$$6 \times \frac{x}{3} = 6 \times \frac{1}{2} \quad \text{(lcm of 3 and 2 is 6)}$$
$$2x = 3$$
$$x = 1\tfrac{1}{2}$$

b
$$y = \frac{2}{5}(y - 1)$$
$$5y = 2(y - 1)$$
$$5y = 2y - 2$$
$$3y = -2$$
$$y = -\tfrac{2}{3}$$

c
$$\frac{x}{3} - \frac{x}{5} = 2$$
$$15\left(\frac{x}{3} - \frac{x}{5}\right) = 15 \times 2 \quad \text{(lcm of 3 and 5 is 15)}$$
$$15 \times \frac{x}{3} - 15 \times \frac{x}{5} = 30$$
$$5x - 3x = 30$$
$$2x = 30$$
$$x = 15$$

EXERCISE 4A

Solve these equations:

1 a $\dfrac{x}{2} = 5$ **b** $\dfrac{y}{3} = 1$ **c** $\dfrac{u}{4} = \dfrac{3}{2}$ **d** $\dfrac{v}{4} = \dfrac{1}{2}$

2 a $\dfrac{m}{3} = -2$ **b** $\dfrac{n}{5} = -1$ **c** $\dfrac{x}{2} = -\dfrac{1}{2}$ **d** $\dfrac{y}{4} = -\dfrac{1}{2}$

3 a $2(x+3) = 6$ **b** $3(x-1) = 1$ **c** $5(t+2) = 0$

4 a $x = \dfrac{1}{2}(x+3)$ **b** $y = \dfrac{1}{3}(y-2)$ **c** $z = \dfrac{1}{4}(z+1)$

5 a $p = \dfrac{2}{3}(2-p)$ **b** $q = \dfrac{3}{4}(1+q)$ **c** $r = \dfrac{3}{5}(r-1)$

6 a $\dfrac{m+2}{4} = 3$ **b** $\dfrac{n-1}{5} = 0$ **c** $\dfrac{t-3}{4} = \dfrac{1}{2}$

7 a $\dfrac{x}{2} - \dfrac{x}{3} = 1$ **b** $\dfrac{y}{2} + \dfrac{y}{4} = 1$ **c** $\dfrac{z}{2} - \dfrac{z}{5} = 0$

8 a $\dfrac{t}{3} - \dfrac{t}{2} = \dfrac{1}{2}$ **b** $\dfrac{u}{3} - \dfrac{u}{5} = \dfrac{1}{3}$ **c** $\dfrac{v}{4} - \dfrac{v}{2} = \dfrac{3}{2}$

9 a $\dfrac{a+1}{2} = \dfrac{a}{3}$ **b** $\dfrac{b-1}{3} = \dfrac{b}{5}$ **c** $\dfrac{c+3}{2} = \dfrac{c}{4}$

10 a $\dfrac{3}{y+1} = 1$ **b** $\dfrac{2}{2x-1} = 3$ **c** $\dfrac{1}{2z-4} = \dfrac{1}{3}$

EXERCISE 4B

Examples Solve:

a
$$\dfrac{x+3}{6} - \dfrac{x-1}{2} = 4$$
$$6\left(\dfrac{x+3}{6} - \dfrac{x-1}{2}\right) = 6 \times 4$$
$$\dfrac{6(x+3)}{6} - \dfrac{6(x-1)}{2} = 24$$
$$x+3-3(x-1) = 24$$
$$x+3-3x+3 = 24$$
$$-2x = 18$$
$$x = -9$$

b
$$2x + \dfrac{5}{x} = 11$$
$$x\left(2x + \dfrac{5}{x}\right) = 11 \times x$$
$$2x^2 + 5 = 11x \quad \text{(a quadratic equation)}$$
$$2x^2 - 11x + 5 = 0 \quad \text{(standard form)}$$
$$(2x-1)(x-5) = 0$$
$$x = \tfrac{1}{2} \text{ or } 5$$

Solve the equations in questions **1–5**.

1 a $\dfrac{x+2}{5} + \dfrac{x}{3} = 2$ **b** $\dfrac{x-3}{3} - \dfrac{x}{2} = 1$

2 a $\dfrac{y+2}{2} + \dfrac{y-1}{4} = 2$ **b** $\dfrac{y}{2} - \dfrac{y-1}{4} = 1$

3 a $\dfrac{a-5}{3} + \dfrac{a}{2} = 0$ **b** $\dfrac{b}{2} - \dfrac{b-3}{5} = 3$

4 a $\dfrac{m+3}{6} + \dfrac{m+1}{2} = 4$ **b** $\dfrac{n+3}{3} - \dfrac{n-5}{5} = 2$

5 a $\dfrac{2x-1}{3} - \dfrac{2x-1}{5} = 2$ **b** $\dfrac{y+1}{2} + \dfrac{y-2}{3} = 0$

In questions **6–9**, make quadratic equations, then solve them.

6 a $x + \dfrac{6}{x} - 5 = 0$ **b** $x - \dfrac{6}{x} + 1 = 0$ **c** $x - \dfrac{10}{x} + 3 = 0$

7 a $2x - \dfrac{3}{x} = -5$ **b** $x + \dfrac{4}{x} = 4$ **c** $2x - \dfrac{12}{x} = 5$

8 a $\dfrac{1}{2}x^2 + \dfrac{3}{2}x = 9$ **b** $\dfrac{x}{2} - \dfrac{3}{x} = \dfrac{5}{2}$ **c** $x - \dfrac{1}{4x} = 0$

9

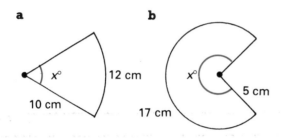

Can you find *two* numbers Sanjay might have started with?

10 Calculate, to the nearest degree, $x°$, the angle at the centre of each sector.

For example, in **a** $12 = \dfrac{x}{360} \times 2 \times \pi \times 10$.

a

$x°$ 12 cm

10 cm

b

$x°$ 5 cm

17 cm

11 Two cyclists took part in a city suburbs race. Their average speeds were 20 km/h and 25 km/h. The faster cyclist finished 6 minutes ahead of the other.

a If they cycled d km, explain why $\dfrac{d}{20} - \dfrac{d}{25} = \dfrac{1}{10}$.

b Solve this equation to find the length of the race.

12 Two sports cars were timed over a distance d km. Their average speeds were 60 km/h and 80 km/h.

a Write down an expression for the time each car took.

b The difference in their times was half an hour. Make an equation, and solve it to find the distance covered.

/ **CHALLENGE**

Find a positive number, correct to 3 decimal places, which is one more than its reciprocal.
(Hint: take x for the number, and make an equation.)

LITERAL EQUATIONS

Remove fractions.
Remove brackets.
Use rules for
solving equations.

Examples
Solve for x (make x the subject):

a $\dfrac{x}{a} = \dfrac{b}{c}$

(Multiply by lcm of denominators, ac)

$ac \times \dfrac{x}{a} = ac \times \dfrac{b}{c}$

$cx = ab$

$x = \dfrac{ab}{c}$

b $y = a(x - n)$
$y = ax - an$
$y + an = ax$
$ax = y + an$
$x = \dfrac{y + an}{a}$

EXERCISE 5A

Solve each equation for x in questions **1–7**.

1 a $x-2=k$ **b** $x-p=q$ **c** $x+5=t$
d $x+m=n$

2 a $\dfrac{x}{2}=d$ **b** $\dfrac{x}{c}=d$ **c** $2x=b$ **d** $ax=b$

3 a $\dfrac{x}{2}=\dfrac{a}{3}$ **b** $\dfrac{x}{c}=\dfrac{4}{5}$ **c** $\dfrac{x}{m}=n$ **d** $\dfrac{x}{b}=\dfrac{1}{2}$

4 a $3x+2=w$ **b** $5x-g=h$
c $ax+b=c$ **d** $px-q=r$

5 a $2(x-a)=b$ **b** $a(x-3)=c$ **c** $a(x+b)=c$

6 a $y=ax-b$ **b** $u=px+q$ **c** $t=1-cx$

7 a $\dfrac{x}{2}+a=b$ **b** $\dfrac{x}{3}-c=d$ **c** $\dfrac{x}{m}-p=q$

In questions **8–14** make the letter in brackets the subject.

8 a $V=\dfrac{1}{3}ah\ldots(h)$ **b** $I=\dfrac{E}{R}\ldots(E)$ and (R)

9 a $C=2\pi r\ldots(r)$ **b** $V=lbh\ldots(h)$

10 a $P=2(x+y)\ldots(x)$ **b** $P=a+b+c\ldots(a)$

11 a $V=\pi r^2h\ldots(h)$ and (r) **b** $y=mx+c\ldots(x)$

12 a $D=ST\ldots(S)$ **b** $P=\dfrac{E^2}{R}\ldots(E)$ and (R)

13 a $v=u+at\ldots(u)$ and (t) **b** $S=\frac{1}{2}gt^2\ldots(t)$

14 a $y=\frac{3}{4}(x+1)\ldots(x)$ **b** $C=\frac{5}{9}(F-32)\ldots(F)$

EXERCISE 5B

Examples
a Solve for t:
$$tu=tv+w$$
$$tu-tv=w \quad (t \text{ terms to one side})$$
$$t(u-v)=w \quad (\text{common factor})$$
$$t=\frac{w}{u-v}$$

b Solve for x: $\qquad y=\dfrac{a+x}{a-x}$
$$(a-x)y=a+x$$
$$ay-xy=a+x$$
$$-x-xy=a-ay \quad (x \text{ terms to one side})$$
$$x+xy=ay-a$$
$$x(1+y)=ay-a \quad (\text{common factor})$$
$$x=\frac{ay-a}{1+y}$$

1 Solve for x:
  a $3x=x+a$ **b** $2x-a=x+b$ **c** $p-x=q-2x$
  d $mx=n$ **e** $(m+1)x=n$ **f** $x(c-d)=y$

2 Solve for t:
  a $at+bt=c$ **b** $pt-qt=r$ **c** $ut=vt+1$
  d $ct=m-nt$ **e** $at+t=b$ **f** $dt=t+d$

3 Solve for y:
  a $ax+by=c$ **b** $ay+by=c$ **c** $ax+by=ay$
  d $ay=by+d$ **e** $py=m-y$ **f** $pq-qy=r$

4 Solve for x:
  a $\dfrac{x}{a}+\dfrac{x}{b}=1$ **b** $\dfrac{x}{c}-\dfrac{x}{d}=2$ **c** $\dfrac{x-1}{a}=\dfrac{x}{b}$
  d $\dfrac{m}{x}=\dfrac{n}{1-x}$ **e** $\dfrac{1-x}{x}=\dfrac{a}{2}$ **f** $\dfrac{a-bx}{x}=a$
  g $y=\dfrac{1-x}{1+x}$ **h** $\dfrac{a}{b}=\dfrac{1-x}{1+x}$ **i** $\dfrac{a+x}{a-x}=\dfrac{3}{2}$

149

CHECK-UP ON FRACTIONS AND EQUATIONS

1 Simplify:

a $\dfrac{mn}{m}$ **b** $\dfrac{x}{x^2}$ **c** $\dfrac{2a}{10}$ **d** $\dfrac{3(u-v)}{4(u-v)}$

2 Factorise, then simplify:

a $\dfrac{3y-12}{3}$ **b** $\dfrac{2}{2x+2}$ **c** $\dfrac{a+2}{a^2-4}$ **d** $\dfrac{b^2+2b+1}{b+1}$

e $\dfrac{2x-2y}{x-y}$ **f** $\dfrac{x^2-x-6}{x^2-5x+6}$ **g** $\dfrac{u^2-v^2}{u-v}$ **h** $\dfrac{(m-n)^2}{m^2-n^2}$

3 Simplify:

a $\dfrac{14}{1}\times\dfrac{t}{7}$ **b** $\dfrac{m^2}{n}\times\dfrac{n}{m}$ **c** $\dfrac{3}{z}\times\dfrac{z}{6}$ **d** $\dfrac{a^2}{b}\div\dfrac{a}{b}$

4 Simplify:

a $\dfrac{x}{5}+\dfrac{x}{2}$ **b** $\dfrac{x}{5}-\dfrac{y}{2}$ **c** $\dfrac{u}{3}-\dfrac{u}{6}$ **d** $\dfrac{1}{a}+\dfrac{1}{b}$

e $\dfrac{a-1}{3}+\dfrac{2a+3}{6}$ **f** $\dfrac{x+2}{2}-\dfrac{x-2}{3}$ **g** $\dfrac{3}{x}-\dfrac{2}{x-1}$

5 Find the area and perimeter of each shape in terms of x:

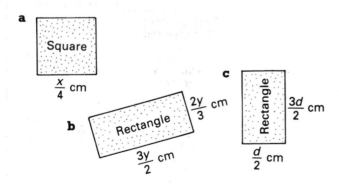

6 Simplify:

a $\dfrac{x+1}{2}+\dfrac{x-1}{3}$ **b** $\dfrac{x}{3}-\dfrac{x-2}{4}$ **c** $\dfrac{x-1}{2}-\dfrac{x+2}{5}$

7 Solve these equations:

a $\dfrac{y-1}{3}=2$ **b** $\dfrac{w-6}{2}=-1$ **c** $1-\dfrac{y-1}{2}=0$

8 Solve:

a $\dfrac{x}{2}-\dfrac{x}{3}=1$ **b** $\dfrac{x+3}{3}+\dfrac{x}{4}=1$ **c** $\dfrac{x+3}{4}-\dfrac{x-1}{2}=0$

9 Arrange these as quadratic equations in standard form, and solve them.

a $x-2-\dfrac{8}{x}=0$ **b** $x+6+\dfrac{9}{x}=0$ **c** $2x-3+\dfrac{1}{x}=0$

10 Solve for x:

a $ax+b=10$ **b** $\dfrac{m}{x}=n$ **c** $p(q-x)=r$

d $3x-4=x$ **e** $ax-4=x$ **f** $ax-b=x$

11 In each formula below make the letter in brackets the subject.

a $M=60H\,..\,(H)$ **b** $P=4x\,..\,(x)$

c $A=\tfrac{1}{2}bh\,..\,(h)$ **d** $V=\dfrac{8p}{c}\,..\,(p)$

e $L=\dfrac{wp}{2000}\,..\,(p)$ **f** $A=4\pi r^2\,..\,(r)$

g $\dfrac{x}{y}=\dfrac{a}{b}\,..\,(x)$ and (y) **h** $R=\dfrac{u}{1-v}\,..\,(u)$ and (v)

12 Remove the fractions in the formula $\dfrac{1}{R}=\dfrac{1}{R_1}+\dfrac{1}{R_2}$, then make R the subject.

13 In a cross-country race, d km in length, Mark's average speed was 5 m/s and Jamal's was 6 m/s. Jamal finished 4 minutes ahead of Mark. Make an equation, and solve it to find the length of the race in km.

12 PROBLEM SOLVING

1 DIAGRAMS

(i) Flowcharts

A flowchart is a diagram with a list of instructions which must be carried out in a certain order. It has a title, and may then have:

START/STOP boxes   Instruction boxes   Decision boxes   Read/write boxes   Loops (to repeat steps)

  No  Yes

Examine the ways in which these are used in the following flowcharts.

Examples

a

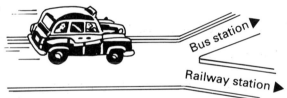

The passenger in the taxi has a choice.
He can take either the bus or the train.

To take the correct road

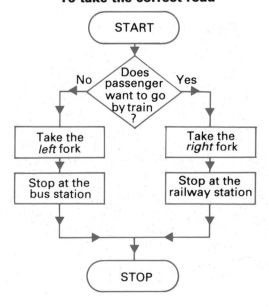

b   To calculate the mean of five numbers

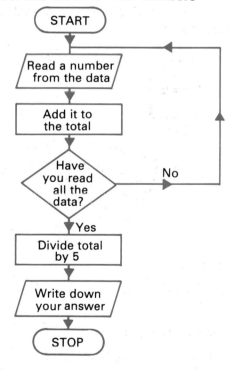

Data: 2, 3, 4, 7, 9

EXERCISE 1

1 Rashid is delivering a parcel to a block of flats. If the flat is on the first or second floor he will use the stairs. If it is above the second floor he will use the lift. Arrange the boxes in the form of a flowchart, and give the flowchart a title.

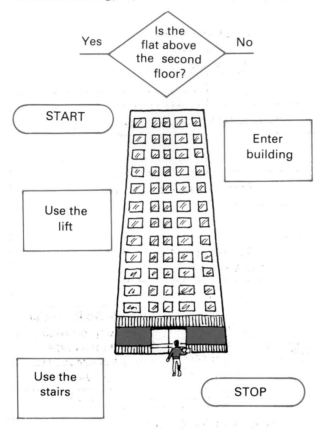

2 Some pupils are helping to plan a weekend trip to the school cottage.

Tom: I'm sure no more than 12 will want to go. A minibus will be big enough.

Ann: What if more than 12 *do* want to go?

Tom: If there are 24, or less, two minibuses will do.

Jill: What if the whole class of 30 decide to go?

Tom: Then we'll need a coach.

Use these boxes to draw a flowchart which describes their plans. Remember to choose a title.

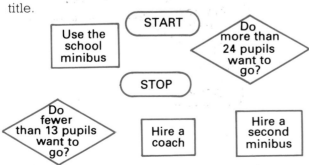

3

A teacher reads out the register to check if students are present. Copy the empty flowchart and use the boxes below to fill it in. Remember to give it a title.

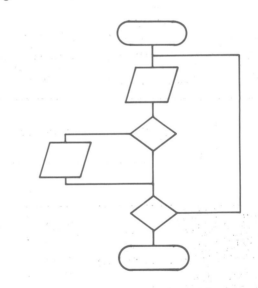

Data: class register

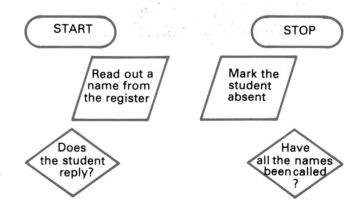

4 Copy this empty flowchart, then fill in the boxes.

A game at the fair

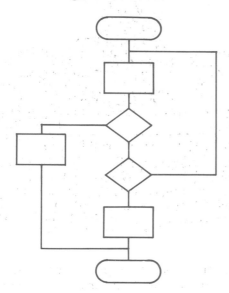

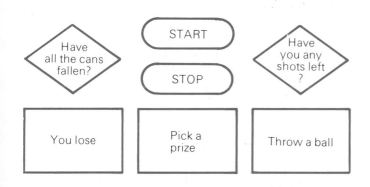

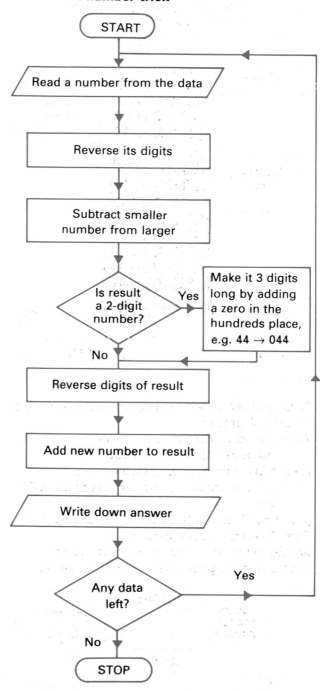

5 a Use this flowchart to process the data listed below.

b What do you find?

c Choose your own data (some 3-digit numbers in each of which the first digit is different from the last one) and try it again.

Data: 432, 257, 372, 892, 754, 890

A number trick

START

Read a number from the data

Reverse its digits

Subtract smaller number from larger

Is result a 2-digit number? — Yes → Make it 3 digits long by adding a zero in the hundreds place, e.g. 44 → 044

No

Reverse digits of result

Add new number to result

Write down answer

Any data left? — Yes

No

STOP

6 The seats in a cinema are arranged so that each row has one more seat than the row in front of it. Using the flowchart the manager is able to calculate the number of seats in any block of rows. The front row has 20 seats, and there are 50 rows.

a How many seats are there:
  (i) in the cinema
  (ii) from the fourth to the fifteenth row?

b Use the flowchart to make a formula for N, the number of seats in the cinema, involving S and R.

7 It is often necessary to arrange lists in some kind of order. This program arranges A, B, C in order of increasing size.

a Try the program for A = 3, B = 2, C = 1, writing down the results at stages (i), (ii) and (iii).

b Try it again for data 30, 50, 40.

c The computer understands > to mean 'is after . . . . .', alphabetically. For example, Becky > Alan. Test the flowchart for Peter, Sophie, Balvinder.

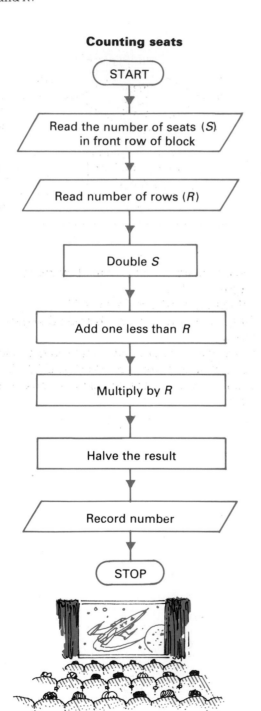

Counting seats

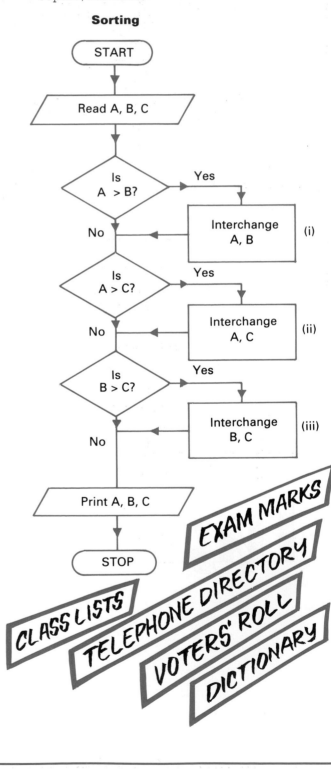

Sorting

8 Here is a flowchart without a title.

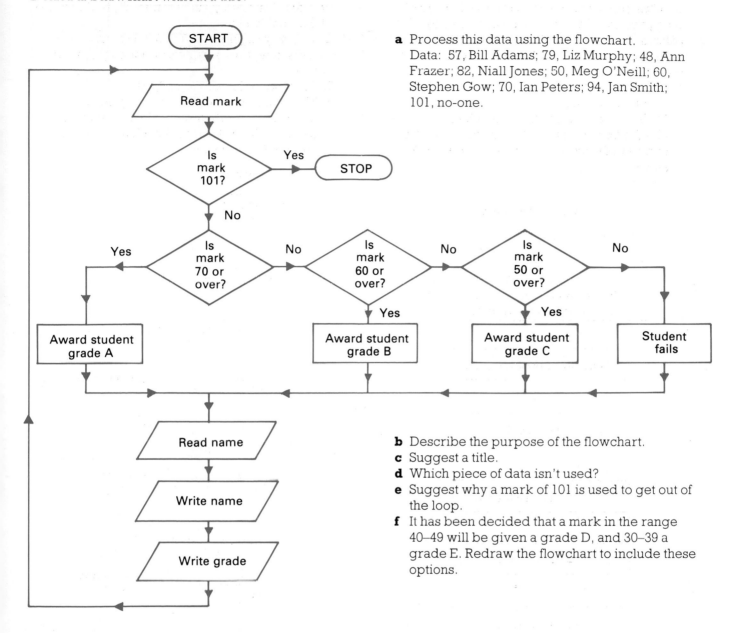

a Process this data using the flowchart.
Data: 57, Bill Adams; 79, Liz Murphy; 48, Ann Frazer; 82, Niall Jones; 50, Meg O'Neill; 60, Stephen Gow; 70, Ian Peters; 94, Jan Smith; 101, no-one.

b Describe the purpose of the flowchart.
c Suggest a title.
d Which piece of data isn't used?
e Suggest why a mark of 101 is used to get out of the loop.
f It has been decided that a mark in the range 40–49 will be given a grade D, and 30–39 a grade E. Redraw the flowchart to include these options.

(ii) Graphs—mathematical pictures

Graphs come in all shapes and sizes, and every one tells a story.

EXERCISE 2

In questions **1–6** decide which graph fits the story above it.

1 From the boundary, Jack throws the cricket ball to the keeper.

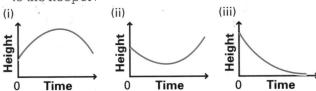

2 The car accelerates away from rest, then stops at a crossroads.

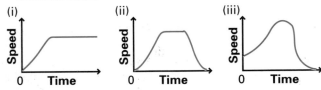

3 A bean is planted. It germinates and grows to its full height. Its height is measured daily.

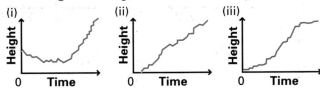

4 A radiator is switched on in a room, and the temperature is measured hourly.

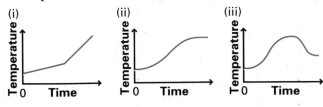

5 Louisa is blowing up a balloon.

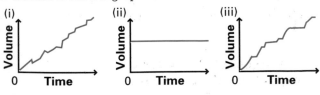

6 Charges for car hire: £50 deposit, then 10p per mile.

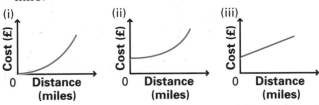

7 Water flows from each of these containers at a steady rate. Match the graphs and the containers.

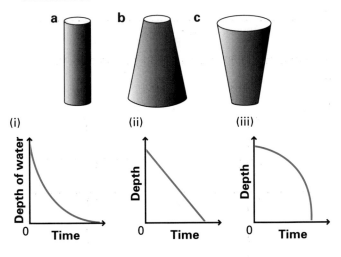

8 These graphs show the time taken for the temperature in a room to fall from 20°C to 18°C, and then to be raised again to 20°C by heaters. Draw a graph over a period of three hours, showing the temperature as the heating goes off at 20°C and on at 18°C.

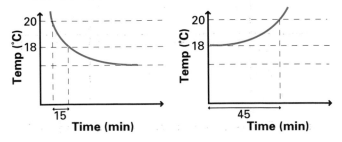

9 The graph illustrates Ali's car journey as he enters the town at New Street. Describe his route, mentioning the traffic lights at which he had to stop.

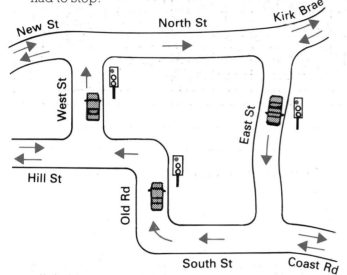

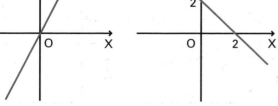

In questions **10–12**, pair each equation with its graph.

10 (i)

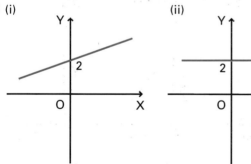

(ii)

(iii)

(iv)

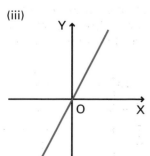

a $y = 2x$ **b** $x + y = 2$ **c** $y = 2$ **d** $y = \frac{1}{2}x + 2$

11 (i)

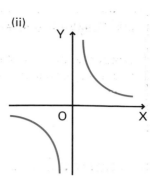

(ii)

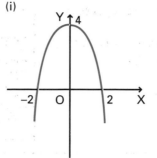

(iii)

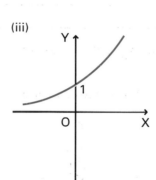

(iv)

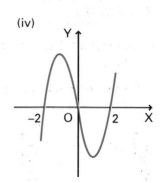

a $y = 2^x$ **b** $y = x^3 - 4x$ **c** $y = \dfrac{4}{x}$ **d** $y = 4 - x^2$

12

(i)

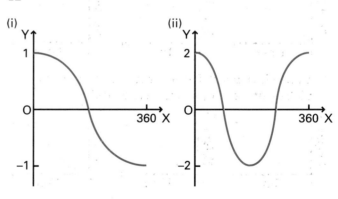

(ii)

(iii)

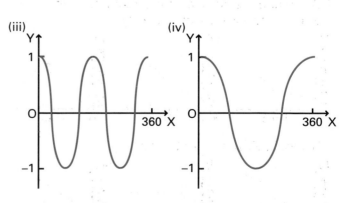

(iv)

a $y = \cos 2x°$ **b** $y = \cos \frac{1}{2}x°$
c $y = 2\cos x°$ **d** $y = \cos x°$

(iii) Venn diagrams

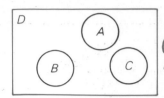

John Venn was an English mathematician who lived from 1834 to 1923.

EXERCISE 3

1

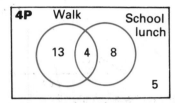

This Venn diagram tells you that: there are 30 students in class 4P; 17 walk to school; 12 take school lunches; 4 walk *and* take school lunches; 5 neither walk to school nor take school lunches. How many of the class walk to school and do not take school lunches?

2

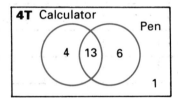

a How many students:
   (i) are in class 4T
   (ii) have their calculators
   (iii) have their calculators and pens?
b Calculate the probability that a pupil in the class, chosen at random, has neither pen nor calculator.

3

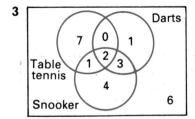

a How many people belong to the Youth Club?
b How many play in:
   (i) all three teams   (ii) the table-tennis team
   (iii) both darts and snooker teams
   (iv) the table-tennis and snooker teams, but *not* in the darts team?
c Calculate the probability that a member chosen at random plays:
   (i) snooker   (ii) only one of the sports.

4 Draw Venn diagrams to illustrate:
   a Class 4D has 27 students. 19 take history, 14 geography and 6 both history and geography. How many take neither subject?
   b Ahmed's catalogue describes 20 games. 7 of them need dice, 12 need counters and 3 need both. How many need neither dice nor counters?

5

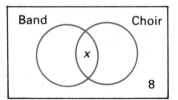

25 students study music. 16 are in the school band, and 10 are in the school choir. 8 are in neither.
   a If x students are in both, write down an expression for the number who are in:
      (i) the band only   (ii) the choir only.
   b Make an equation in x, and solve it. How many are in both band and choir?

6 In a group of 40 students, 25 study French, 32 German and 6 study neither language. Draw a Venn diagram, and use the method of question **5** to find the number of students who take both French and German.

7 A survey of the use of records, tapes and CDs by 90 people found that 12 used records only, 15 used tapes only, 23 used CDs only, 14 used records and tapes, 19 tapes and CDs, 18 records and CDs, and 7 used none at all.
   a Copy the Venn diagram, and fill in all the regions in terms of x.
   b Make an equation and solve it to find the number who used records, tapes *and* CDs.

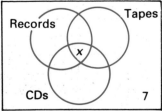

2 SHAPE AND SPACE

(i) Similar shapes (area and volume)

Reminder
Two shapes are **similar** if one is a
scaled copy of the other.
This means that:
a their corresponding angles are equal
b their corresponding sides are in the
same ratio (have the same scale
factor).
For triangles, either condition is sufficient.
These two triangles are similar because:
   a corresponding angles are equal
     (30°, 30°; 60°, 60°; 90°, 90°)
or b corresponding sides have scale factor 2:1.

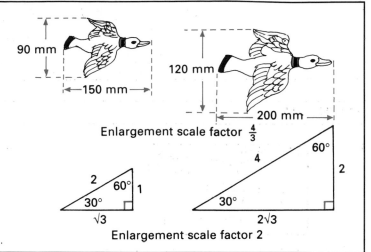

Enlargement scale factor $\frac{4}{3}$

Enlargement scale factor 2

EXERCISE 4

1 Why are all squares similar?
Copy and complete:

Enlargement from	(i) to (ii)	(i) to (iii)	(i) to (iv)
Linear scale factor	2:1 = 2		
Area scale factor	4:1 = 4		

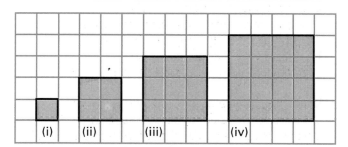

2 The tiling below is made of congruent triangles.
Why are the shaded triangles similar?
Copy and complete (count the small triangles for
the areas):

Enlargement from	(i) to (ii)	(i) to (iii)	(i) to (iv)
Linear scale factor			
Area scale factor			

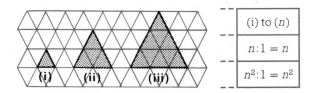

(i) to (n)
n:1 = n
n²:1 = n²

3 Copy and complete this table for the 'nest' of
similar hexagons.

Enlargement from	(i) to (ii)	(i) to (iii)	(i) to (iv)
Linear scale factor			
Area scale factor			

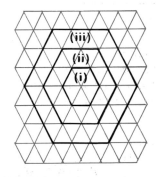

(i) to (n)

If the linear scale factor for two similar shapes is
n, then their area scale factor is n^2.

4 Check the 'area scale factor' = (linear scale
factor)² rule for the two triangles in the box
above Exercise 4.

5 One square has a side 1 cm long, another has a
side 1 m long. Calculate the scale factor of the
enlargement of:
a the lengths of the sides
b the areas.

6 These radiators are similar, with linear scale factor of enlargement 2.

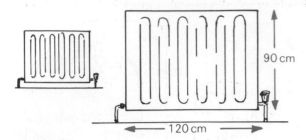

90 cm

120 cm

Calculate:
a the length and breadth of the smaller radiator
b the areas of the front faces of the radiators
c the area scale factor of enlargement.
d Is area scale factor = (linear scale factor)²?

7 The linear enlargement scale factor for these two similar tents is 3.

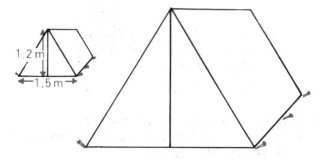

1.2 m

1.5 m

Calculate:
a the width and height of the front of the larger tent
b the areas of the fronts of the tents
c the area enlargement scale factor.
d Check that the 'n^2 rule' holds.

8 This is a photograph of the moon, and an enlargement of it.

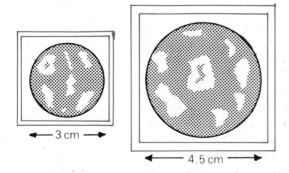

3 cm

4.5 cm

Calculate:
a the linear scale factor of the enlargement
b the area scale factor.

9 One television screen is 51 cm size (the length of its diagonal), and the other is 59 cm. Calculate, correct to 2 decimal places, the area scale factor of enlargement between the screens.

10 Two similar oval mirrors have widths of 20 cm and 30 cm. The smaller one costs £24. What would you consider to be a fair price for the larger one?

11 The enlargement scale factor is 3. Calculate the area of photographic paper needed for the enlargement.

Length in MM

54

84

12 a Write down pairs of equal angles in the diagram below. Are the triangles similar?
b Calculate the scale factors of the enlargement of the sides and areas from △ABC to △ADE.
c The area of △ABC is 360 mm². Calculate the area of △ADE.

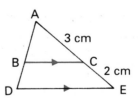

A
3 cm
B   C
2 cm
D   E

13 a Why are △s PQR and PST similar?
b Calculate the scale factors of the reduction of the sides and areas from △PST to △PQR.
c The area of △PST is 800 mm². Calculate the area of △PQR.

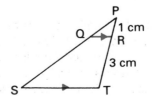

P
1 cm
Q
R
3 cm
S   T

EXERCISE 5

1 Each small cube has a 1 cm edge.

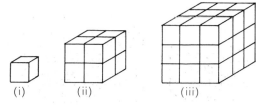

Copy and complete the table.

Enlargement from	(i) to (ii)	(i) to (iii)	(i) to (iv)
Linear scale factor			
Volume scale factor			

	(i) to (n)

> If the linear scale factor for two similar shapes is n, then their volume scale factor is n^3.

2

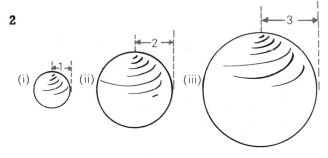

Copy and complete this table for spheres:

Enlargement from	(i) to (ii)	(i) to (iii)	(i) to (iv)
Linear scale factor			
Volume scale factor			

	(i) to (n)

3 Perfume is sold in similar bottles of three
different sizes. Corresponding edges of the
bottles are 1 cm, 2 cm and 3 cm long. The
smallest bottle holds 2 ml of perfume.
How much does each of the others hold?

4 These two cylindrical tins of paint are similar.

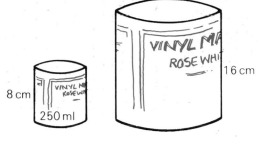

Calculate:
a the linear scale factor of enlargement
b the volume scale factor
c the volume of the larger tin.

5 The flower pots have similar shapes. The
smallest one can hold 720 cm^3 of soil.
How much can each of the others hold?

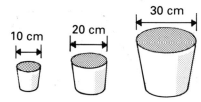

6 A model car has a scale factor of 1:50.
a The model is 7.5 cm long. Calculate the length
of the real car, in metres.
b The area of the model's windscreen is 10 cm^2.
Calculate the area of the windscreen on the
real car in: (i) cm^2 (ii) m^2.
c The car's petrol tank holds 50 litres. How
much will the model's tank hold, in ml?

7 One cube has an edge 1 mm long, and another
has an edge 1 cm long. Calculate the
enlargement scale factor of:
a the edges   **b** the surface areas
c the volumes.

8 This standard lamp throws
two similar cones of light
onto the floor and ceiling.
Calculate the scale factors
for:
a the heights of the cones
b the areas of the pools of
light on the floor and
ceiling
c the volumes of the two
cones of light.

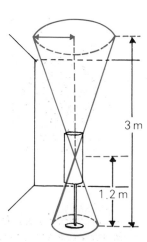

161

9 Star Cereals give a free sample packet (linear scale factor ⅔) with every new large packet. The coloured design on the large packet covers 200 cm². Calculate:

a the area of the design on the free sample
b the volume of each packet
c the area of card needed for each.

BRAINSTORMER

Many photocopiers have a 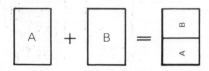 *button for reducing the size of a copy. This allows two A4 sheets to be printed onto one A4 page.*

***a** Why 71%? Why not 50%?*

***b** What happens if you put a reduced sheet through again?*

***c** What percentage button would reduce an A4 sheet to 65.6% of its area after two reductions?*

10 Repeat question **9** for two cylindrical cartons of juice (with scale factor ⅖). The larger one has height 20 cm and diameter of base 10 cm, with a coloured design covering 80 cm². Give answers correct to 3 significant figures, where necessary.

11 The weight of a new statue for the Town Square will be 18 tonnes. What would the weight of a similar statue, made of the same material, but only half the height?

(ii) Locus

A locus is a set of points defined by a given rule.
The points may trace a path if movement is involved in the definition.
In these diagrams the dotted lines show the locus of points on the page which are:

a 1 cm from A   **b** 1 cm from BC   **c** equidistant from D and E   **d** equidistant from FG and GH

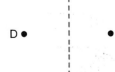

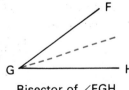

A circle, centre A   Two parallel lines   Perpendicular bisector of DE   Bisector of ∠FGH

EXERCISE 6

1 Describe or sketch the locus of points traced out by:

a a corner of the rising lift

b the weight on the swinging pendulum

c a point on the floor of the escalator

d the centre of the ball in flight

e the tip of the rotating blade

f the centre of the golf ball after it is struck towards the green.

2 Molly is a landscape gardener. She has to plant a tree T_3 which is the same distance from trees T_1 and T_2. Draw a line 4 cm long to represent T_1T_2, and mark all the places where she could put T_3 (the locus of T_3).

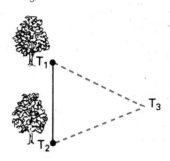

3 The master of the cruiser *Starlight* (S) has to steer to the harbour H, keeping the same distance from the sandbanks HA and HB. Copy the diagram, and draw his course (the locus of S).

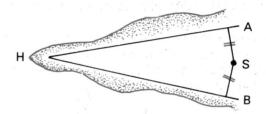

4 a On squared paper, draw the locus of points:
    (i) 1 unit from the *x*-axis (more than one set?)
    (ii) 2 units from the *y*-axis
    (iii) equidistant from both axes.
b Write down the equation of each locus.

5 Two walls XY and AB are perpendicular. A lamp-post has to be sited 2 m from XY and 3 m from AB. Make a diagram, which shows possible positions of the lamp-post.

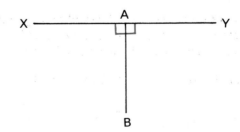

6 PQRS is a rectangular room. PQ = 6 m and QR = 4 m. A standard lamp has to be placed so that it is equidistant from walls PQ and QR, *and* 3 m from R.
Make a scale drawing, and show clearly where the lamp might be placed.

7 On squared paper, show the locus of points
d units from the origin where:
a $d = 1$ **b** $d \leqslant 1$ (unshaded)
c $2 < d < 3$ (unshaded).

8 Allcall's new radio phone transmitter can reach
places up to 3 km away. The diagram shows it
based at Weston.

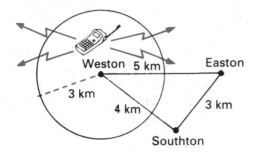

a Make a scale drawing and show the locus of
places served by the transmitter at Weston,
Easton and Southton.
b Shade the region where one transmitter could
be placed which would serve all three villages.

9 a In diagram (i), PQ is fixed in position, but R can
vary. What is the locus of R if the area of △PQR
remains constant?

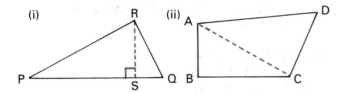

(i)   (ii)

b In diagram (ii), A, B and C are fixed, but D can
vary. What is the locus of D if the area of
quadrilateral ABCD remains constant?

*Find the locus of the base
of the valve as the wheel
rolls along a horizontal
surface.*

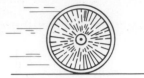

PRACTICAL PROJECTS

1 *A rod AB is 10 cm long, and its ends slide in
perpendicular grooves PQ and PR. Make a full-
size diagram to construct the locus of the midpoint
AB.*

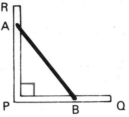

2 *Fix pins at A and B. Make a suitable loop of string,
put it round the pins and, keeping it taut with a
pencil point, trace the locus of P. Find out how the
locus varies as the distance between A and B is
altered.*

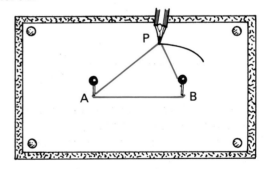

3 REASONING AND DEDUCTION—THINKING THINGS OUT

(i) Geometry

**In mathematics, each step should be set down clearly, and in order. Give reasons
where possible in this section of work.**

Example

Prove that the exterior angle,
ACD, of △ABC is equal to
the sum of the two interior
opposite angles, ABC and BAC.

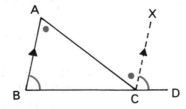

Proof
Draw CX ∥ BA.
∠DCX = ∠DBA (corresponding ∠s)
∠ACX = ∠BAC (alternate ∠s)
So ∠ACD = ∠ABC + ∠BAC.

EXERCISE 7

1 Prove that $\angle DEY = \angle CBX$.

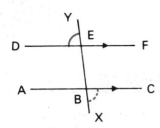

2 Using the diagram for question **1**, prove that $\angle DEB + \angle ABE = 180°$.

3 Prove that the three angles of a triangle add up to 180°.
(*Hint* Copy $\triangle ABC$, and draw $XCY \parallel AB$.)

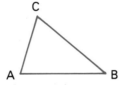

4 Prove that the three exterior angles of a triangle add up to 360°.
(*Hint* Question **3**.)

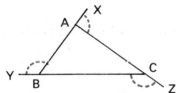

5 A snooker ball is struck and bounces off a cushion, as shown in diagram (i).
 a Prove that in diagram (ii), $\angle$s ABX and DCZ are complementary.
 b Copy diagram (ii) and draw CP perpendicular to YZ. Prove that $CD \parallel BA$.

(i) 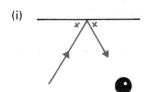 (ii)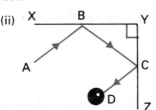

6 Copy this diagram, and prove that the angles of $\triangle PQR$ are in the ratio $1:2:3$.

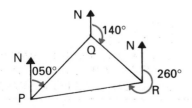

7 Semi-circles are drawn on the sides of the right-angled triangle ABC. Prove that area P = area Q + area R.
(*Hint* Pythagoras' Theorem.)

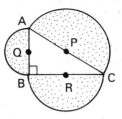

8

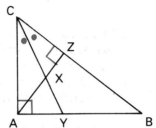

ABCD and DEFG are squares. Prove that triangles ADG and CDE are equal in area.
(*Hint* Area of $\triangle = \frac{1}{2}ab \sin C$)

9 Prove that:
 a $\angle CXZ = \angle CYA$
 b $\triangle AXY$ is isosceles.

10 Prove that if $\triangle$s ABC and DEF are:
 a congruent, then they are similar
 b similar, then they may or may not be congruent.

11 $AB \parallel DC$. Prove that:
 a $\triangle$s ABX and CXD are similar
 b $AX.XD = BX.XC$
 c $\triangle$s AXD and BXC have the same area.

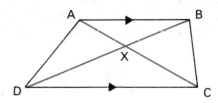

12 O is the centre of the circle in diagram (i) below. Prove that $\angle OQR = 3\angle OPR$.

(i) 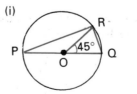 (ii)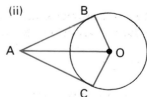

13 O is the centre of the circle in diagram (ii) above, and AB and AC are tangents to the circle.
 a Prove that $AB = AC$.
 b If AO and BC cross at M, prove that $BM = MC$.

(ii) Algebra

A conversation overheard

If you square an odd number you always get an odd number.

$1^2 = 1$, $3^2 = 9$, $5^2 = 25$, $9^2 = 81$. It seems to work but...

I'll prove it. $2n$ must be an even number, so $2n+1$ must be odd, $(2n+1)^2 = 4n^2 + 4n + 1 = 4n(n+1) + 1$.

Right $4n(n+1)$ must be even, so adding 1 gives an odd number.

EXERCISE 8

1 The formula for changing temperatures in Fahrenheit to Celsius is $C = \dfrac{5}{9}(F - 32)$.

Find the temperature where the numerical values of C and F are equal.

2 Flares are fired from A and B at the same time.

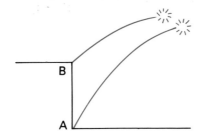

For A, $h = 60t - 2t^2$, and for B, $h = 360 + 22t - t^2$, where h is height in metres and t is time in seconds. Mike claims that flare A will never be higher than B. Is he right?
(*Hint* Make a quadratic equation, and solve it.)

3 Prove that the OUT number will always be double the IN number.
(*Hint* Try some numbers. Then let the IN number be n.)

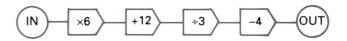

$$\text{IN} - \boxed{\times 6} - \boxed{+12} - \boxed{\div 3} - \boxed{-4} - \text{OUT}$$

4 This mobile is pivoted at A, B and C. The sun shape ● weighs 2 g. Find the weight of each of the other shapes if the mobile remains balanced.

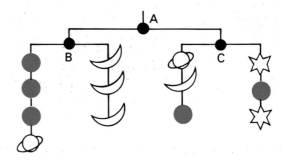

5 Eve finds that the graphs of $y = 2^x$ and $y = x^3$ meet twice, between $x = 1$ and $x = 2$, and between $x = 9.9$ and $x = 10$. Use iteration to find x in each case, correct to 2 decimal places.

6 a Write down an expansion for $(x + y)^2$.
  b Prove that $(x + y)^3 = x^3 + 3x^2y + 3xy^2 + y^3$.
  c Write down, then check, an expansion for $(x + y)^4$.

EXERCISE 9

1 a n is a whole number. Check for some values of n that:
  (i) $2n$ is even, and $2n+1$ is odd
  (ii) n, $n+1$, $n+2$ are consecutive whole numbers
  (iii) the sum of an even and an odd number is odd, and their product is even
  (iv) the square of an even number is even.
  b Prove the results in **a** (iii) and (iv).

2 Prove that:
  a the sum of three consecutive whole numbers is a multiple of 3
  b the sum of three consecutive even numbers is a multiple of 6.

3 In Margaret's family there are five sisters, with each one 3 years younger than the one before her.

  a Prove that the sum of their ages is a multiple of 5.
  b Find their ages, if these total 260 years.

4 Prove that the difference between the squares of two consecutive whole numbers is odd.

5 Sums of numbers 1 to 10:

$$S = 1+ 2+ 3+ \ldots + 9+10$$
$$\underline{S = 10+ 9+ 8+ \ldots + 2+ 1}$$
$$\text{Add: } 2S = 11+11+11+ \ldots +11+11 = 10 \times 11$$
$$S = \frac{10 \times 11}{2} = 55$$

Use this method to show that:
  a $1+2+3+ \ldots +100 = 5050$
  b $1+2+3+ \ldots n = \frac{1}{2}n(n+1)$.

6

For numbers from 10 to 99, the difference between the chosen number and the number obtained by reversing its digits is always a multiple of 9.

  a Try this for 23, 32; 71, 17; etc.
  b Prove that the statement is true.
  (*Hint* $23 = (2 \times 10)+3$. Let the number with digits x, y be $10x +y$.)
  c Investigate for numbers from 100 to 999.

7 Prove that for the sequence $1, \frac{1}{2}, \frac{1}{3}, \frac{1}{4}, \ldots$ the difference between:
  a the 9th and 10th terms is $\frac{1}{90}$
  b the nth and $(n+1)$th terms is $\dfrac{1}{n(n+1)}$.

EXERCISE 10

1 Use the road-sign to complete a table of distances like this:

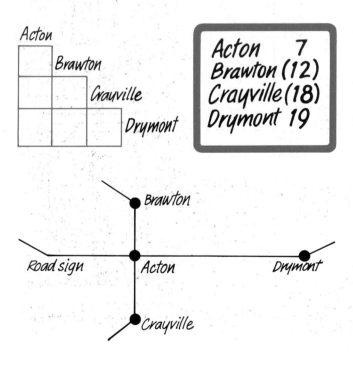

Acton 7
Brawton (12)
Crayville (18)
Drymont 19

2 Sean is an interior decorator. He spray-paints panels. Spraying takes no time, but he must then wait one hour for the paint to dry before he can turn the panel over and spray the other side. He has enough space to have two panels drying at the same time. What is the shortest time he can take to complete both sides of:
a 1 panel **b** 2 panels **c** 3 panels?

3 Rose Dawn is an abstract painter. Each disc takes 10 minutes to paint, but must then be left to dry before another can be painted on top of it.
Drying times in minutes are:
red 20, blue 30, yellow 40.
The white background is already done.

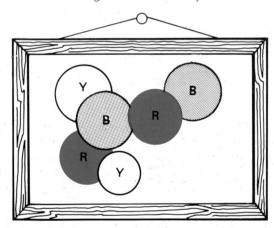

What is the shortest time in which she can produce a finished, dried painting, like the one above?

4

Each letter represents a digit.
The same letters represent the same digit.
Different letters represent different digits.
The letter N represents zero.
What do the other letters represent?

5 This diagram shows how a house can be built by a construction firm in nine weeks.
Notice that some jobs must wait for others to be completed, while others can be done at the same time.
Work out a timetable for the same firm to build two houses without increasing their equipment or workforce.
The time should be as short as possible, and definitely *not* 18 weeks.

House programme – 1 unit		Week											
Job	**Resource**	1	2	3	4	5	6	7	8	9	10	11	12
Site strip	Digger	▓											
Foundation	Bricklayer		▓	▓									
Kit make	Base joiner		▓	▓									
Kit erection	Site joiner				▓	▓							
Drainage	Digger		▓										
Glazing	Glazier						▓						
Roof tiling	Slater							▓					
Brick skin	Bricklayer							▓	▓				
Roughcast, etc.	Decorator									▓			

TOPICS TO EXPLORE

1 Seeing red

A wooden cube is painted red, and is then cut into eight identical cubes.

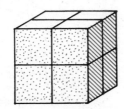

a How many red faces has each of these cubes?
b Investigate the same problem if the original cube is cut into:
(i) 27 smaller cubes   (ii) 64 cubes.
Can you go further than this?

2 Multiple measures

These jars hold 2 measures and 7 measures of liquid. Explain how you could use them to pour 1, 2, 3, . . . 9 measures of liquid.

3 The snowflake sequence

Each 'flake' is based on equilateral triangles.

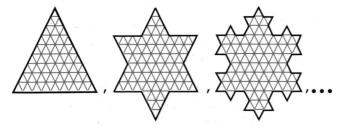

a Write down the number of sides in:
(i) each of the first three flakes
(ii) the fourth and fifth flakes
(iii) the nth flake.
b Use first and second differences to explore the sequence of:
(i) perimeter lengths of the 'snowflakes'
(ii) their areas.

4 Flower petals

You know how to fix the position of a point using *cartesian coordinates* (x, y). Another way is to use *polar coordinates* $(r, \theta°)$. P is the point $(6.4, 20°)$.

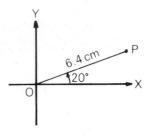

a Copy and complete this table, correct to 1 decimal place:

θ	0	10	20	30			90
2θ	0	20	40				
$r = 10\sin 2\theta°$	0	3.4	6.4				

b Plot the points $(r, \theta°)$, and then draw the graph of $r = 10\sin 2\theta°$ for $0 \leqslant \theta \leqslant 90$.
c Continue the table at 10° intervals, until you can complete the four 'flower petals' (symmetry can help you here).
d Investigate the graph of $r = 10\sin\frac{1}{2}\theta°$ for $\theta = 0, 30, 60, \ldots, 360$. The shape may surprise you.

5 Grid lengths

You can join points on this 1 by 1 grid by straight lines of lengths 1 unit and $\sqrt{2}$ units.

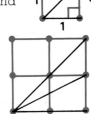

a On this 2 by 2 grid there are three more lengths. Use Pythagoras' Theorem to calculate these in square root form.

b Draw a 3 by 3 grid, and calculate four more lengths.
c Copy and complete this table, from a 1 by 1 to a 5 by 5 grid.

Grid	New lengths	Total number
1 by 1	$1, \sqrt{2}$	2
2 by 2		$2+3 = 5$

d Simplify the surds, where possible.

6 The snooker player

a Johnny's snookered. He has to hit the black, but another ball is in the way. Make a larger copy of the diagram and, assuming that the angle of rebound is equal to the angle of approach of the ball to the cushion, try to find the point X.

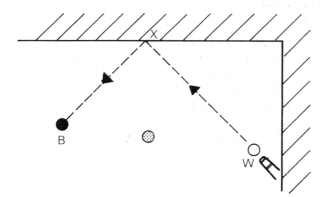

b Is there a mathematical solution to Johnny's problem?
I is the image of the black ball in the cushion. Copy the diagram, and explain why
$\angle WCE = \angle BCD$.

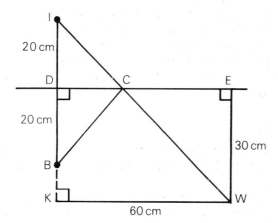

c Calculate:
   (i) $\angle KIW$
   (ii) $\angle WCE$, the angle of approach
   (iii) CE

7 Expansions

a Copy these squares and rectangles. By filling in areas, check that $(n+1)^2 = n^2 + 2n + 1$.

b A red cube with side $n+1$ units has been 'exploded' to show the eight cuboids that make it up. Write down the volume of each part, A to H, and find an expansion for $(n+1)^3$.

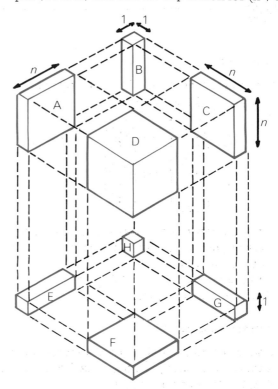

c Why would this method not work for $(n+1)^4$? Find its expansion, using
$(n+1)^4 = (n+1)(n+1)^3$.

8 Polydiags and the 'Mystic Rose'

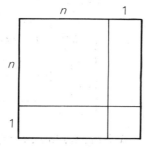

a (i) Carefully count the number of diagonals in the square, pentagon and hexagon.
   (ii) Continue for polygons with 7, 8, 9, ... sides
   (iii) Check that the formula $N = \frac{1}{2}n(n-3)$ gives the number of sides N in an n-sided polygon, as far as you have gone.

b To make a 'Mystic Rose' you draw all possible lines from every vertex. That means all the sides *and* diagonals.
   (i) How many lines are needed for polygons with 3, 4, 5, ... sides?
   (ii) Use the formula in **a**(iii) to find a formula for the number of lines L in an n-sided Mystic Rose.

9 Communications around the world

Deepspace International plan to put three communication satellites in the same orbit around the Earth. The satellites must be able to communicate directly with each other, and must cover the whole of the Earth's circumference between them.

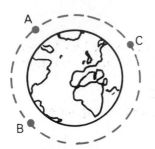
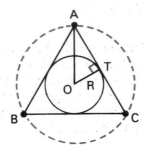

a The sketch on the right shows how they could be placed. If the Earth's radius is R km, show that the radius of the satellites' orbit must be at least $2R$ km.

b Investigate the same problem for 4, 5 and 6 satellites.

10 A calculator search

This feeding-trough has a cross-section in the shape of a trapezium. The base and sloping edges of the trough are 1 m long. Each edge makes an angle $\theta°$ with the ground.

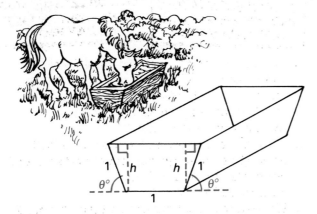

a Find an expression for h in terms of $\sin\theta°$, $\cos\theta°$ or $\tan\theta°$.

b Show that the area of the cross-section is $(1+\cos\theta°)\sin\theta°$.

c Use your calculator to investigate the areas given by different values of $\theta°$.

d Find the value of θ that maximises the capacity of the trough.

11 A pyramid puzzle

The HI-IQ Toy Company wants a design for sets of pyramids that can fit together to make cubes of side 16 cm. Sketch one of the pyramids, and calculate its dimensions. If you have time you could check by making the cube.

12 Domino dots

Ray and Keith make sets of dominoes. Ray makes the wooden shapes, and Keith etches the dots on the dominoes.

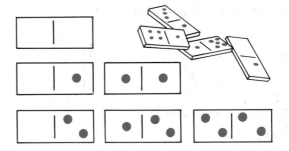

a Extend the sketch above to rows of double 3 and double 4 dominoes.

b Copy and complete this table.

Highest double	0	1	2	3		6
Number of dominoes in set	1	3	6			

c (i) Check that the formula $N = \frac{1}{2}(n+1)(n+2)$ gives the number of dominoes N for a highest double of n.

    (ii) How many dominoes are there for a highest double of 10?

d Keith needs to know the number of dots he has to etch in order to work out the cost.

    (i) Show that in the second row of this table second differences are constant, and in the third row third differences are constant.

    (ii) Extend each sequence in (i) to 'highest double 8'.

Highest double	0	1	2	3		6
Extra number of dots to etch	0	3	9	18		
Total number of dots to etch	0	3	12	30		

CHAPTER REVISION EXERCISES

1 Tahir leaves the level road, and toils up the hill. Which graph best represents his journey:
  a up the hill
  b down the hill on the other side?

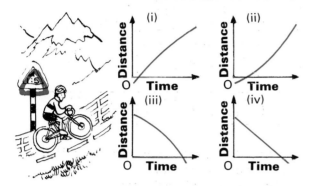

2 Find the gradient of each line:
  a $y = 8x + 7$ **b** $y - x = 1$ **c** $2x - y = 0$

3 L is the point $(-3, 3)$, M(3, 0), N(4, 4) and P$(-2, 7)$. Show that LMNP is a parallelogram.

4 Sketch the line:
  a through the origin, with gradient $\frac{1}{2}$
  b through $(-3, 0)$ with gradient $-\frac{1}{2}$
  c with equation $3x - 4y = 12$.

5 Laser Light Show Ltd produce cloud pictures by firing laser beams at a computer controlled mirror. They fire a laser beam from A along AB. Which point does this beam strike, P, Q or R?

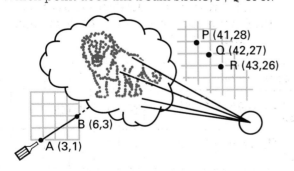

6 Find the equation of the line joining each pair of points:
  a D(0, 0), E$(-3, -1)$ **b** F$(-1, 2)$, G$(1, -2)$
  c H$(-4, 0)$, K$(-2, -2)$ **d** M$(6, -8)$, N$(2, -2)$

7 Find the point of intersection of the line through $(-1, 7)$ with gradient -2, and the line through $(5, 4)$ with gradient 1 by:
  a drawing graphs of the lines
  b finding their equations, and solving them simultaneously.

8 Dan is practising his diving. His diving speed is measured every half-second.

Time (T s)	0	0.5	1	1.5	2
Speed (S m/s)	0	5	10	15	20

  a Draw a graph of S against T for $0 \leqslant T \leqslant 2$.
  b Read off Dan's speed after:
    (i) 0.25 second (ii) 1.75 seconds.
  c Copy and complete:
    $S = \ldots T$

9

'SPARKS' ELECTRICIANS
CALL-OUT CHARGE £12
THEN £10 AN HOUR

'SUREFIRE' ELECTRICIANS
NO CALL-OUT CHARGE
£13 AN HOUR

  a How much does each firm charge for a job which takes:
    (i) 1 hour (call-out + 1 hour's charge)
    (ii) 2 hours (iii) 3 hours
    (iv) 4 hours (v) 8 hours?
  b Draw a graph showing the charges of both firms. (Use 2 mm squared paper and scales of: horizontally 1 hour = 2 cm, vertically £20 = 2 cm.)
  c Write down equations giving their charges £C for N hours.

10 By changing the resistance, Denise can vary the current and voltage. She records her results:

Current (I amps)	0.3	0.4	0.5	0.6
Voltage (V volts)	3.5	5.0	6.0	7.5

  a Plot the mean point and the four points in the table, then draw the best-fitting straight line.
  b Find the equation of the graph, and use it to calculate the voltage for a current of 0.75 amp.

REVISION EXERCISE ON CHAPTER 2: FUNCTIONS AND GRAPHS

1 Write down the input set in **a**, and the output set in **b**.

a $f: \ldots \to 12$
$f: \ldots \to 30$
$f: \ldots \to 42$
f means '$\times 6$'

b

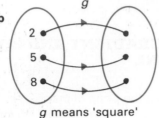

g

g means 'square'

2 $f(x) = \dfrac{1}{x}$, $x \neq 0$. Calculate:

a $f(1)$ **b** $f(2)$ **c** $f(\frac{1}{2})$

3 $h : x \to (x-2)^2$. Find the value of h at:

a $x = 0$ **b** $x = 2$ **c** $x = -2$

4 $p(x) = 5 - 2x$. For what value of x is:

a $p(x) = 0$ **b** $p(x) = 3$?

5 a The side of the crate is square. Prove that its area, $A(x)\,\text{m}^2$ is given by the formula $A(x) = x^2 + 4$.

2 m

x m

b Calculate $A(1)$, $A(2)$ and $A(3)$.
c Given $A(a) = 40$, find a.

6 Anita is an architect given the job of designing a bridge which is supported by a parabolic arch. As a mathematical model, she chooses the equation $y = 8x - x^2$.

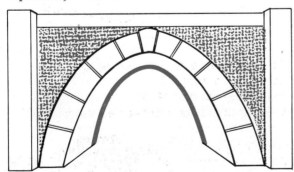

a Make a table of values for $x = 0, 1, 2, \ldots 6$.
b Draw the graph of the parabola.
c From your graph estimate the height and width of the arch (all measurements are in metres).

7 The Caring Car Company makes 20 cars each week:

x cars are saloons, and y cars are hatchbacks.
a Write down a formula for y in terms of x.
b Draw a graph of y against x.

8 The Flash-fire Fighter goes into a parabolic dive. The model for its height H km above the ground after t seconds is $H = t^2 - 3t + 8$.

a Using $t = 0, 1, 2, 3, 4$, draw a graph.
b How close to the ground does the plane come? When is this?
c What was the pilot's problem following his next parabolic dive with equation $H = (t-3)^2$?

9 a Use the data in the table to draw a graph.

x	36	12	9	6	4	3	2	1
y	1	3	4	6	9	12	18	36

b Which of these equations matches the graph?

(i) $y = ax$ (ii) $y = ax^2$ (iii) $y = ax^3$ (iv) $y = \dfrac{a}{x}$

c Use your graph to find a formula for the function.
d Calculate $f(10)$.

10

Hannah and Hal rent $100\,\text{m}^2$ of floor area in the Indoor Craft Market. Which rectangular shape should they choose to keep the perimeter of their table to a minimum? Make a mathematical model. Take x metres for the length.

a Prove that the floor's perimeter, P m, is

$$P = 2\left(x + \frac{100}{x}\right).$$

b Draw a graph, taking $x = 4, 6, 8, 10, 12, 14, 16$.
c Find x for the minimum perimeter.

REVISION EXERCISE ON CHAPTER 3: SYMMETRY IN THE CIRCLE

1 Copy this diagram, and fill in as many lengths and angles as you can.

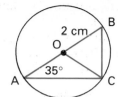

2 Explain why each diagram below contains a right angle, and calculate *y*, *d* and *x*.

a

b

c

d

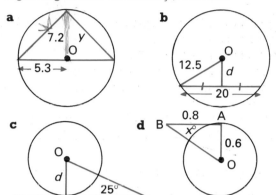

3 Calculate the distance from:
a O **b** A
c B, to the chord XY.

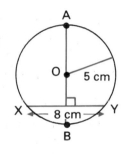

4 M is the centre of the circle, and TCD is a tangent. Copy the diagram, and mark all the angles, given ∠ACT = 50°.

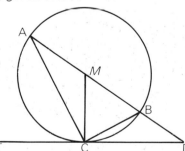

5 The latitude of London is $51\frac{1}{2}°$, and the radius of a cross-section of the Earth is 6400 km. Calculate the length of a flight from London direct to the equator, to the nearest 10 km.

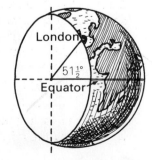

6 Calculate the area, to the nearest cm², of the end of the park bench.

7 The picture shows a hand-held circular saw, with a guard over the blade. The radius of the saw is 50 mm, and the radius of the guard is 55 mm.

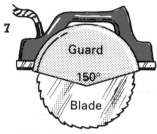

Calculate:
a the length of the exposed cutting edge of the saw
b the area of the guard.

8 The windscreen wiper sweeps through an angle of 100°.

Calculate the area, to the nearest cm², of:
a the large sector OAB
b the smaller sector OCD
c the part of the windscreen kept clean.

9 The area of the end of this open sports bag is 3205 cm², and its radius is 35 cm. Calculate, to the nearest degree, the angle on the end marked with an arc.

REVISION EXERCISE ON CHAPTER 4: INEQUALITIES

1 Solve these inequalities, and illustrate the solutions on the number line.
  a $3x \geqslant 9$ **b** $5x < -5$ **c** $-2x < 5$

2 Solve:
  a $3u + 5 > 11$ **b** $2v - 1 < 6$ **c** $3w + 7 \geqslant 1$
  d $7t - 3 \geqslant 4t + 9$ **e** $5p - 2(p + 1) \leqslant 7$

3 The perimeter of the square is greater than the perimeter of the rectangle. Make an inequality in m, and solve it. The lengths are in centimetres.

4 The mixing cylinder has a capacity of 32 litres, but a 2-litre space must be left free at the top for stirring. Six tins of paint are poured in.

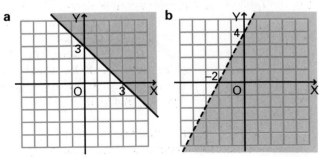

If each tin holds x litres of paint, write down an inequality; then solve it to find the maximum capacity of a tin.

5 Find the smallest whole number for which:
  a $2p - 11 > 0$ **b** $3t - 8 > t$ **c** $3 - 4t < -12$

6 For **a** and **b** below:
  (i) find the equation of the boundary line of the clear region. (Remember $y = mx + c$.)
  (ii) write down an inequality which defines the region.

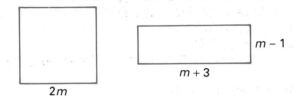

7 By first drawing the boundary of the region, illustrate these inequalities on the coordinate plane.
  a $x + y > 6$ **b** $2x - y \geqslant 6$ **c** $5x + 4y \leqslant 20$

8

Eva has x sessions in the gym.
  a Make an inequality to show when partial membership costs less than complete membership.
  b How many sessions would she have to attend to make complete membership worthwhile?

9 Gardeners from the Parks Department plan to plant some trees in a special area. There is enough space to plant eight trees of type A, or five of type B. They will plant at least one of each type, but not more than ten altogether.

  a Make a set of inequalities, taking x for the number of type A trees and y for type B.
  b Illustrate the inequalities in a diagram.

10 a Use a set of inequalities to define the clear region.
  b Find the maximum and minimum values of $4x + 3y$ in the region.

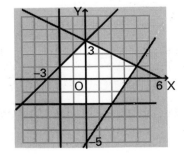

REVISION EXERCISE ON CHAPTER 5: TRIGONOMETRY—CALCULATIONS, GRAPHS AND EQUATIONS

1 Calculate x, correct to 1 decimal place.

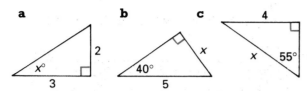

a   **b**   **c**

2 a Sketch the x and y-axes, and plot the points R(4, 3) and S(-4, -3).
   b Write down ratios for:
      (i) $\sin$ XOR, $\tan$ XOR   (ii) $\cos$ XOS, $\tan$ XOS.

3 Given $\cos A = \frac{21}{29}$, and $0° \leqslant A \leqslant 90°$, construct a right-angled triangle.
   a Calculate the length of the third side.
   b Write down ratios for $\sin A$ and $\tan A$.

4 Use the sides of the half-square and half-equilateral triangle to copy and complete the table.

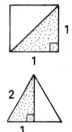

A	$\sin A$	$\cos A$	$\tan A$
30°		$\frac{\sqrt{3}}{2}$	
45°	$\frac{1}{\sqrt{2}}$		
60°			$\sqrt{3}$

5 Air Traffic Control at A detects a plane at G, 12 km east, 5 km north and 1.1 km high. Calculate:
   a the distance AC
   b the angle of elevation of the plane from A.

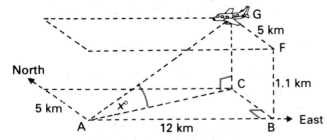

6 a On 2 mm squared paper draw the graph of $y = 2 + 2\cos x°$, for $0 \leqslant x \leqslant 360$, calculating $\cos x°$ at 30° intervals, correct to 1 decimal place.
   b Write down the maximum and minimum values of y, and the corresponding values of x.

7 The vertical ends of the prism are isosceles triangles, and the three sides are rectangles. EG is perpendicular to the base. (Units are cm.)

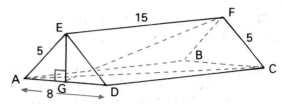

   a Sketch the right-angled $\triangle$ACD, and calculate: (i) AC   (ii) $\angle$DAC.
   b Calculate EG.
   c Sketch $\triangle$EFG.
      (i) Why is $\angle$GEF = 90°?   (ii) Calculate $\angle$EGF.

8 Sketch the graphs of:
   a $y = -\sin x°$ **b** $y = \sin x° - 1$ **c** $y = \sin 4x°$

9 The equation of this curve is $y = a + b\cos cx°$. Find the values of a, b and c.

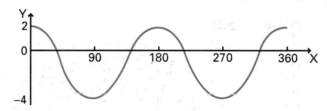

10 John rides along on his bike. The height h cm of his foot above the ground after t seconds is given by $h = 20 + 10\sin 30t°$.
   a Write down the maximum and minimum values of h.
   b Calculate the height, to the nearest cm, after 10 seconds.
   c What is the period of the graph of h?

11 Solve these equations, to the nearest degree, for $0 \leqslant x \leqslant 360$:
   a $\tan x° = -1$ **b** $\sin x° = 0.1$ **c** $\cos x° = -0.7$
   d $8\sin x° + 5 = 0$ **e** $7\cos x° - 3 = 0$

12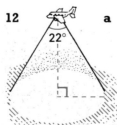
   a Calculate, to the nearest 10 m:
      (i) the height at which the plane must fly to photograph a circular area of diameter 1 km
      (ii) the diameter of the circular area it can photograph from a height of 500 m.
   b What apex angle would give a circle of diameter 1 km from a height of 1 km?

REVISION EXERCISE ON CHAPTER 6: QUADRATIC EQUATIONS

1 Use the graph to solve these quadratic equations:
  a $x^2 - 4x + 1 = 1$ **b** $x^2 - 4x + 1 = 6$
  c $x^2 - 4x + 1 = -2$ **d** $x^2 - 4x + 1 = -3$

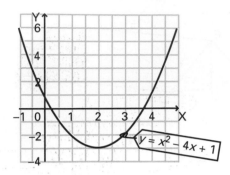

2 Solve each equation in question **1** by rearranging it in standard form $ax^2 + bx + c = 0$, and factorising.

3 Use factors to solve:
  a $x^2 + x - 2 = 0$ **b** $x^2 - 3x - 10 = 0$
  c $m^2 - 4m = 0$ **d** $4y^2 - 9 = 0$
  e $2n^2 + 8n - 24 = 0$ **f** $x^2 + 7x - 18 = 0$

4 Find the coordinates of A and B.

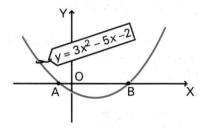

5 Rearrange in standard form, and solve:
  a $30 = 5x^2 - 5x$ **b** $(x+5)^2 = 16$
  c $(y+2)(y-3) = 6$ **d** $3(n+2)^2 - 27 = 0$

6 Solve the following equations, giving the solutions correct to 1 decimal place.
  a $3x^2 - 2x - 2 = 0$ **b** $y^2 - 3y + 1 = 0$
  c $5x = 2x^2 + 1$ **d** $5x^2 = 3 - x$

7 Find the coordinates of A and B in each diagram below.

a
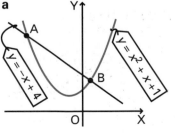

b
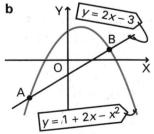

8 In a sports league, each team plays another twice, once at home and once away. For n teams, $n^2 - n$ games must be played.
  a Last season, 132 games had to be played. How many teams were involved?
  b Another season 100 games were played. Did each team play at home and away? Explain.

9 The height of the mini TV screen is 3 cm less than the breadth.

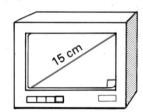

  a Taking x cm for the breadth, show that $x^2 - 3x - 108 = 0$.
  b Find the dimensions of the screen.

10 a Show that $x = 1$ is one root of the equation $x^3 - 8x + 7 = 0$.

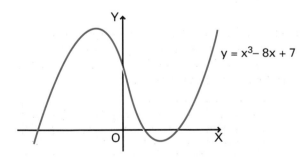

  b Show that another root lies between 2 and 3, and use iteration to find it, correct to 1 decimal place.
  c Find the third root of $x^3 - 8x + 7 = 0$, correct to 2 decimal places.

REVISION EXERCISE ON CHAPTER 7: PROPORTION IN PRACTICE

1 Which of these graphs have equations of the form:

a $y = kx$ **b** $y = \dfrac{k}{x}, k > 0$?

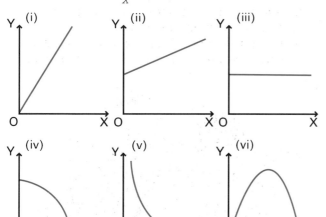

2 $P \propto Q$, and $P = 135$ when $Q = 9$. Calculate:
a P when $Q = 20$ **b** Q when $P = 60$.

3 y varies inversely as the square of x. When $x = 6$, $y = 3$.
a Find a formula connecting x and y.
b Calculate: (i) y when $x = 3$ (ii) x when $y = 3$.

4 A pilot ejects from his jet plane. Until his parachute opens he falls at a speed (v m/s) which varies as the square root of the distance (d m) he has fallen.
a Write down an equation connecting v and d.
b After he has fallen 4 m, his speed is 8 m/s. Find a formula for v in terms of d.
c Calculate his speed after he has fallen 25 m.
d How far has he fallen when his speed reaches 40 m/s?

5 Nick and Harry read that electrical power (W watts) is directly proportional to the voltage (V volts) in the circuit. They set up an experiment and recorded these results:

V	2	3	4	6	10	12	18
W	0.7	0.8	1.1	1.9	2.8	3.4	5.4

a Plot W against V. Draw the best-fitting straight line.
b Do their results agree with what they had read? Give a reason.
c Find a formula for W in terms of V.

6 The distance, d km, of the horizon varies as the square root of the height h m of the observation point above sea-level. At a height of 4 m, the distance is 5.2 km. Calculate the distance at a height of 9 m.

7 The number of toy cubes (n) that can be fitted into a toy box varies inversely as the volume of a cube (v cm³). 512 cubes of side 5 cm fill the box.
a Find a formula connecting n and v.
b How many 8 cm cubes will fill the box?

8 The time (T s) that the cassette tape will run varies directly as the length (L ft) of the tape, and inversely as its speed (S inches/s).

A tape 450 ft long runs for 24 minutes at $3\frac{3}{4}$ inches/s.
a Find a formula for T.
b Calculate the running time of a tape 1000 ft long at $7\frac{1}{2}$ inches/s.

9 What happens to P, A, V, S and d in the relationships below if r is doubled?

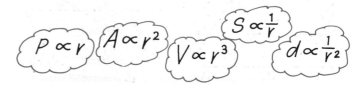

$P \propto r$ $A \propto r^2$ $V \propto r^3$ $S \propto \dfrac{1}{r}$ $d \propto \dfrac{1}{r^2}$

REVISION EXERCISE ON CHAPTER 8: HANDLING DATA

1 A survey was carried out among 150 smokers, in which the number of cigarettes they smoked daily was noted.

Number of cigarettes	1–5	6–10	11–15
Frequency	10	25	30

16–20	21–25	26–30	31–35	36–40
35	22	16	8	4

a Draw a histogram and a frequency polygon of the data.
b Calculate the probability that a person in the survey, chosen at random, smoked:
 (i) no more than 20 a day
 (ii) more than 10 a day.

2 Describe these methods of sampling, and give an example of a situation where each might be used:
a systematic **b** random **c** stratified

3 A market research company in Eurostate requires a stratified sample of 2500 of the country's electorate. The sample has to be based on the number who voted for each party at the last election, shown in this table.

Party	Socialist	Environmental
Votes (million)	8	2

Social Democrat	Democrat	Nationalist
18	13	9

Calculate the composition of the stratified sample.

4 a Calculate the probability of winning the car.
b How should the promoter protect himself against a win?

SIX SUCCESSIVE SIXES WINS A CAR

SIX THROWS FOR £1

5 This histogram shows the lengths, in seconds, of phone calls made by a business on a particular day.

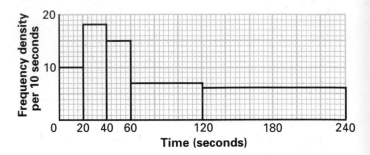

a Make a table, showing the number of calls in each class interval.
b Calculate the probability, correct to 1 decimal place, of a call lasting more than one minute.
c Taking the midpoints of the class intervals as 10, 30, 50, 90 and 180, calculate the mean length of a call, to the nearest second.

6 The spinner is spun and the dice rolled.

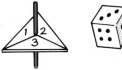

a Copy and complete this table:

		Dice					
		1	2	3	4	5	6
	1	(1, 1)	(1, 2)				
Spinner	2	(2, 1)					
	3						

b Calculate:
 (i) P(same score on both)
 (ii) P(total of 3 or more)
 (iii) P(at least one giving a score of 3).
c P(at least one 3) = P(3 on dice) + P(3 on spinner). True or false? Explain.
d How often would you expect a total of 6 or more in 100 spins and throws?

7 Three new students are about to join the class.
a Assuming P(male) = $\frac{1}{2}$, what is the probability that all three will be boys?
b If you are told that one is a boy, what is the probability now that all three will be boys?

REVISION EXERCISE ON CHAPTER 9: INDICES AND SURDS

1 Use the $\boxed{y^x}$ key on your calculator to express these numbers, in standard form, to 3 significant figures.
a 2^{45} **b** 3^{-17}

2 Simplify, and finish with positive indices:
a $x^4 \times x^{-3}$ **b** $3y^3 \times 2y^{-3}$ **c** $4z^4 \div 2z$

d $(p^{-2})^{-1}$ **e** $x^{-1}(x^2 - x)$ **f** $\dfrac{t^6}{t^{-2} \times t^3}$

3 Write down the value of:
a 2^3 **b** 2^{-3} **c** 2^0 **d** $9^{1/2}$ **e** $9^{3/2}$
f $8^{1/3}$ **g** $27^{-1/3}$ **h** $100^{1/2}$ **i** $100^{-1/2}$

4 $f(x) = 16^x$. Calculate, in simplest form:
a $f(1)$ **b** $f(-1)$ **c** $f(\frac{1}{2})$ **d** $f(\frac{1}{4})$ **e** $f(-\frac{1}{4})$

5 Find the value of:
a $3x^{-1/2}$ when $x = 4$ **b** $3x^{-3/2}$ when $x = 9$
c $m^{3/2} + n^{1/2}$ when $m = 4$ and $n = \frac{1}{4}$

6 Simplify:
a $a^{1/3}(a^{2/3} - a^{-1/3})$ **b** $b^{-3/2}(b^{-1/2} + b^{3/2})$

7 Evaluate these, when $p = 1$, $q = 8$, $r = 9$:
a $\dfrac{p^3 q^{2/3} r^{3/2}}{12}$ **b** $\dfrac{p^0 q^{1/3}}{6r^{1/2}}$

8 Multiply out and simplify:
a $(x^{1/2} + 1)(x^{1/2} - 1)$ **b** $(y^{3/2} + 1)^2$

9 The area of one side of this cube is A cm², and its volume is V cm³. Write the length of an edge in index form in terms of: **a** A **b** V

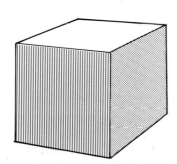

10 Use the graph of $y = 2^x$ (top right) to estimate, correct to 1 decimal place:
a $2^{-1/2}$ **b** $2^{1/2}$ **c** $2^{3/2}$ **d** $2^{5/2}$

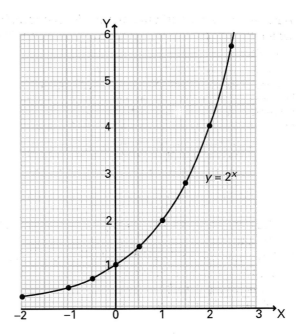

11 Find the two values of x in the solution of the equation $2^x = 2x$ by:
a drawing the graphs of $y = 2^x$ and $y = 2x$
b trial and improvement.

12 The present population of Novaton is 30 000, and its expected population, P, t years later, is given by the formula $P = 30\,000 \times 1.2^{0.1t}$. Estimate:
a the population after 25 years
b the time taken for the present population to double.

13 Simplify:
a $\sqrt{8}$ **b** $\sqrt{18}$ **c** $\sqrt{32}$ **d** $\sqrt{98}$ **e** $\sqrt{700}$
f $\sqrt{3} + \sqrt{3}$ **g** $5\sqrt{2} - \sqrt{2}$ **h** $\sqrt{8} - \sqrt{2}$
i $\sqrt{18} - 3\sqrt{2}$ **j** $\sqrt{5} \times \sqrt{5}$ **k** $3\sqrt{2} \times 2\sqrt{2}$

14 Use surds to write down in simplest form the length of:
a EB **b** DB **c** BC
(All lengths are in cm.)

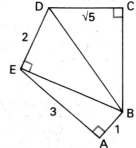

15 Rationalise these denominators:
a $\dfrac{2}{\sqrt{2}}$ **b** $\dfrac{6}{\sqrt{3}}$ **c** $\dfrac{10}{\sqrt{5}}$ **d** $\dfrac{2}{\sqrt{3} + \sqrt{2}} \times \dfrac{\sqrt{3} - \sqrt{2}}{\sqrt{3} - \sqrt{2}}$

REVISION EXERCISE ON CHAPTER 10: TRIGONOMETRY—TRIANGLE CALCULATIONS

1 Calculate x in each triangle:

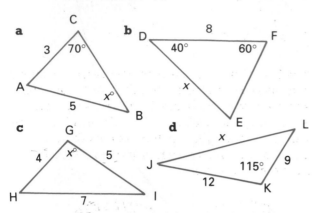

2 Sketch $\triangle$ABC in which $\angle A = 112°$, $\angle B = 51°$ and $b = 18$ cm. Calculate:
  a a **b** $\angle C$ **c** the area of $\triangle$ABC.

3 Sketch $\triangle$DEF in which $\angle D = 124°$, $e = 23$ cm and $f = 32$ cm. Calculate:
  a d **b** the area of $\triangle$DEF.

4 The lengths in this metal framework are in metres. Calculate all the unmarked lengths and angles.

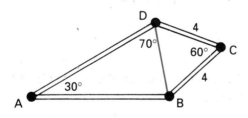

5 From a point P, level with the foot of the hill, the angle of elevation of S, the top of the hill, is 15°. From a point Q, 1200 m nearer the foot of the hill, the angle of elevation of the top is 35°. Calculate:
  a QS **b** the height of the hill, RS.

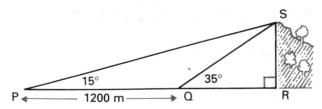

6 A stained glass window consists of 120 regular hexagonal panels. The side of each panel is 4 cm long. Calculate the total area of the glass.

7 A farmer uses two sections of fencing against a wall to enclose an area of 26 m². One section is 12 m long and the other is 9 m long. Calculate:
  a two possible values of angle ABC
  b the corresponding lengths of AC.

8 Cables are laid in the ground as shown below. Calculate all the unmarked lengths and angles. (The lengths are in metres.)

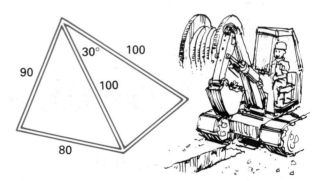

9 Mast AB is 40 m high, standing on horizontal ground.

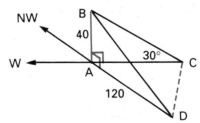

  a When the sun is due west the shadow of the mast is AC, and $\angle$ACB = 30°. Find the length of AC.
  b When the sun is north-west the shadow AD is 120 m long. Find the angle of elevation of the sun.
  c Calculate the distance CD.

10 An aircraft flies from its base 500 km on a bearing 025°, then 750 km on a bearing 280°, then returns to base. Calculate the length and bearing of the last leg of its flight.

REVISION EXERCISE ON CHAPTER 11: FRACTIONS AND EQUATIONS

1 Simplify:

a $\dfrac{ab}{a}$ **b** $\dfrac{x}{x^2}$ **c** $\dfrac{a-1}{a(a-1)}$

d $\dfrac{3x}{6xy}$ **e** $\dfrac{8mn^2}{4m^2n}$ **f** $\dfrac{(x-y)(x+y)}{(x+y)^2}$

2 Simplify, by first factorising:

a $\dfrac{2a-4}{3a-6}$ **b** $\dfrac{3x}{x^2+x}$ **c** $\dfrac{3-3y}{2-2y}$

d $\dfrac{x^2+x-2}{x+2}$ **e** $\dfrac{a^2-b^2}{2a-2b}$ **f** $\dfrac{4x^2-y^2}{2ax-ay}$

g $\dfrac{x^2+7x}{2x^2-98}$ **h** $\dfrac{m^2-7m+12}{m^2-3m-4}$ **i** $\dfrac{6x^2+x-2}{4x^2-1}$

3 Find expressions for:
(i) the area   (ii) the perimeter
of each rectangle.

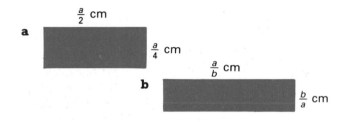

a $\frac{a}{2}$ cm

$\frac{a}{4}$ cm

b $\frac{a}{b}$ cm

$\frac{b}{a}$ cm

4

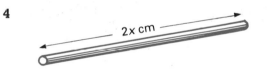

2x cm

a Find the length of each piece if the rod is
divided into these numbers of equal lengths:
(i) 8   (ii) x (iii) $2n$ (iv) x^2
b $\frac{1}{4}$ of the length is removed. What length is left?

5 Write each with a common denominator, and
simplify where possible:

a $\dfrac{3}{y}+\dfrac{1}{3}$ **b** $\dfrac{2}{5}-\dfrac{3}{x}$ **c** $\dfrac{5}{a}+\dfrac{2}{b}$

d $\dfrac{1}{x^2}-\dfrac{5}{x}$ **e** $\dfrac{3a}{7}+\dfrac{b}{14}$ **f** $\dfrac{3a}{2x}-\dfrac{a}{x}$

g $\dfrac{3}{2n}-\dfrac{8}{3n}$ **h** $\dfrac{2}{m^2}+\dfrac{5}{m}$ **i** $\dfrac{2a}{5}+\dfrac{a+5b}{10}$

j $\dfrac{x}{2}-\dfrac{x-3}{4}$ **k** $\dfrac{y}{5}-\dfrac{y+1}{10}$ **l** $\dfrac{a}{3}-\dfrac{2-a}{2}$

m $\dfrac{8}{k}-\dfrac{2k+1}{k^2}$ **n** $\dfrac{1}{x-2}+\dfrac{1}{x+3}$ **o** $\dfrac{3}{m-n}+\dfrac{2}{m+n}$

p $\dfrac{1}{3y+1}-\dfrac{1}{3y-1}$

6 Solve these equations.

a $\dfrac{x}{10}=\dfrac{3}{2}$ **b** $\dfrac{x-2}{5}=3$ **c** $\dfrac{y-1}{2}+\dfrac{y+1}{3}=4$

d $\dfrac{t-2}{3}-\dfrac{t-1}{4}=1$ **e** $\dfrac{u}{4}-\dfrac{u+2}{8}=2$

7 The Superlink express runs between two stations
at an average speed of 80 mph. The Streamliner
service covers the same distance, d km, at an
average speed of 60 mph. If the Streamliner takes
half an hour longer than the express, form an
equation in d and solve it to find the distance
between the stations.

8 Arrange these as quadratic equations in standard
form, then solve them.

a $x-5+\dfrac{4}{x}=0$ **b** $y=1+\dfrac{6}{y}$

c $u+\dfrac{1}{u}=2$ **d** $6v+5-\dfrac{6}{v}=0$

9 Make the letter in brackets the subject in each of
the following:

a $V=\dfrac{I}{R}\ ..\ (R)$ **b** $D=\dfrac{T-t}{R}\ ..\ (t)$

c $A=2\pi(1+x)\ ..\ (x)$ **d** $\dfrac{V}{W}=\dfrac{AC}{XZ}\ ..\ (Z)$

e $A+d=\dfrac{V}{t}\ ..\ (t)$ **f** $E=\dfrac{1+a}{1-b}\ ..\ (b)$

g $\dfrac{1+a}{1-a}=\dfrac{b}{c}\ ..\ (a)$ **h** $\dfrac{4+A}{A-3}=\dfrac{t}{2}\ ..\ (A)$

i $r=\dfrac{1000T}{1000+T}\ ..\ (T)$

GENERAL REVISION EXERCISES

1 Write down two more numbers for each sequence, and state the rule you use.
  a $1, 4, 9, 16, \ldots$ **b** $1, -2, 4, -8, \ldots$
  c $1, 3, 6, 10, \ldots$

2 Simplify:
  a $3p + 2p$ **b** $3p \times 2p$ **c** $2q - q - q$
  d $a + 2a + 3a$ **e** $a \times 2a \times 3a^2$

3 ABC is a straight line, as shown in the diagram.

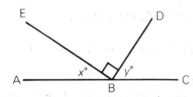

  a Write down an equation involving x and y.
  b If $x = 35$, find y.
  c If $x > 30$, what can you say about y?
  d If $x = y$, write down the values of x and y.

4 June saves £1 coins in this tube. Each coin is 3 mm thick. How much money will she have when the tube is full?

9 cm

5 $x = -1$, $y = -4$ and $z = 2$. Calculate the value of:
  a $x + y + z$ **b** xyz **c** x^2 **d** $2y^2$ **e** z^3

6 A table-top football pitch is a scaled down version of the real thing. The scale is $1 : 50$. Calculate:
  a the breadth of the model if the breadth of a real pitch is 75 m
  b the length of the real pitch if the model is 2.2 m long.

7 Solve the equations:
  a $6x - 3 = 2x + 9$ **b** $t^2 - 3t - 4 = 0$

8 This diagram consists of an isosceles triangle and a parallelogram. Calculate a, b and c.

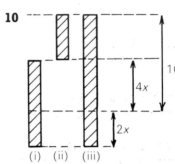

9 Sketch the graphs, for $0 \leqslant x \leqslant 360$, of:
  a $y = \sin x°$ **b** $y = 2 \sin x°$ **c** $y = \sin 2x°$.

10
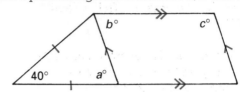
(i) (ii) (iii)

  a Write down an expression for the length of each of the three planks (in metres). The total length of the three planks is 28 metres.
  b Make an equation in x and solve it.
  c Write down the lengths of the planks.

11 During a balloon race, one of the balloons drifts for 5 km on a bearing 070°. The wind changes, and the balloon is blown another 6 km on a bearing 100°, before it bursts.
  a Make a scale drawing of its flight.
  b Measure the distance (correct to 0.1 km) and bearing (to the nearest degree) from where it starts to where it bursts.

12 This diagram shows the side of a garden frame.
  a Write down the gradient of the top, as a fraction in its simplest form.
  b Calculate $\angle$ ABC.

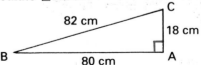

13 Central High School has 90 fifteen-year-old students who travel by bus; 30 from Midton, 40 from Easton and 20 from Weston. Illustrate this data in an accurately drawn:
  a bar graph **b** pie chart.

GENERAL REVISION EXERCISE 1B

1 Solve:
a $x + 2 = -1$ **b** $2x - 4 = -6$ **c** $5y + 4 = 3y$
d $a - 2 = 2a - 3$ **e** $3t + 2 \geqslant 5$ **f** $2(n-1) < 8$

2 a On squared paper draw the triangle with vertices A(6, 5), B(3, 4) and C(3, 2).
b Draw △DEF, the image of △ABC under reflection in the y-axis.
c Draw △GHI, the image of △DEF in the x-axis. How could you obtain △GHI directly from △ABC?

3 a Use Pythagoras' Theorem to calculate:
(i) x (ii) y, in the diagram below.
b Calculate z, correct to 0.1°.

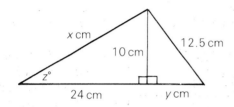

4 a $f(x) = x^2 + 2x + 1$. Find the value of $f(-1)$.
b $f(y) = 1 - y$. Find the value of $f(a) + f(-a)$.

5 A rectangular tank measures 3 m by 2.5 m by 1.2 m. Calculate the number of litres of water the tank can hold when it is half full.

6 The time taken by Mr Hughes to drive between two service stations on a motorway is inversely proportional to his average speed. He takes 45 minutes at an average speed of 48 km/h. Calculate his time for the journey at an average speed of 90 km/h.

7 Multiply out:
a $(a+b)^2$ **b** $(a-b)^2$ **c** $(3x+1)(x-1)$
d $(2t+3)^2$ **e** $\left(x - \dfrac{1}{x}\right)^2$ **f** $(a+b)(a-b+1)$

8 Find a formula for the nth term of each sequence:
a 1, 9, 17, 25, . . .   **b** 4, 9, 16, 25, 36, . . .

9 ACE is a straight line, and △s ABC and CDE are isosceles.

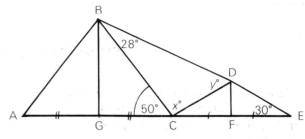

a Why must GB be parallel to FD?
b Copy the diagram, and find x and y.

10 When £P is invested at $r\%$ per annum compound interest, it grows to an amount £A after n years. $A = P\left(1 + \dfrac{r}{100}\right)^n$. Calculate the amount to which £250 grows at 7% in eight years.

11 A straight line has equation $y = 5x - 10$. Write down:
a its gradient
b the coordinates of the points A and B where it cuts the x and y-axes
c the area of △OAB, where O is the origin.

12 a Calculate the area of this trapezium.
b An enlargement of the trapezium has scale factor 2.5. What is its area?

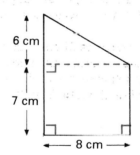

13 a Arrange each of these sets of marks in class intervals of 5: 35–39, 40–44, . . .
b Draw frequency diagrams, and calculate the mean mark for each set, to the nearest whole number.

(i) 44 50 43 45 43 43 46 35 77
     70 62 51 55 44 54 53 47 42
     51 43 69 70 71 52 56 35 50

(ii) 83 88 89 66 65 76 77 58 48
     52 54 46 46 56 44 50 42 46
     41 47 74 58 61 43 45 50 36

14 a Use your frequency tables in question **13** to draw cumulative frequency curves.
b Estimate the median and inter-quartile range for each set of marks.

GENERAL REVISION EXERCISE 2A

1 At Top Prints which film offers the best value (least cost per exposure)?

Number of exposures	20	24	36
Price (£)	3.00	3.36	5.22

2 A glass contains 32 ml orange squash and 48 ml water. Express the volume of squash in the glass as:
  a a fraction in its simplest form
  b a decimal fraction
  c a percentage, of the total volume of liquid.

3 Solve:
  a $9x - 70 = 11$ **b** $3y = y - 2$
  c $x + 7 = 87 - x$ **d** $6n - 12 = 4n + 2$

4 Copy these diagrams, and fill in the sizes of as many angles as you can.

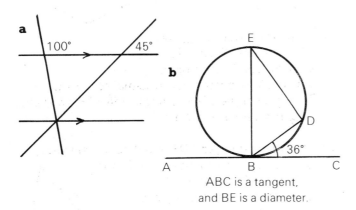

a

100°   45°

b

ABC is a tangent,
and BE is a diameter.

5 Neptune is 4500 million km from the sun, and the eccentricity of its orbit is 0.00855. Write both of these numbers in standard form, $a \times 10^n$.

6 Copy this table, and fill in all the boxes.

a	3	-2	4	-3		-1
b	2	-1	-2	5	5	
$a + b$					3	
$a - b$						0

7 In $\triangle$ABC, $\angle$B = 90°, AB = 14 cm and BC = 48 cm. Calculate:
  a the length of AC
  b the size of $\angle$A, correct to 0.1°.

8 Calculate the perimeter and area of this metal plate. All the angles are right angles. Make a sketch first.

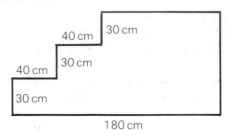

40 cm   30 cm
40 cm   30 cm
30 cm
180 cm

9 On squared paper draw:
  a the line from the origin O to the point A(7, 7)
  b the triangle with vertices (1, 1), (1, 6) and (3, 6)
  c the image of the triangle under reflection in OA. Write down the coordinates of its vertices.

10 The three short straws have the same total length as the long straw. Make an equation, solve it and calculate the length of each type of straw.

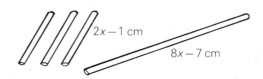

$2x - 1$ cm
$8x - 7$ cm

11 Mrs Watt's electricity bill drops into her letterbox.

Standing charge: £15.50
Day rate: 8.33p per unit
Night rate: 3.18p per unit
VAT is charged at 8%.

Look at the readings below and work out how much the bill is for.

Readings	Present	Previous
Day rate	10436	10178
Night rate	02041	01118

12 Factorise:
  a $m^2 - mn$ **b** $m^2 - n^2$ **c** $m^2 + m - 6$

13 Find the mean, median and mode of:
  a £s: 12, 13, 13, 13, 14, 15, 15, 18, 22
  b cm: 8, 9, 7, 8, 6, 6, 9, 7, 9, 10, 9

GENERAL REVISION EXERCISE 2B

1 Find the value of:
a $9^{1/2}$ **b** 4^0 **c** 5^{-2} **d** $8^{-1/3}$ **e** $(3^2)^{-1}$

2 Each bag contains x weights of 1 kg. The weights on the scales are also 1 kg each.
a Make an inequality for each picture, and solve it.
b Use the two solutions to find the possible number of weights in the bags.

(i)   (ii)

3 The value of a car depreciates each year by 12% of its value at the beginning of the year. Damian's new car costs £15 000. Calculate its value after:
a 1 year **b** 5 years, to the nearest £.

4 AB is a diameter of the circle.
Calculate:
a BC
b AC, correct to the nearest 0.1 cm
c the area of △ABC, correct to the nearest cm².

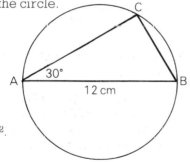

5 Solve for t:
a $\dfrac{t}{2} - \dfrac{t}{3} = 1$ **b** $\dfrac{3t}{2} = -6$
c $2t + a = 3b$ **d** $p = q + \sqrt{t}$

6 Investigate whether $y \propto x$, $y \propto \dfrac{1}{x}$, or neither, for each table.

a

x	20	40	60	100
y	2.5	5	7.5	12.5

b

x	2	3	4	6
y	30	20	15	10

7 Find the maximum and minimum values of y, and the corresponding values of x ($0 \leqslant x \leqslant 360$), for:
a $y = 5\cos x°$ **b** $y = 2 + \sin(x-90)°$

8 The Earth travels 9.4×10^{11} m round the sun in a year of 2.9×10^4 seconds. Calculate its average speed in m/s, in standard form, correct to 1 decimal place.

9 Simplify:
a $\dfrac{x^2 - 9}{5x - 15}$ **b** $\dfrac{x^2 + 2x - 8}{2x^2 - 3x - 2}$ **c** $\dfrac{ax + bx}{cx + dx}$

10 Find an expression for:
a the total volume of the three boxes (the lengths are in metres)
b the total exposed surface area of the boxes when stacked as shown.

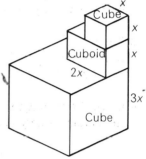

11 The cosine rule for △ABC is $a^2 = b^2 + c^2 - 2bc\cos A$.
a Make cos A the subject.
b Calculate, correct to 1 decimal place, the largest angle of the triangle with sides 55 mm, 75 mm and 95 mm long.

12 a Explain why △s ADE and ABC are similar.
b What is the reduction scale factor from △ABC to △ADE?
c Write down a ratio equal to $\dfrac{x}{x+4}$, and make an equation.
d Calculate x (the lengths are in cm).

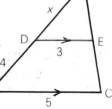

13 Sketch the graphs of:
a $y = x^2$ **b** $y = x^2 + 1$ **c** $y = (x+1)^2$

14 a Draw a frequency diagram for this table of the duration in minutes of a sample of telephone calls.

Duration	0	1	2	3	4	5	6	7	8
Frequency	3	20	31	35	28	18	5	8	2

b How many calls lasted more than five minutes?
c What percentage of calls lasted less than one minute?
d What is the probability that a call chosen at random lasted three minutes?

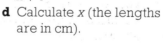

187

GENERAL REVISION EXERCISE 3A

1 Solve:

  a $3(x+2) \geqslant 12$ **b** $\left.\begin{array}{l} 2x+3y = 1 \\ 3x-2y = 8 \end{array}\right\}$

2 a Name an angle:

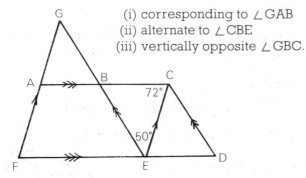

    (i) corresponding to $\angle GAB$
    (ii) alternate to $\angle CBE$
    (iii) vertically opposite $\angle GBC$.

  b Copy the diagram, and fill in the sizes of all the angles.

3 Calculate:

  a $40-(3\times11)$ **b** $\dfrac{9+(6\div2)}{(4\times1)-1}$ **c** $7+(\tfrac{1}{2}\text{ of }1\tfrac{1}{2})$

  d $\tfrac{1}{7}$ as a decimal, rounded to 3 significant figures.

4 Multiply out, and simplify where possible:

  a $5(2t-n)$ **b** $a(a^2+1)$ **c** $d(d^2-d)$
  d $-2(x-y)$ **e** $-(p+q)$ **f** $3(1-u+2v)$
  g $5+2(1-x)$ **h** $3-2(1-x)$

5 How many cartons of Juicy can be packed in a box 1.2 m by 0.8 m by 0.45 m?

16 cm · 12 cm · 15 cm

6 How much interest would £1800 earn in each bank in eight months?

MONEYBANK
Interest—
$7\tfrac{1}{2}$% p.a.

BRITBANK
Interest—
7% p.a.

7 The area of a triangle is given by the formula
$A = \sqrt{s(s-a)(s-b)(s-c)}$, where
$s = \tfrac{1}{2}(a+b+c)$.
Calculate A, to the nearest whole number, when
$a = 5$, $b = 8$ and $c = 9$.

8 Happy Hire charge £25 a day for car hire, plus 30p a mile, with a minimum charge of 20 miles. After 100 miles, the rate is reduced to 15p a mile. Follow the flowchart to find the hire charge for a mileage of:

  a 18 miles **b** 30 miles **c** 90 miles **d** 200 miles

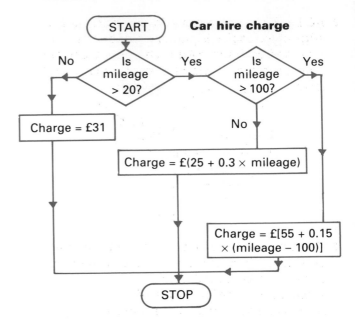

9 The ladder is one metre longer than the distance it reaches up the wall. Make an equation, and solve it to find the distance the ladder reaches up the wall.

Wall

4 m

10 A game has a square board of side 50 cm, with a circular track of width 4 cm touching the sides.

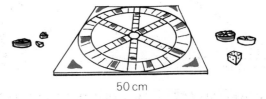

50 cm

Calculate, correct to 3 significant figures:
  a the circumference of the outside circle
  b the area of the track.

11 a Draw a tiling based on the kite O(0, 0), A(1, 2), B(4, 0), C(1, −2).
  b Calculate the area of OABC.

GENERAL REVISION EXERCISE 3B

1 Solve:
a $2(1-2x) = 2-3(x-1)$ **b** $2(x+1)-3(x-1) = 6$

2 A meal at the Ritz Restaurant costs Karen £14.10, including VAT at 17.5%. What is the cost of the meal before VAT?

3 ACB is the cross-section of a rain gutter at the edge of the roof. It is part of a circle of radius 6 cm, and its depth is 4 cm. Calculate the width AB of the gutter, in simplest surd (square root) form.

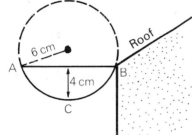

4 Tom drives for 15 minutes at an average speed of 48 km/h, then for half an hour at an average speed of 72 km/h. Calculate:
a the distance he has travelled
b his average speed for the whole journey.

5 Each edge of a skeleton cube is 2 cm long. Calculate, as surds, the lengths of:
a a face diagonal **b** a space diagonal.

6 Measurements are made on a base-line AB to find the height of the steeple CD. Calculate, correct to the nearest metre:
a BC **b** CD.

7 Find the cost of one jar of jam and the cost of one roll. (Remember to check your answer.)

Total cost £4.20

Total cost £6

8 a Match up each point below with the conditions it satisfies.

Conditions	Points
(i) $x \geqslant 2$ and $y \leqslant 3$	O(0, 0)
(ii) $1 \leqslant y \leqslant 3$	A(2, 2)
(iii) $x \leqslant 2$ and $y \geqslant -2$	B(3, 1)

b Illustrate the regions of the XOY plane defined by (i), (ii) and (iii) in separate sketches.

9 Simplify:
a $\dfrac{x^4 \times x^6}{x^2}$ **b** $y^{1/3}(y^{2/3}+y^{-1/3})$ **c** $(t^{-1/2})^4$
d $(x^{1/2}-x^{-1/2})^2$ **e** $(x^{1/4}-1)(x^{-1/4}+1)$

10 Boxes of Fruitos are made in two sizes. The small boxes are similar to the large ones.
a Use the heights of the boxes to write down the enlargement scale factor.

b A small box is 6 cm high. Calculate the height of a large box.
c The front of a small box has area 27 cm². Calculate the area of the front of a large box.
d The volume of a small box is 54 cm³. Calculate the volume of a large box.

11 a A function f is defined by $f(x) = (2x-1)^2$.
Calculate: (i) $f(1)$ (ii) $f(-2)$ (iii) $f(\frac{1}{2})$.
b For another function g, $g(x) = \sin x°$.
Calculate:
(i) $g(30)$
(ii) $g(123)$, correct to 2 decimal places.

12 Quickfix have a call-out charge of £25, plus an hourly charge of £15.
a On squared paper draw the graph of cost (£c) against time (t hours).
b Write down the equation for c in terms of t.
c A customer pays £85. How many hours work were involved?

13 a Use the formula $C = \frac{5}{9}(F-32)$ to calculate C when:
(i) $F = 59$ (ii) $F = 5$ (iii) $F = -4$
b Change the subject of the formula to F.

14 Solve, correct to 3 significant figures:
a $x^2+x-1 = 0$ **b** $2x^2-x-5 = 0$ **c** $x(x-2) = 9$.

GENERAL REVISION EXERCISE 4A

1 a From 15 May to 23 August (including both dates) a ferry makes four trips daily. How many trips is this altogether?

b A train leaves London Euston at 22 50, and arrives at Glasgow Central at 07 35, after a delay at Carlisle from 04 50 to 05 25. How long would the journey have taken without the delay?

2 Solve:
a $6(x+1)-2x = x+4$ **b** $2y^2-5y-3 = 0$

3 Each side of a triangular plot ABC is 100 m long. A TV aerial has to be put on the plot, subject to these conditions:
a It must be at least 25 m from each side of the plot.
b It must be within 55 m of A.
Draw a diagram to show where the aerial can go.

4 Fab Fashions increased its yearly profits from £140 000 to £185 000.
a Calculate the percentage increase in profits, correct to 1 decimal place.
b As a result, employees were given a 15% discount on all purchases. How much would they pay for this scarf and coat?

(i)
SCARF
£3.60

(ii)
COAT
£45.40

5 A bottle of diameter 8 cm sits in a rack. The points of contact P and R are 3 cm from A.
Calculate:
a AT
b ∠PAR, to the nearest degree.

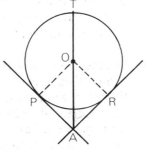

6 Mohammed is a surveyor. He measures the length and breadth of the rectangular base of a house: 12 m and 8 m, *to the nearest metre.* Calculate the maximum and minimum area and perimeter of the base.

7 Solve one of these pairs of equations by drawing graphs, one by substitution of x or y, and one by eliminating x or y.
a $2y+x = 12$ **b** $y = x$ **c** $x+2y = 12$
  $3y-x = 18$ $y = 2x+11$ $2x-y = -11$

8 Laurie drives a van from Glasgow to Preston.

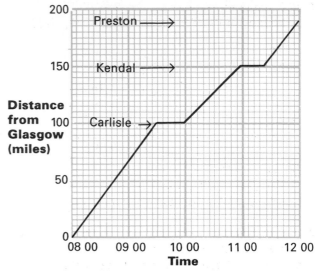

Calculate, to the nearest whole number where necessary:
a the length of each stop he makes
b his average speed on each of the three parts of his journey
c his average speed for the whole journey
  (i) including stops   (ii) excluding stops.

9 On squared paper, show the region defined by $x > 0$, $y > 0$ and $y < -2x+6$.

10 Which cylindrical bottle contains more liquid? How much more, to the nearest 0.1 cm³?

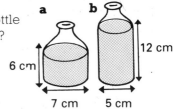

11 z varies directly as x and inversely as y. When $x = 12$ and $y = 8$, $z = 3$. Find z when $x = 6$ and $y = 4$.

12 Christopher tosses two coins.
a Make a tree diagram showing all possible outcomes.
b Calculate the probability that he has:
  (i) 2 heads
  (ii) 1 head and 1 tail (in any order)
  (iii) no heads   (iv) no heads or tails.

GENERAL REVISION EXERCISE 4B

1 a Calculate:
   (i) $2\frac{3}{4}+1\frac{3}{4}$ (ii) $4\frac{1}{5}-2\frac{2}{5}$ (iii) $3\frac{3}{4}\times1\frac{1}{5}$ (iv) $2\frac{5}{8}\div1\frac{3}{4}$
b How many $\frac{3}{4}$ kg bags of salt can be filled from a 60 kg supply?
c What length is halfway between $\frac{4}{5}$ mm and $\frac{9}{10}$ mm?

2 a Calculate:
   (i) the length of BD   (ii) the area of $\triangle$ACD

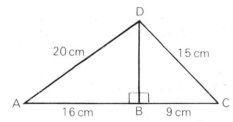

b Prove that:
   (i) $\triangle$ACD is right-angled
   (ii) $\triangle$s ABD and CBD are similar.

3 The height (h metres) of a rocket after t seconds is given by the formula $h=20t-4t^2$.
a Copy and complete this table of values:

t	0	0.5	1	2	3	4	4.5	5
h	0	9						

b Draw a graph of h against t.
c How long is the rocket in the air?
d Solve: (i) $20t-4t^2=0$ (ii) $20t-4t^2=21$
e When is the rocket 12 m above the ground?

4 Calculate the area of the car's windscreen swept clear by the wiper, correct to 2 significant figures.

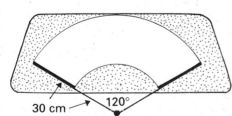

5 Solve for x:
a $3x+4=2$ **b** $ax+b=c$ **c** $y=mx+c$
d $\frac{x-3}{2}=1$ **e** $\frac{x-c}{d}=p$ **f** $t=\frac{n}{1-x}$

6 Solve these equations to the nearest degree, for $0<x<360$:
a $2\sin x°-1=0$ **b** $3\cos x°+2=0$.

7 Two ships leave port P at the same time. One sails 40 km on course 040° to A. The other sails 50 km on course 097° to B. Calculate, to the nearest metre and degree:
a AB   **b** $\angle$PAB   **c** the bearing of B from A.

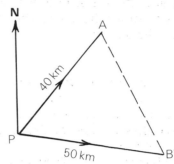

8 Solve:
a $2(t-3)-4\leqslant t-3(t+1)$
b $(x-3)^2>(1-x)^2$

9 a Sketch the region defined by:
   $y\geqslant x,\ y\leqslant 2$ and $x\geqslant -2$
b Calculate its area.

10

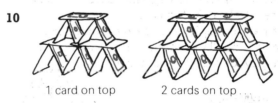

1 card on top   2 cards on top

a Copy and complete:

Number of cards on top (n)	1	2	3	4
Total number of horizontal cards (h)	3			
Total number of cards (t)	13			

b Find a formula for:
   (i) h in terms of n (ii) t in terms of n
   (iii) t in terms of h.

11 Tom flies his model plane in a circle at the end of a wire. The tension in the wire varies directly as the square of the plane's speed, and inversely as the radius of the circle. The tension is 8 newtons for a speed of 8 m/s and a radius of 6 m. Calculate the tension for a speed of 10 m/s and a radius of 5 m.

12 Use a step-by-step (iterative) method to find a root, correct to 1 decimal place for:
a $2x^2-x-2=0$ (root between 1 and 2)
b $x^3-6x+2=0$ (root between 2 and 3).

GENERAL REVISION EXERCISE 5A

1 a Before their holiday the Hill family changed £1200 to Swiss francs at 2.40 francs to the £. How many francs did they receive?

  b On the ferry home they changed their remaining 173 Swiss francs to £s at 2.36 to the £. How much money were they given?

2 Calculate:

  a the area of the end of the doll's house

  b the volume of the house.

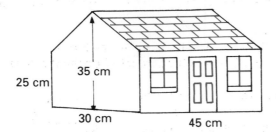

25 cm   35 cm   30 cm   45 cm

3 Sketch the graphs of the function f defined by:

  a $f(x) = 2x$ **b** $f(x) = 2 - x$ **c** $f(x) = (2 - x)^2$

4 The sum $S°$ of the angles of a polygon with n sides is given by the formula $S = 180(n - 2)$.

  a Calculate:

    (i) the sum of the angles of a 15-sided polygon

    (ii) the size of each angle if the polygon in (i) is regular.

  b Change the subject of the formula to n, and calculate the number of sides of the polygon with angle sum 900°.

5 a Copy and complete this table of outcomes for two spins.

Second spin

First spin	1	2	3
1	(1, 1)		
2			
3			

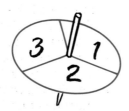

  b Calculate the probability that in two spins:

    (i) the first number is 3

    (ii) both numbers are 3

    (iii) the first number is less than the second

    (iv) the sum of the two numbers is less than 5.

6 Simplify:

  a $\dfrac{2}{x} + \dfrac{3}{y}$ **b** $\dfrac{3}{x+2} + \dfrac{2}{x-1}$ **c** $\dfrac{2}{y-1} - \dfrac{3}{y-2}$

7 A piece of elastic is pinned at B and C, so that BC = 30 cm. It is then pulled out to A, so that $\triangle$ABC is isosceles.

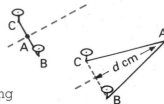

  a How long is AC:

    (i) before stretching

    (ii) when $d = 20$?

  b The elastic is stretched from its initial position until its length (CA + AB) is increased by a factor of 2.6. Calculate d now.

8 The hypotenuse of a right-angled triangle is $2x + 3$ cm long, and the other two sides have lengths x cm and $x + 7$ cm. Make an equation, solve it and find the lengths of the three sides.

9 A is the point $(1, -2)$ and B is $(3, 2)$. Find:

  a the length of AB, correct to 1 decimal place

  b the gradient of AB

  c the equation of the straight line through A and B.

10 a On the same diagram, draw graphs which illustrate the cost of car hire from these companies:

    Speedy £20, plus 10p per mile;

    Rentacar £30, plus 5p per mile;

    Costacar £50, and no mileage charge.

  b Which company is least expensive for hires of: (i) 100 miles   (ii) 200 miles   (iii) 400 miles   (iv) 500 miles?

11 O is the centre of the circle. Calculate the difference, correct to 1 decimal place, between the areas of $\triangle$OAB and sector OAB.

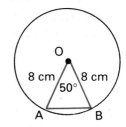

12 On a ferry crossing the cost for three cars and two lorries is £165, and the cost for five cars and one lorry is £170. Make two equations, and solve them to find the cost for a car and for a lorry.

13 a List all the prime numbers less than 50.

  b How many are:

    (i) 1 more than a multiple of 6

    (ii) 1 less than a multiple of 6

    (iii) neither (i) nor (ii)?

  c Calculate the percentage of each type, to the nearest whole number.

GENERAL REVISION EXERCISE 5B

1 Solve:

a $\dfrac{1}{x}+\dfrac{1}{2}=0$ **b** $\frac{1}{2}(2y-1)<-3$

c $\dfrac{x-1}{2}+\dfrac{x+1}{3}=4$ **d** $\dfrac{x}{2}+\dfrac{2}{x}=2$

2 a Explain why:
  (i) in $\triangle ABC$,
    $\angle ACB = 90°$
  (ii) AB is a diameter
    of the circle.
b Calculate the
  perpendicular
  distance from
  the centre of the
  circle to:
  (i) BC   (ii) AC.

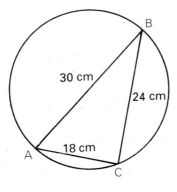

30 cm, 24 cm, 18 cm

3 24 can be written as the product of several pairs
of factors: $1\times24,\ 2\times12,\ \dots,\ -1\times-24,\ \dots$
  a Write down all the pairs you can find, like this:
    $(1, 24), (2, 12), \dots, (-1, -24), \dots, (-24, -1)$.
  b Plot these as points on squared paper, and
    draw a smooth curve through them.
  c What is the equation of the graph?
  d Is the graph a parabola or a hyperbola?

4 Write in a simpler surd form:
  a $\sqrt{20}$ **b** $4\sqrt{3}-2\sqrt{3}$ **c** $\sqrt{6}(\sqrt{2}+\sqrt{3})$
  d $(\sqrt{3}-\sqrt{2})^2$ **e** $\dfrac{2}{\sqrt{2}}$ **f** $\dfrac{3}{2\sqrt{6}}$

5 a Sketch the graphs of $y = \sin x°$ and $y = \sin 2x°$
  on the same diagram.
  b How many roots has the equation
  $\sin x° = \sin 2x°$, for $0 \leqslant x \leqslant 360$?

6 a Sketch the graphs of $y = \sin x°$ and $y = \sin\frac{1}{2}x°$
  on the same diagram.
  b Estimate the root of $\sin x° = \sin\frac{1}{2}x°$ for
  $0 < x < 360$, then calculate it using a
  step-by-step (iterative) method.

7 The length and breadth of a rectangle are each
increased by 10%. Calculate the percentage
increase in its area.

8 Simplify:
  a $\dfrac{5n+15}{3n+9}$ **b** $\dfrac{2x+6}{x^2+2x-3}$ **c** $\dfrac{a^2-b^2}{3a-3b}$
  d $\dfrac{2u^2-5uv+3v^2}{2u^2-uv-3v^2}$ **e** $\dfrac{3y^2-12}{2y^2+3y-2}$

9

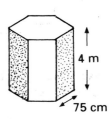

d_1, $n-1$, d_2, $n-2$, d_3, $n-3$
$n+1$, $n+2$, $n+3$

  a Find expressions for:
    (i) d_1^2, d_2^2 and d_3^2 (ii) $d_2^2-d_1^2$ and $d_3^2-d_2^2$.
  b Continuing the sequence, write down the
    value of $d_4^2-d_3^2$, and a formula for $d_{n+1}^2-d_n^2$.

10 Solve:
  a $(2x-1)^2-9=0$ **b** $4x^2+4x-3=0$
  c $2x^2+3x-4=0$, correct to 2 decimal places.

11 The cross-section of this
4 m high column is a
regular hexagon of side
75 cm. Calculate the
volume of stone in the
column, in m^3, correct to
3 decimal places.

4 m, 75 cm

12 Calculate, in standard form:
  a $(1.9\times10^8)\times(0.7\times10^{-9})$
  b $(3.6\times10^{-5})\div(0.8\times10^{-8})$

13 This list shows the different prices charged for a
gallon of petrol (in £s) over a number of years.

1.60	1.85	1.50	2.12	1.98	2.60	2.48
2.66	2.35	2.60	1.95	2.10	1.65	1.78
1.85	1.90	2.12	1.84	2.45	2.50	1.86
2.00	2.35	2.05	1.58	1.75	1.94	

  a Construct a frequency table, with class
    intervals 1.50–1.64, etc.
  b Use your table to calculate the mean price, to
    the nearest penny.
  c Add a cumulative frequency column, and
    draw a cumulative frequency curve.
  d Use the curve to estimate the median cost, and
    the inter-quartile range.

14 Find a formula for the number of squares of *all*
sizes in the nth picture of this sequence:

   • • •

ANSWERS

THE GRADIENT AND EQUATION OF A STRAIGHT LINE

Page 1 Looking Back

1a (i) Black (ii) blue (iii) red **b** blue **2a** 4 **b** 2 **c** −1
3c 6, 3 **d** $\frac{1}{2}$ **4a, b, d** **5a** (i) AB (ii) at O and C
b by the slope of the curve–the steeper, the faster
6a −1 **b** 5 **c** −7 **d** −2 **7a** −2 **b** −3 **c** $\frac{1}{2}$ **d** 0
8a (4, 0), (0, 4) **b** (1, 0), (0, −1) **c** (2, 0), (0, 3) **9c** Yes; the greater the number of goals against, the lower the number of points held **10a** $x = 2, y = 10$ **b** $x = 6, y = 60$

Page 2 Exercise 1

1a (i) The second (ii) 3, 4 **b** (i) the first (ii) 2, $\frac{3}{2}$
2a $\frac{3}{4}$ **b** 4 **c** 1 **d** $\frac{1}{2}$ **e** $\frac{3}{2}$ **f** 1 **g** $\frac{1}{3}$ **h** 2 **i** 1 **3a** $\frac{3}{5}$ **b** $\frac{2}{3}$
4 3, 0, 2, 0, 2 **5a** 0.04 **b** 0.004 **6a** (i) AB, CD (ii) BC, DE
(iii) EF **b** (i) CD (ii) BC **c** (i) CD (ii) EF
7a AB 2, CD $\frac{2}{3}$ **b** AB 3, CD 6 **c** AB 2, CD $2\frac{2}{3}$

Page 4 Exercise 2A

1a $\frac{1}{4}$ **b** −1 **c** 2 **d** $-\frac{1}{2}$ **2** AB 1, CD $\frac{1}{4}$, EF 0, GH −2
3 PQ 4, RS −1, TV −3 **4a** Angles made with OX are: (i) 45°
(ii) 45° (iii) 72° (iv) 72° (v) 14° (vi) 14° (vii) 84°
(viii) 0° **b** those with gradients 1 and −1 **5b** (i) $\frac{1}{3}$ (ii) $\frac{1}{3}$
(iii) $-\frac{3}{2}$ (iv) 1 (v) 5 (vi) $-\frac{1}{2}$ **c** (i) they are the same
(ii) the lines are parallel
6 Yes. $m_{AB} = m_{DC} = \frac{1}{4}$; $m_{AD} = m_{BC} = 3$
7a $m_{AB} = \frac{1}{2}, m_{BC} = -\frac{1}{2}, m_{CD} = \frac{5}{2}, m_{AD} = -\frac{5}{2}.$
Gradients of KN and LM = $\frac{1}{2}$; gradients of KL and NM = 2.
Gradients of EF and HG = 1; gradients of EH and FG = −1
b (i) parallelogram (ii) square
c equal in size, opposite in sign, in pairs **8a** (i) $\frac{1}{2}$ (ii) $\frac{1}{2}$
(iii) $\frac{1}{2}$ (iv) $\frac{1}{2}$ **b** they all lie on the same straight line
9 Only U, T, S are

Page 6 Exercise 2B

1a 2 **b** −3 **c** $-\frac{1}{2}$ **d** $\frac{1}{2}$ **e** −2 **f** −3 **g** −1
2a $\frac{3}{4}$ **b** $-\frac{1}{3}$ **c** 1 **d** 0 **3a** (i) **b** (iii) **c** (ii) **d** (iv)
4 Gradients: AB, 1; BC, −3; AC, 0
5a Gradients: PQ, 1; QR, $-\frac{1}{3}$; RS, 1; PS, −7 **b** trapezium
6a (i) $\frac{3}{2}$ (ii) $\frac{3}{2}$ (iii) $\frac{3}{2}$ **b** they are in a straight line **7** S
8 Gradients of PQ and SR are $-\frac{1}{2}$. Gradients of PS and QR are 4. So opposite sides are parallel **9** AD and BC

10
b is steepest

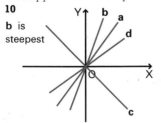

11

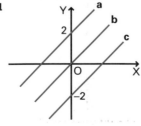

Page 8 Exercise 3A

1a 2, 5 **b** $\frac{1}{2}$, −4 **c** −1, 1 **d** −8, −8 **e** 3, 0 **f** −2, 0

2a 1, (0, 2) **b** −3, (0, −1) **c** 5, (0, −5) **d** −9, (0, 1)
e 2, (0, 0) **f** 0, (0, 4) **3a** 1, 0; 1, 4 **b** 2, 0; 2, −5
c −1, 0; −1, 3 **d** −2, 0; −2, −1 **4a** $y = 5x$ **b** $y = \frac{1}{4}x$
c $y = -\frac{1}{2}x$ **d** $y = 0$ **e** $y = \frac{3}{2}x$ **6a** 1, 3; $y = x + 3$
b $\frac{1}{2}$, 1; $y = \frac{1}{2}x + 1$ **c** $-\frac{1}{4}$, −2; $y = -\frac{1}{4}x - 2$
7a $y = 3x + 2$ **b** $y = 3x - 1$ **c** $y = 3x + 6$ **d** $y = 3x - \frac{1}{2}$
8 a, b

Page 8 Exercise 3B

1 $c = 6, y = -2x + 6$ **2a** $y = 3x + 2$ **b** $y = 3x - 10$
c $y = 3x + 6$ **3a** $y = x + 3$ **b** $y = \frac{1}{2}x + 3$ **c** $y = 2x + 1$
d $y = x - 3$ **e** $y = 3x$ **f** $y = 20x + 2$
4a −1, 6 **b** 2, −3 **c** 2, 3 **d** $-\frac{1}{2}$, −2 **e** $-\frac{3}{2}$, 3 **f** −1, −1
g 1, −3 **h** 2, −1 **i** 1, −5 **j** −2, 2 **k** 3, 0 **l** $\frac{4}{3}$, $-\frac{8}{3}$
5a $S = T + 3$ **b** $H = -\frac{1}{2}W + 7$ **c** $V = -\frac{2}{3}L + 4$
d $A = -2B + 11$

Page 9 Exercise 4A

1a (i) $\frac{1}{5}$, 2 (ii) $C = \frac{1}{5}T + 2$ **b** (i) −2, 4 (ii) $V = -2H + 4$
2a 2 **b** −100 **3a** $\frac{3}{2}$ **b** $C = \frac{3}{2}R$ **c** 12 m **4a** (i) £20
(ii) £10 **b** (i) 10 (ii) 20 **c** $C = 10T + 20$ **d** £140
5a (i) −20, 1200 (ii) $H = -20T + 1200$ **b** 60 s
6a $C = 2M + 25$ **b** £45 **7a** $V = 8000 - 800Y$ **b** 10 years

Page 10 Exercise 4B

1a (i) Row: 20, 25, 30, 35, 40, 45
b (i) Row: 0, 10, 20, 30, 40, 50 **c** 4, £40 **d** (i) Speedwheels
(ii) Maximiles **e** (i) $C = 20 + 5N, C = 10N$ (ii) $N = 4$
2a Rows: 30, 35, 40, 45, 50, 55; 0, 15, 30, 45, 60, 75 **c** 3, £45
d (i) Fast Hire (ii) Happy Hire **e** (i) $C = 30 + 5N, C = 15N$
(ii) $N = 3$ **3a** (i) Row: 350, 500, 650, 800, 950
(ii) 250, 500, 750, 1000, 1250 **c** 20
d (i) $C = 200 + 15N, C = 25N$ (ii) $N = 20$
4a 10, 15, 20, 25, 30 **b** 0, 10, 20, 30, 40 **d** (i) £20 (ii) 100
e North Gas Board **f** (i) $C = \frac{1}{5}N$ (ii) $N = 100$

Page 12 Exercise 5

(Answers depend on the choice of best-fitting line.)
1a 2.5 s, 375 m **d** 150 **e** $D = 150T$ **f** 150 km/h
2a (7, 65) **c** −5 **d** $H = -5T + 100$; 20 s **e** 5 cm/min
3a (24, 192) **b** when $V = 0, M = 0$ **c** $M = 8V$ **d** 8 g/cm³
4a (2.5, 161) **b** $A = -15T + 200$, 10 hours
c 15 mg/ml per hour **5b** $S = 5T$ **c** 5 cm/s per second

Page 14 Check-up on The Gradient and Equation of a Straight Line

1a AB, CD, GH, MN **b** EF, KL, PQ **c** IJ
2 AB 1, CD 4, EF −1, GH 1, IJ 0, KL $-\frac{1}{3}$, MN $\frac{1}{3}$, PQ −3
3a (iii), **b** (iv), **c** (ii), **d** (i) **4a** 1, 0 **b** −2, 1 **c** 3, 2
d −1, 0 **5** $m_{AB} = m_{DC} = \frac{1}{5}, m_{AD} = m_{BC} = -2,$
so opposite sides are parallel **6** $m_{AC} = \dfrac{3}{4}, m_{CE} = \dfrac{14-5}{18-6} = \dfrac{3}{4}$
7a, b, d 8a, c 9a 1, 1 **b** −2, 0 **c** 3, −2 **10a** $y = 4x + 1$
b $y = -3x - 1$ **11a** $y = 2x + 1$ **b** $y = -2x - 2$
12a Rows: 2, 3.5, 5, 6.5, 8, 9.5, 11 **c** $C = \frac{3}{2}D + 2$; £62
13a (3, 18.5) **c** $V = 1.5T + 14$; 12 minutes

2 FUNCTIONS AND GRAPHS

Page 15 Looking Back

1a 15 **b** 54 **c** $5+a$ **d** $5a$ **2a** 13 **b** -2 **c** -5 **d** 18
3a 5 **b** $2\frac{1}{2}$ **c** 2 **4c** $\frac{1}{2}$, $y = \frac{1}{2}x - \frac{1}{2}$ **5a** (i) about 167 (ii) 1.67
b £60 **c** less steep **6a** (i) $(4, 0)$ (ii) $(0, 2)$
7a (i) $(2, 0)$ (ii) $(0, -6)$ **9a** 3 **b** 7 **c** 12
10a 56 m **b** 15 s **c** (i) after 5 s and 10 s from the start
(ii) because it goes up and then comes down **d** 34 m

Page 17 Exercise 1

1a $\{6, 12, 18, 24\}$ **b** $\{6, 7, 8, 9\}$ **c** $\{-1, 0, 1, 2\}$
2a $\{6, 3, 12\}$ **b** $\{8, 5, 1\}$ **3a** Divide by 2 **b** multiply by 10
4 Function 'divide by 5'; output $\{2, 4, 6, 8, x\}$
5 Function 'divide by 50'; output $\{1, 2, 3, x\}$
6

a 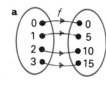 **b** 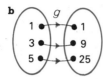 **c**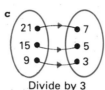

Divide by 3

d 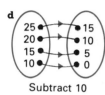 **e** **f**

Subtract 10

7a (i) $\{1, 2, 3\}$ (ii) $\{4, 5, 6\}$ **b** add 3
c

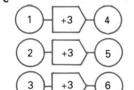

$f : 1 \to 4$
$f : 2 \to 5$
$f : 3 \to 6$

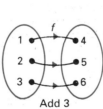

Add 3

Page 18 Exercise 2A

1a (i) 8 (ii) 72 (iii) 0 **b** (i) 1 (ii) 100 (iii) 49
2a (i) 8 (ii) 17 (iii) 26 **b** (i) -4 (ii) 2 (iii) -10
3a (i) 6 (ii) 7 (iii) 8 **b** (i) 4 (ii) 0 (iii) 8 **4a** 6 **b** 12
c 18 **5a** $\frac{3}{2}$ **b** 3 **c** 6 **6a** (i) 28 (ii) 31 (iii) 34 **b** £43
7 7 **8** 5 **9** $2\frac{1}{2}$ **10** -2 **11** 0 **12** 1

Page 19 Exercise 2B

1a (i) 2 (ii) 2000 **b** (i) $f(t) = 2t^3$ (ii) $f(a) = 2a^3$
2a -8 **b** -8 **c** 0 **d** 0 **3a** (i) 9 (ii) 36 **b** $f(a) = (a + 3)^2$
4a (i) 65 (ii) 100 **b** (i) 9 (ii) 42 **5a** (i) 60 (ii) 30 (iii) 20
b (i) 200 mph (ii) 300 mph **6a** (i) 24 (ii) 4 (iii) -12 **b** 3
7a (i) 1 (ii) 4 (iii) 9 **b** 25
8a $f(2a) = 5(2a) = 10a$ **b** $f(a+1) = 5(a+1)$
9a $g(2a) = (2a)^2 = 4a^2$ **b** $g(a-1) = (a-1)^2$ **10** -4
11a $2a + b = 5$, $a + b = 4$ **b** $a = 1$, $b = 3$ **c** $f(x) = x + 3$
12a $5a + b = 7$, $a + b = 3$; $a = 1$, $b = 2$ **b** $g(x) = x + 2$
13a $p(x) = 2x - 3$ **b** $q(x) = 2x$

(In the remaining exercises in this chapter, sketches of the graphs are given, showing some of their main features.)

Page 21 Exercise 3A

1a y: $-1, 0, 1, 2, 3, 4, 5$

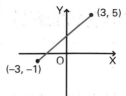

2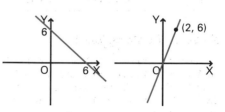

3a y: 16, 9, 4, 1, 0, 1, 4, 9, 16
b $x = 0$

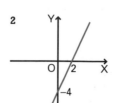

4a y: 12, 5, 0, -3, -4, -3, 0, 5, 12
b -4, at $x = 0$
c -2 and 2

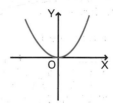

5a 8, at $x = 1$ **b** (i) $-1, 3$ (ii) $-2, 4$
6a -12.25 at $x = 1.5$ **b** (i) $-2, 5$ (ii) 0, 3
7a y: $-5, 0, 3, 4, 3, 0, -5$
b max 4, at $x = 1$
c $-1, 3$

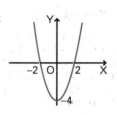

8a

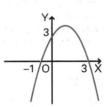

b min -1, at $x = 1$
c 0, 2

9a

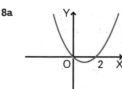

b max 3, at $x = 0$
c $-1, 1$

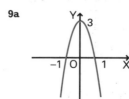

10a
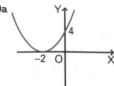
b min 0, at $x = -2$
c -2

11a
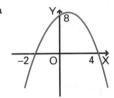
b max 9, at $x = 1$
c $-2, 4$

Page 22 Exercise 3B

1a 2000 m, 20 s **b** 40 s **c** 900 m **d** 10 s, 30 s

2a
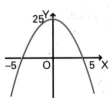
b (i) 11 (ii) 3.5
c (i) 180 (ii) 5

3a
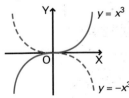
b (i) 12.8 (ii) 22.8
c 6.3 units

4a D: 20, 80, 180, 320 **b**
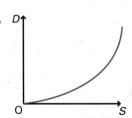
c (i) 45 ft, 245 ft
(ii) 63 mph, 89 mph

Page 24 Exercise 4

1a Graph is shown above Exercise 4 **b** at the origin **c** no

2a
b (0, 0)
c $x = 0, y = 0$
$y = x^3$
$y = -x^3$

3a y: $-15, 0, 3, 0, -3, 0, 15$

b (i) max. 3.1 at $x = -1.2$;
min. -3.1 at $x = 1.2$
(ii) $-2, 0, 2$

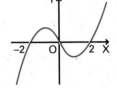

4a
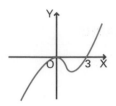
b (i) max. 0 at $x = 0$;
min. -4 at $x = 2$
(ii) 0, 3

5a Length × breadth × height
$= (10-2x)(10-2x)x$
$= x(10-2x)^2$
b
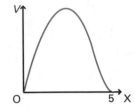

c 74 at $x = 1.7$;
6.6 cm by 6.6 cm by 1.7 cm

Page 25 Exercise 5

1a See text **b** (i) axes of symmetry are $y = x$ and $y = -x$
(ii) centre of symmetry is the origin
c decreases; gets closer and closer to $y = 0$
d increases; gets closer and closer to $x = 0$
2a As in question **1** **b** axes of symmetry $y = x, y = -x$;
symmetrical about the origin
3a Mirror image in the y-axis of the graph in question **2**
b same as question **2**

4a
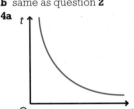
b (i) 80 s
(ii) 48 s

5a B: 48, 40, 30, 24, 20, 16, 15, 12, 10, 8, 6, 5
b
c $B \times L = 240$; yes

Page 26 Making Sure

2a (iv) **b** (i) **c** (ii) **d** (iii) **e** (i) **f** (iii) **g** (iv) **h** (ii)
i (i) **j** (iv)

Page 27 Exercise 6

1a $y = 2x$ **b** $y = x^2$ **c** $y = \frac{1}{4}x^3$ **d** $y = \frac{12}{x}$

2b **1a**, $y = 3x$ **c** (i) 15 volts (ii) 30 volts
3b $y = 5x^2$ **c** (i) 7.2 m (ii) 16.2 m
4b Yes; $y = 4x^3$ **c** (i) 62.5 cm³ (ii) 171.5 cm³
5b **1d** **c** $xy = 240$ **d** (i) 12 amps (ii) 1.6 amps
6b **1b** **c** $y = 9x^2$ **d** (i) 56.25 m² (ii) 144 m²

Page 29 Check-up on Functions and Graphs

1a 9, at $x = 3$ **b** (i) 0, 6 (ii) 2, 4
2a 1, 2, 7, 8; 7, 14, 49, 56 **b** 64, 48, 40, 8; 8, 6, 5, 1
c 1, 4, 2, 3; 1, 64, 8, 27 **d** 5, -5, 10, 17; 0, -10, 5, 12
3a (i) 13 (ii) -2 (iii) -7 **b** (i) -9 (ii) 0 (iii) -8
4a 3 **b** $\frac{1}{2}$ **5b** 51 **c** 6

6a $f(x)$: 7, 0, −5, −8, −9, −8, −5, 0, 7

b

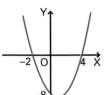

c −9, 1   **d** −2, 4

7a (i);   **b** (iv);   **c** (ii);   **d** (iii)

8a

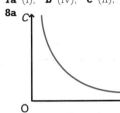

b one branch of a hyperbola; $NC = 72$

c (i) £14 400   (ii) £7200

---

3 SYMMETRY IN THE CIRCLE

(Degree symbols are not shown in answer diagrams.)

Page 30   Looking Back

1

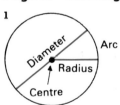

2a 360°   **b** (i) 285   (ii) 60   **3a** 180°   **b** (i) 40   (ii) 55
4a (i) $C = \pi D$ (ii) $A = \pi r^2$ **b** (i) 157.1 cm   (ii) 1963.5 cm²
5a 26 cm   **b** 1.5 cm   **6** 29.7°   **7a** 6.8 cm   **b** 4.2 cm

Page 31   Exercise 1

1a 40   **b** 110   **2a** 31   **b** 30   **3a** 128   **b** 25   **4a** 45   **b** 67.5
5

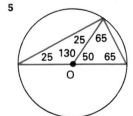

6 a

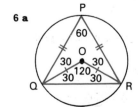

b

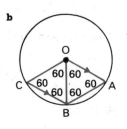

Page 32   Exercise 2

1a 60   **b** 15   **2a** $a = 90, b = 30$ **b** $c = 33, d = 57$
3a $e = 47, f = 20$ **b** $g = 45$
4a $x = 25, y = 25$ **b** $x = 110, y = 55$
5 semi-circle; Pythagoras' Theorem; 20; $d = 4.5$ **6a** 7.2
b 6.6   **7** semi-circle; 41.4
8a $d = 13, m = 22.6$ **b** $d = 10.4, m = 60$ **9a** 17.2   **b** 16.3
10a 113.1 cm   **b** 10 000 cm²
11a Isosceles △OAC   **b** isosceles △OBC
c sum of angles of △ABC = 180°   **d** 90°
12 ∠s ADB and ADC are right angles (angles in semi-circles). So $\angle ADB + \angle ADC = 180°$

Page 34   Exercise 3

1 a

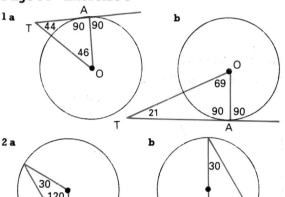

b

2 a

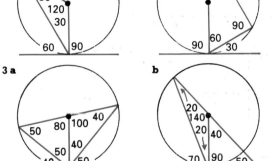

b

3 a

b

4a 6.9   **b** 3.2   **5a** $d = 10, x = 36.9$ **b** $d = 24, x = 67.4$
6a 24 cm; 24 cm   **b** a kite   **7** $a = 50, b = 40, c = 40, d = 10$
8 120 mm
9a $\angle BAD = \angle BCD = 90°, \angle ABC = 120°, \angle ADC = 60°$
b 27.7 cm   **10a** 1 m   **b** 1.4 m

Page 36   Exercise 4A

1 a

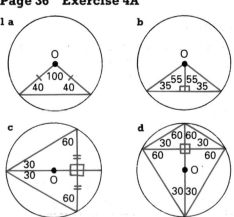

b

c

d

2a 12   **b** 5   **3a** 12   **b** 24   **4a** 6.5   **b** 6
5a $x = 41.4, y = 48.6$ **b** $x = 30, y = 30$
6 5 m 24 cm   **7** 40 cm   **8** 6 m

Page 37 Exercise 4B

1 35 mm **2a** 180 mm **b** 576 mm **3a** 40 cm **b** 34.6 cm, 40 cm, 34.6 cm **4a** (i) AB (ii) any angle at M (iii) AC = AD, BC = BD, CM = MD **b** a kite; two pairs of adjacent sides equal, or one diagonal bisects the other at right angles **5a** 19.4 mm **b** 17.3 mm **c** 13.2 mm **6a** AB, by 1.3 cm **b** TS, by 0.9 cm

Page 38 Exercise 5

2 Each fold makes a diameter **4** Draw the perpendicular bisectors of two of AB, BC, CA (and the third as a check)

Page 39 Class Discussion/Exercise 6

1a (i) $\frac{1}{6}$ (ii) $\frac{1}{6}$ (iii) $\frac{1}{6}$ **b** 60° **2a** (i) $\frac{1}{8}$ (ii) $\frac{1}{8}$ (iii) $\frac{1}{8}$ **b** 45° **3** Rows: 90°, 60°, 45°, 36°, 30°; $\frac{1}{4}, \frac{1}{6}, \frac{1}{8}, \frac{1}{10}, \frac{1}{12}$; $\frac{1}{4}, \frac{1}{6}, \frac{1}{8}, \frac{1}{10}, \frac{1}{12}$; $\frac{1}{4}, \frac{1}{6}, \frac{1}{8}, \frac{1}{10}, \frac{1}{12}$

Page 40 Exercise 7

1a (i) $\frac{1}{2}$ (ii) 18.8 cm **b** (i) $\frac{1}{6}$ (ii) 8.4 cm **c** (i) $\frac{1}{8}$ (ii) 3.9 cm **d** (i) $\frac{1}{9}$ (ii) 8.4 cm **e** (i) $\frac{3}{4}$ (ii) 70.7 cm **f** (i) $\frac{2}{3}$ (ii) 83.8 cm **2a** $\frac{1}{3}$ **b** 52.4 cm **3** 209 cm **4a** 36° **b** (i) 6.3 m (ii) 62.8 m **5** 15.1 m **6** The outer rail is 2.1 cm longer **7** Over the North pole by 1431 miles **8a** 47.7 **b** 214.9 **9a** 69.1 cm **b** 113.1°

Page 42 Exercise 8

1a 8.7 cm² **b** 150.8 m² **2** 6.5 cm² **3** 314.2 cm² **4a** 349.1 cm² **b** 3.1 m² **5** 6283 mm² **6a** 3487 cm² **b** 280 cm² **c** 3207 cm² **7** 151 cm², 7540 cm³ **8a** 78.5 cm² **b** 50 cm² **c** 28.5 cm² **9a** 33.4° **b** 287.6° **10a** 407 m **b** 37 600 − 13 800 = 23 800 m²

Page 44 Check-up on Symmetry in the Circle

1

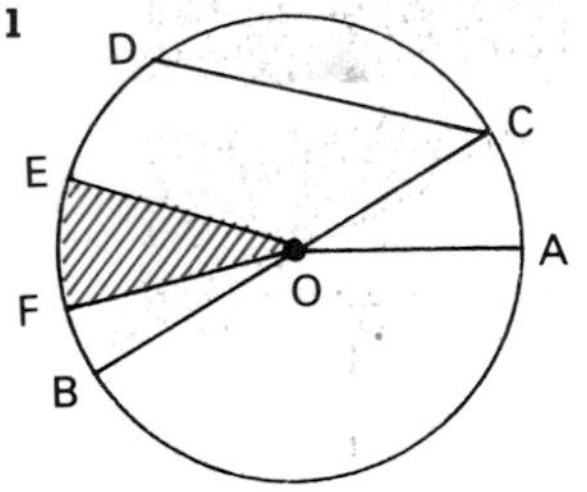

2a ∠ABC (in a semi-circle) **b** ∠s OED, OEF (angle between tangent and radius) **c** ∠s OQP, OQR (OQ is on axis of symmetry) **3a** 35 **b** 52 **c** 25 **d** 45 **e** 15 **4a** $d = 13$, $m = 22.6$ **b** $d = 5.9$, $m = 49.1$ **5a** 90° **b** 5.6 cm **6a** 13 m **b** 12 m **c** 45.2° **7a** (i) 7.9 m (ii) 19.6 m² **b** (i) 12.6 cm (ii) 75.4 cm² **8** 5.2 m **9a** 139.6 cm **b** 5585 cm² **10a** 20.9 cm **b** 1570.8 cm²

4 INEQUALITIES

Page 45 Looking Back

1a 4 **b** 5 **c** −4 **d** −2

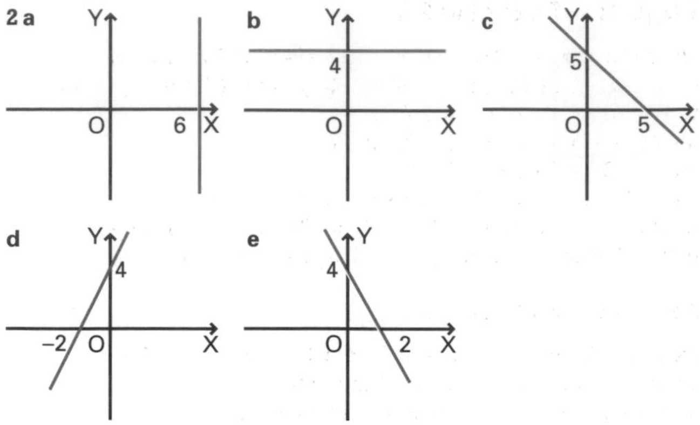

3b (i) T (ii) T (iii) F (iv) T (v) F (vi) T (vii) T (viii) T **4a** $5 > 3$ **b** $1 < 2$ **c** $1 > 0$ **d** $-1 < 0$ **e** $2 > -2$ **f** $-2 < 2$ **g** $-3 > -4$ **h** $5 > -1$ **5a** 12 **b** 9 **6a** $m \leqslant 100$ **b** $a \geqslant 14$ **c** $w \leqslant 7.5$ **d** $d \geqslant 200$ **7a** 2 **b** −2 **c** 0, 1, 2 **d** 0, −1, −2 **e** 2 **f** 0, −1, −2 **g** 2, −2, **h** −2 **8** $t \geqslant -3$ and $t \leqslant 5$

Page 46 Exercise 1

1a $x > 2$ **b** $x \geqslant -1$ **c** $x < -2$ **d** $x \leqslant 1$ **2a** $1 \leqslant x \leqslant 4$ **b** $-3 < x < 0$ **c** $x < -2$ or $x > 3$ **d** $x \leqslant 0$ or $x \geqslant 1$

3

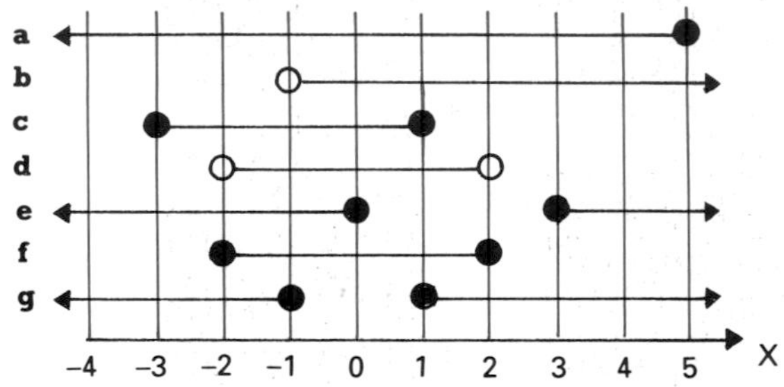

4a $x > -4$ **b** $x \geqslant 1$ **c** $x \leqslant -1$ **d** $-2 < x \leqslant 3$ **e** $x < -2$ or $x > 2$

5a $d \leqslant 5$ 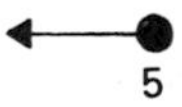

b $w > 2$ 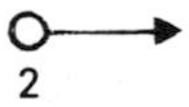

c $2 \leqslant h \leqslant 3$ 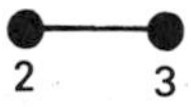

d $t < 3$ or $t > 10$ 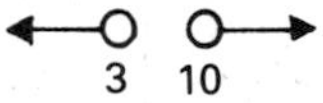

e $3 \leqslant t \leqslant 10$ 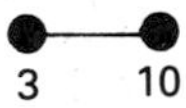

6a (i) $s \geqslant 8$ (ii) $s \leqslant 30$ (iii) $8 \leqslant s \leqslant 30$

b (i) 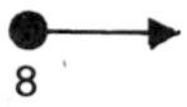

(ii) 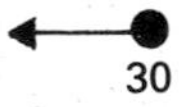

(iii) 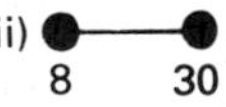

Page 47 Exercise 2A

1a $y > 2$ **b** $x < -1$ **c** $m > 5$ **d** $n < 1$ **e** $k \geqslant 1$ **f** $t \leqslant -2$ **g** $u \geqslant 3$ **h** $v \leqslant 1$ **i** $w > 6$ **j** $p \leqslant 0$ **k** $z \leqslant -3$ **l** $t < -4$ **2a** $y < 3$ **b** $x < 4$ **c** $m > 2$ **d** $n < -1$ **e** $k \geqslant 2$ **f** $t \leqslant -2$ **3a** $y > 3$ **b** $x < 3$ **c** $m > 5$ **d** $n < -1$ **e** $k \geqslant 2$ **f** $t \leqslant 3$ **g** $u \geqslant -2$ **h** $v \leqslant 0$ **i** $p < -2$ **4a** 3 **b** 6 **c** 4 **5a** $x > 3$ **b** $x > 10$ **c** $x < 4$ **d** $y \leqslant 6$ **e** $y \leqslant 0$ **f** $y \geqslant 7$ **6a** $t > -1$ **b** $u < -2$ **c** $v > -6$ **d** $w \leqslant -7$ **e** $x \geqslant -2$ **f** $y \leqslant -6$ **7a** $x > -2$ **b** $y < -1$ **c** $t < 2$ **d** $u < -2$ **e** $y > -3$ **f** $z \leqslant 1$ **g** $x > -4$ **h** $y \leqslant 2$ **i** $p \geqslant -2$ **8a** $p > 3$ **b** $q < 9$ **c** $r > 4$ **d** $s \geqslant 3$ **e** $t \leqslant 3$ **f** $u \geqslant 5$ **9a** $x > 5$ **b** $y < 6$ **c** $z \leqslant 1$ **d** $x < -2$ **e** $y < 5$ **f** $t \leqslant 4$ **10a** $t \geqslant -3$ **b** $x > -2$ **c** $y \leqslant 4$ **d** $p \geqslant 5$ **e** $u < 4$ **f** $r \leqslant 4$

Page 48 Exercise 2B

1b $x \leqslant 6$ **2b** $x \leqslant 160$, 160 ml **3a** $5x + 10 \leqslant 100$; $x \leqslant 18$
b 18 **4a** $20x + 40 \leqslant 840$; $x \leqslant 40$ **b** (i) yes (ii) yes (iii) no
5 $4x + 70 + 40 \leqslant 160$; $x \leqslant 12\frac{1}{2}$; 12
6a $750 + 15x \geqslant 1000$; $x \geqslant 16\frac{2}{3}$ **b** 17
7a $36 + 2x \geqslant 200$; $x \geqslant 82$ **b** 82
8a £$(25 + x)$, £$(5 + 3x)$ **b** $25 + x < 5 + 3x$; $x > 10$
c (i) Carl's (ii) either (iii) Otto's **9a** £$(8x + 1)$, £$(6x + 10)$
b $8x + 1 < 6x + 10$; $x < 4\frac{1}{2}$ **c** 1, 2, 3 or 4 calculators

Page 49 Exercise 3

1a $x \geqslant -2$ **b** $x > 3$ **c** $x \geqslant 0$ **d** $y \geqslant 0$ **e** $x \leqslant 1$ **f** $y < 1$
2a $x \geqslant 0$ and $y \geqslant 0$ **b** $x \geqslant -2$ and $y > -1$
c $x \geqslant -2$ and $y \geqslant -2$ **d** $x > -1$ and $y < 3$
e $x < 0$ and $y \geqslant 0$ **f** $x \geqslant 0$ and $y \leqslant 0$

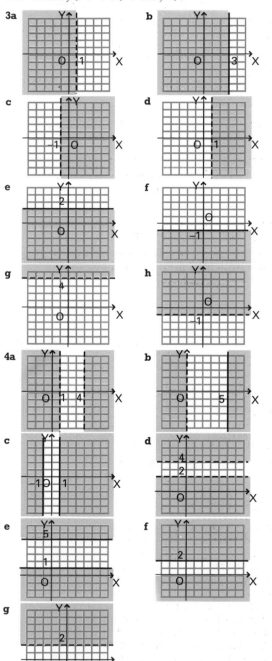

5a $-2 \leqslant x \leqslant 2$ and $-2 \leqslant y \leqslant 2$
b $-3 \leqslant x \leqslant 0$ and $-3 \leqslant y \leqslant 0$
6a $0 \leqslant x \leqslant 1$ and $2 \leqslant y \leqslant 3$ **b** $0 \leqslant x \leqslant 3$ and $0 \leqslant y \leqslant 1$
c $-2 \leqslant x \leqslant 0$ and $-1 \leqslant y \leqslant 2$ **7a** E **b** S, T, α, β

Page 51 Exercise 4

1a $y \leqslant x + 1$ **b** $y < x - 2$ **c** $y \geqslant 2 - x$ **d** $y < 1 - 2x$
2a $y < -2x + 6$ **b** $y \geqslant x + 4$ **c** $y < -x - 3$ **d** $y \geqslant x - 3$
3a (i) $y = x + 2$ (ii) $y \geqslant x + 2$ **b** (i) $y = x + 3$ (ii) $y < x + 3$
c (i) $y = -x - 2$ (ii) $y \leqslant -x - 2$ **d** (i) $y = -2x + 2$
(ii) $y < -2x + 2$ **e** (i) $y = x + 1$ (ii) $y \leqslant x + 1$
f (i) $y = -\frac{1}{2}x + 2$ (ii) $y \leqslant -\frac{1}{2}x + 2$

Page 53 Exercise 5A

1a 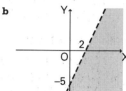 **b**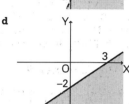

c 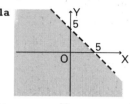 **d**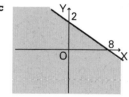

e 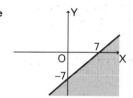 **f**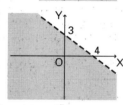

g 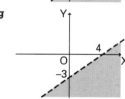 **h**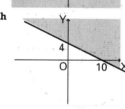

2a $x \geqslant 0$, $y \geqslant 0$, $y \leqslant -2x + 6$ **b** $x > 0$, $y > 0$, $y < -2x + 6$
c $x \geqslant -2$, $y \geqslant -2$, $y \leqslant 3 - x$ **d** $x \geqslant -2$, $y > -2$, $y < 3 - x$

3a 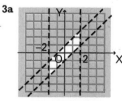 **b**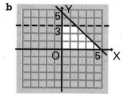

c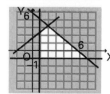

4a $y \geqslant -1$, $y \leqslant \frac{1}{2}x + 2$, $y \leqslant -\frac{1}{2}x + 2$
b $y > -1$, $y < \frac{1}{2}x + 2$, $y < -\frac{1}{2}x + 2$
c $x \geqslant 0$, $y \geqslant 1$, $y \leqslant -2x + 12$, $y \leqslant -\frac{1}{2}x + 6$
d $y \leqslant \frac{2}{3}x + 2$, $y \leqslant -\frac{2}{3}x + 2$, $y \geqslant \frac{5}{3}x - 5$, $y \geqslant -\frac{5}{3}x - 5$

Page 53 Exercise 5B

1a $x > 0$,
$x < 5$,
$y \geqslant 8$,
$x + y \leqslant 15$

b
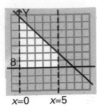
$x=0 \quad x=5$

2a $x > 2$,
$y > 2$,
$x + y \geqslant 5$,
$x + y \leqslant 10$

b
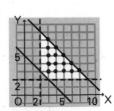

c (S, J): (3, 3), (3, 4), (3, 5), (3, 6),
(3, 7), (4, 3), (4, 4), (4, 5), (4, 6),
(5, 3), (5, 4), (5, 5), (6, 3), (6, 4),
(7, 3)

3a $x \geqslant 1$,
$y \geqslant 2$,
$x + y \leqslant 8$,
$y - x \leqslant 3$

b
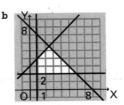

4a $x \geqslant 3$,
$y \geqslant 5$,
$y \leqslant 2x$,
$x + y \leqslant 12$

b (i), (ii)

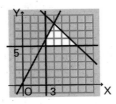

Page 54 Exercise 6B

1a 14, 0 **b** 12, 0 **c** 14, −3 **2a** 13 **b** 4 **c** 32
3a 0 **b** −4 **c** 1 **4a** 8, 2 **b** 7, −5 **c** 17, −11 **d** 36, 4
5

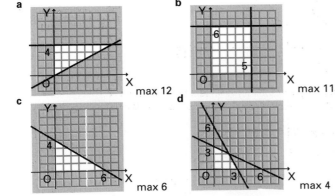

a max 12   **b** max 11   **c** max 6   **d** max 4

6 22, 3

Page 55 Check-up on Inequalities

1a $x > -1$ **b** $x \geqslant 0$ **c** $x \leqslant 1$ **d** $-4 < x \leqslant 4$
e $x < -1$ or $x > 1$ **2a** $x \geqslant 10$ **b** $y < 8$ **c** $z > -1$
d $t \geqslant 2\frac{1}{2}$ **e** $p > -4$ **f** $u \geqslant -2$ **3a** $5x + 2 \leqslant 22$
b $x \leqslant 4$, 4m **4a** $x \leqslant -7$ **b** $y < 0$ **c** $n \leqslant 3$ **d** $k \geqslant 1$
5a $10 + 2x < 3x$ **b** $x > 10$ **6a** 3 **b** 4 **c** 4
7 $-2 \leqslant x \leqslant 4$, $-1 \leqslant y \leqslant 4$
8a $y \leqslant x$ **b** $y > -x$ **c** $y \leqslant x + 2$ **d** $y > -x + 4$
9

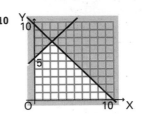
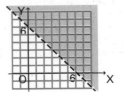

10

11 10, 1; 4, −19 **12** 12

---

5 TRIGONOMETRY – CALCULATIONS, GRAPHS AND EQUATIONS

Page 56 Looking Back

1a 25 **b** 10 **c** 34.5 **d** 1.7
2a $\dfrac{3}{5}, \dfrac{4}{5}, \dfrac{3}{4}$ **b** $\dfrac{y}{r}, \dfrac{x}{r}, \dfrac{y}{x}$ **c** $\dfrac{12}{13}, \dfrac{5}{13}, \dfrac{12}{5}$ **d** $\dfrac{u}{w}, \dfrac{v}{w}, \dfrac{u}{v}$
3a 8.7 **b** 7.2 **c** 3.0 **d** 3.3 **4a** 38.7 **b** 41.8 **c** 62.0
d 30.0 **5a** 8 cm, 48 cm² **b** 14.7 cm, 382.2 (383.4) cm²

Page 57 Exercise 1

1a $\dfrac{3}{5}, \dfrac{4}{5}$ **b** $\dfrac{12}{13}, \dfrac{5}{12}$ **c** $\dfrac{7}{25}, \dfrac{7}{24}$

2 Hypotenuse $= \sqrt{(1+1)} = \sqrt{2}$; $\dfrac{1}{\sqrt{2}}, \dfrac{1}{\sqrt{2}}, 1$

3a Third side $= \sqrt{(2^2 - 1^2)} = \sqrt{3}$ **b** (i) $\dfrac{1}{2}, \dfrac{\sqrt{3}}{2}, \dfrac{1}{\sqrt{3}}$

(ii) $\dfrac{\sqrt{3}}{2}, \dfrac{1}{2}, \sqrt{3}$ **4a** 13 km **b** 18 km **5** 10.8 m

6 (6, 6) **7** 112.1 m **8** 0.15°

Page 58 Exercise 2

1 ∠s OPK, OPN, OPT; OPQ, OPR, OPS **2b** 59.0°, 68.2°, 63.4°
3a 14.1 cm **b** 35.3° **4a** 5 m **b** 5.8 m **c** 31.0° **5a** 13.4
b 63.4° **c** 53.1° **6a** 5.7 cm **b** 9.4 cm **7a** 17.0 m **b** 8.5 m
c 18.1 m **d** 64.8° **8a** 10 cm **b** 5 cm **c** 67.4° **9a** 1800 m
b 2600 m **c** 3200 m

Page 59 Exercise 3A

1 Rows: $4, 3, 5, \frac{3}{5}, \frac{4}{5}, \frac{3}{4}$; $-4, 3, 5, \frac{3}{5}, -\frac{4}{5}, -\frac{3}{4}$; $-4, -3, 5, -\frac{3}{5}, -\frac{4}{5}, \frac{3}{4}$; $4, -3, 5, -\frac{3}{5}, \frac{4}{5}, -\frac{3}{4}$ **2a** $1, 2$ **b** $1, 4$ **c** $1, 3$ **d** 1

3b $5, 12, 13, \frac{12}{13}, \frac{5}{13}, \frac{12}{5}$; $-5, 12, 13, \frac{12}{13}, -\frac{5}{13}, -\frac{12}{5}$; $-5, -12, 13, -\frac{12}{13}, -\frac{5}{13}, \frac{12}{5}$; $5, -12, 13, -\frac{12}{13}, \frac{5}{13}, -\frac{12}{5}$ **c** same as question **2**

4a pos. **b** neg. **c** neg. **d** neg. **e** neg. **f** pos. **g** pos. **h** neg. **5a** 0.985 **b** -0.174 **c** -5.671 **d** -0.342 **e** -0.940 **f** 0.364 **g** 0.5 **h** -0.866 **6a** neg. **b** pos. **c** pos. **d** neg. **e** neg. **f** pos. **g** neg. **h** pos.

7a -1.540 **b** 0.891 **c** 0.996 **d** -0.176 **e** -0.574 **f** 0.996 **g** -0.276 **h** 0.577 **8a** $+$ **b** $-$ **c** $-$

9a Rows: $0, 1, 0, -1, 0; 1, 0, -1, 0, 1$ **c** 0, error, 0, error, 0; cannot divide by zero **10** $\frac{4}{5}, \frac{3}{4}$ **11** $\frac{8}{17}, \frac{15}{17}$

Page 61 Exercise 3B

1a $(180-80)°$ **b** $(180-10)°$ **c** $(180+10)°$ **d** $(180+40)°$ **e** $(360-60)°$ **f** $(360-30)°$ **2a** $\sin 80°$ **b** $-\cos 80°$ **c** $-\tan 80°$ **d** $-\sin 40°$ **e** $-\cos 40°$ **f** $\tan 40°$ **g** $-\sin 60°$ **h** $\cos 60°$ **i** $-\tan 60°$ **j** $\sin 70°$ **k** $-\cos 20°$ **l** $-\tan 20°$ **m** $\sin 55°$ **n** $\cos 25°$ **o** $-\tan 35°$

3a $\dfrac{1}{\sqrt{2}}, -\dfrac{1}{\sqrt{2}}, -1$ **b** $-\dfrac{1}{\sqrt{2}}, -\dfrac{1}{\sqrt{2}}, 1$ **c** $-\dfrac{1}{\sqrt{2}}, \dfrac{1}{\sqrt{2}}, -1$

4a $\dfrac{\sqrt{3}}{2}, -\dfrac{\sqrt{3}}{2}, -\dfrac{\sqrt{3}}{2}$ **b** $-\dfrac{1}{2}, -\dfrac{1}{2}, 1$ **c** $-\sqrt{3}, \sqrt{3}, -\sqrt{3}$

Page 62 Exercise 4

1 $0, 0.5, 0.9, 1, 0.9, 0.5, 0, -0.5, -0.9, -1, -0.9, -0.5, 0$

2a (i) $0, 180, 360$ (ii) 90 (iii) 270

b $B(150, 0.5)$, $C(390, 0.5)$, $D(510, 0.5)$

3 $1, 0.9, 0.5, 0, -0.5, -0.9, -1, -0.9, -0.5, 0, 0.5, 0.9, 1$

4a (i) $90, 270$ (ii) $0, 360$ (iii) 180 **b** $x = 180$

5 $0, 0.6, 1.7, 3.7; -3.7, -1.7, -0.6, 0, 0.6, 1.7, 3.7; -3.7, -1.7, -0.6, 0$

Page 63 Exercise 5A

1a $3, -3$ **b**

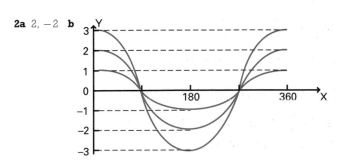

2a $2, -2$ **b**

3

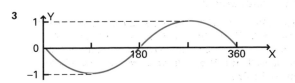

4

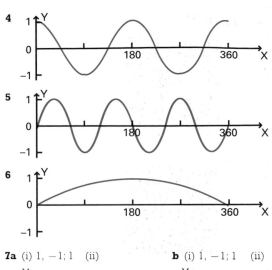

5

6

7a (i) $1, -1; 1$ (ii) **b** (i) $1, -1; 1$ (ii)

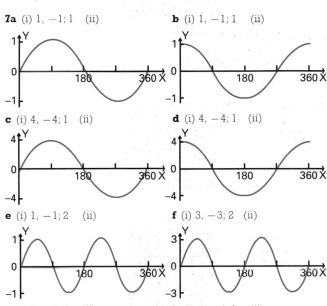

c (i) $4, -4; 1$ (ii) **d** (i) $4, -4; 1$ (ii)

e (i) $1, -1; 2$ (ii) **f** (i) $3, -3; 2$ (ii)

g (i) $1, -1; 2$ (ii) **h** (i) $4, -4; 2$ (ii)

i (i) $5, -5; \frac{1}{2}$ (ii)

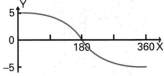

8a (i) $y = \sin x°$ (ii) $y = 2\sin x°$ **b** (i) $y = \cos x°$ (ii) $y = \cos 2x°$ **c** $y = 10\sin x°$ **d** $y = 3\sin 2x°$

Page 65 Exercise 5B

1a $3, 1$ **b**

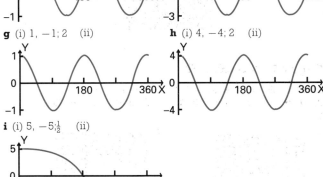

2a 0, −2 **b**

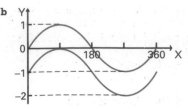

3a (i) 2, 0 (ii) 0, −2 **b**

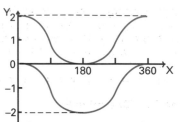

4a **b**

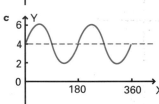

c **d**

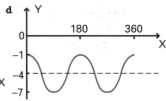

5 $y = 1 + \cos 3x°$
6a 16 m, 4 m **b** 10 m **c**

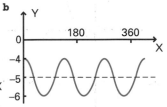

7a (i) 20, 0 (ii) 0 **b**

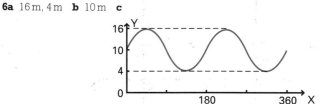

8a 1050, 950 **b** 36 hours **c**

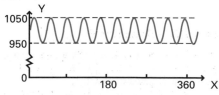

Page 66 Exercise 6

1a 30, 150 **b** 60, 300 **c** 45, 225 **2a** 210, 330 **b** 120, 240
c 135, 315 **3a** 44, 136 **b** 78, 282 **c** 63, 243 **4a** 12, 168
b 139, 221 **5a** 194, 346 **6a** 55, 305 **b** 6, 174
7a 113, 293 **b** 23, 203 **8a** 199, 341 **b** 41, 319 **9a** 90
b 0, 360 **c** 270 **d** 180 **e** 0, 180, 360 **f** 90, 270
10a 30, 150, 210, 330 **b** 60, 120, 240, 300 **c** 84, 96, 264, 276
11a 14, 166 **b** 115, 245

Page 67 Exercise 7B

2 $\sin^2 x° = 1 - 0.7^2$, $\sin x° = \sqrt{0.51} = 0.7$ **3a** 0.6 **b** 0.8
4a 0.9 **b** 0.9 **5** 1 **6a** 0.36 **b** 1.8
7 $\tan x° = 1.5$, $x = 56°$ or $180° + 56° = 236°$
8a 53, 233 **b** 45, 225 **c** 72, 252 **d** 22, 202

Page 68 Check-up on Trigonometry— Calculations, Graphs and Equations

1a 8.7 **b** 8.0 **c** 5.0 **d** 54.0 **2** 6.7 m **3a** 90° **b** 45°
4a 164 cm **b** 168.8 cm **c** 13.7°
5a OP = OQ = 10 **b** (i) $\frac{3}{5}, \frac{4}{5}, \frac{3}{4}$ (ii) $\frac{3}{5}, -\frac{4}{5}, -\frac{3}{4}$
6a

Sin +	All +
Tan +	Cos +

b (i) neg. (ii) pos. (iii) pos. (iv) pos.
c (i) −0.342 (ii) 0.087 (iii) 1.732 (iv) 0.799

7a **b**

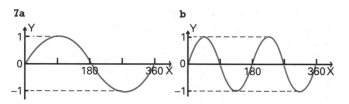

c

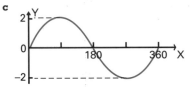

8

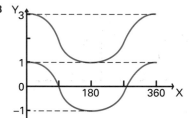

9a $y = \cos 2x°$ **b** $y = \sin \frac{1}{2}x°$
10a 20 days **b** max 3; min 1, 2 **11a** 45.6, 314.4
b 11.5, 168.5 **c** 98.1, 278.1 **d** 14.5, 165.5 **e** 109.5, 250.5
f 58.0, 238.0 **12** $a = 4, b = 2, n = 3$

6 QUADRATIC EQUATIONS

Page 69 Looking Back

1a (i) 18 m (ii) 3 min **b** 5 min
2a 40 **b** 19 **3a** $2\frac{1}{2}$ **b** −2 **c** $\frac{1}{2}$ **4a** $y = -2x + 6$
b $y = x - 1$ **c** $y = 3x - 4$ **5a** 4.9 **b** −0.3
6a (i) 400 m (ii) 20 s (iii) 10 s **b** (i) 76 m (ii) 256 m
7 −3, 1 **8a** $x^2 - 2x$ **b** $y^2 + 2y + 1$ **c** $p^2 - 6p + 9$
d $t^2 + 4t + 3$ **e** $u^2 - 5u + 6$ **f** $v^2 - 3v - 4$ **9a** $x(x-1)$ **b** $2u(1-u)$
c $(a+b)(a-b)$ **d** $(x+3)(x+1)$ **e** $(y-1)^2$ **f** $(2c-1)(c+1)$
10a $2^3 = 8, 3^3 = 27$ **b** $2.4^3 = 13.8, 2.5^3 = 15.6$

Page 71 Exercise 1

1 0, 4 **2** $-2\frac{1}{2}$, 1 **3** −2, 2 **4a** (i) 0 (ii) 6 **b** 0, 6
5a (i) 0 (ii) 8 **b** 0, 8 **6a** A(−50, 0), B(50, 0) **b** 100 m
7a M(−20, 0), N(20, 0) **b** 40 m

8a 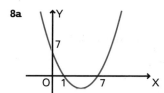 **b** 1, 7

9a 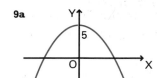 **b** −2.2, 2.2

Page 72 Exercise 2

1a 5 **b** 3 **c** 0 **d** $1\frac{1}{2}$ **e** −2 **f** $-\frac{4}{3}$, i.e. $-1\frac{1}{3}$
2a 1, 2 **b** −4, 7 **c** 0, 8 **d** 0, −4 **e** 0, −5 **f** −3, 3
g $0, \frac{1}{2}$ **h** $\frac{1}{2}, -\frac{2}{3}$ **3a** $-6, 1\frac{1}{2}$ **b** 0, 1 **c** $-\frac{4}{3}, \frac{8}{5}$ **d** $\frac{1}{4}, -\frac{1}{4}$
e 1 **f** $-\frac{1}{2}$ **g** $-\frac{1}{4}, -1\frac{1}{2}$ **h** $\frac{2}{3}, -\frac{1}{2}$ **4a** $A(-\frac{1}{2}, 0), B(2, 0)$
b $A(\frac{1}{2}, 0), B(3, 0)$ **c** $O(0, 0), A(4, 0)$ **d** $(-\frac{2}{3}, 0), (2\frac{1}{2}, 0)$
5a $(1, 0), (4\frac{1}{2}, 0)$ **b** $(0, 0), (5, 0)$ **c** $(-2\frac{1}{2}, 0), (\frac{2}{3}, 0)$
d $(-7, 0), (\frac{5}{3}, 0)$ **e** $(0, 0)$ **f** $(-2, 0)$
6a (i) $(-2, 0), (2, 0)$ (ii) $(0, -4)$ **b**

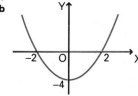

7a (i) $(-3, 0), (3, 0)$ (ii) $(0, 9)$

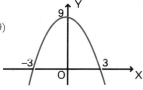

Page 73 Exercise 3A

1a $3(x^2+2)$ **b** $5(y^2+2)$ **c** $2(3z^2+4)$ **d** $2(2-k^2)$
e $12(1-m)$ **f** $a(a+3)$ **g** $b(b-5)$ **h** $x(x+1)$ **i** $2d(d+2)$
j $4y(2-3y)$ **k** $p(p-1)$ **l** $3q(q+3)$
2a $(x-y)(x+y)$ **b** $(p-q)(p+q)$ **c** $(m-2)(m+2)$
d $(x-4)(x+4)$ **e** $(k-1)(k+1)$ **f** $(2x-1)(2x+1)$
g $(3y-2)(3y+2)$ **h** $(4-z)(4+z)$ **i** $(y-10)(y+10)$
j $(4c-5)(4c+5)$ **k** $(t-9)(t+9)$ **l** $(2t-9)(2t+9)$
3a $(x+2)(x+1)$ **b** $(x+5)(x+2)$ **c** $(y+1)^2$ **d** $(y+3)^2$
e $(a-1)^2$ **f** $(b-4)^2$ **g** $(c-3)(c+2)$ **h** $(d+5)(d-2)$
i $(2x+1)(x+1)$ **j** $(3y+2)(y+1)$ **k** $(2x-1)(x-3)$
l $(2y+3)(4y-1)$

Page 73 Exercise 3B

1a $x(2x-3)$ **b** $(x-3)(x+3)$ **c** $(x+4)^2$ **d** $(t-2)^2$
e $(5x-2)(5x+2)$ **f** $5x(x+3)$ **g** $a(a-1)$ **h** $(m-1)^2$
i $(3y+1)^2$ **j** $(3-2n)(3+2n)$ **k** $5x(1-4x)$ **l** $(4x-3)(x-2)$
m $(3-x)(2+x)$ **n** $(3+y)(2-y)$ **o** $(3-z)(2-z)$
2a $2(x-2)(x+2)$ **b** $5(y-1)(y+1)$ **c** $3(a-1)(a+1)$
d $4(c-3)(c+3)$ **e** $2(2x+1)(x+2)$ **f** $2(2y+1)^2$
g $(2x+1)(x-3)$ **h** $(2x-3)(3x-2)$ **i** $2(4-x)(4+x)$
j $2(3y-2)(2y+3)$ **k** $2(2t-1)(t+4)$ **l** $30(a+2)(a-1)$

Page 74 Exercise 4A

1a $(x+5), x+5 = 0, -5$ **b** $(y+4), y+4 = 0, -4$
c $(x+1), x+1 = 0, x = -1, -1$ **d** $(t+1), t+1 = 0, t = -1$

2a $x = 0, 2$ **b** $y = -2, 1$ **c** $a = -3, 3$ **d** $b = -2, 4$
e $k = 0, -6$ **f** $t = -2, 10$ **g** $u = -9, 0$ **h** $x = -1, 1$
i $m = 2, 1$ **j** $x = 3, 4$ **k** $c = 5, 1$ **l** $x = 3, -2$
m $r = -5, 3$ **n** $x = -1, -4$ **o** $x = -4, 4$ **p** $x = -\frac{1}{2}, \frac{1}{2}$
q $y = 0, \frac{1}{2}$ **r** $m = 0, \frac{2}{5}$ **s** $x = -7, -3$ **t** $y = 3$ **u** $z = -10$
v $t = 2, \frac{1}{2}$ **w** $a = \frac{1}{2}, -3$ **x** $x = 1\frac{1}{2}, 1$

Page 74 Exercise 4B

1a $O(0, 0), A(7, 0)$ **b** $A(-2\frac{1}{2}, 0), B(3, 0)$
2a $(-3, 0), (3, 0)$ **b** $(0, 0), (4, 0)$ **c** $(-\frac{1}{2}, 0), (\frac{2}{3}, 0)$ **d** $(\frac{3}{4}, 0)$
3a $(-3, 0), (7, 0)$ **b** 10 m **4a** $(-40, 0), (40, 0)$ **b** 50 cm
5a $-1\frac{1}{2}, -1$ **b** $\frac{1}{3}, 3$ **c** $-\frac{1}{3}$ **d** $\frac{1}{3}, \frac{1}{2}$ **e** 0, 1 **f** −3, 3
g −1, 2 **h** 0
6a $-1\frac{1}{2}, -\frac{1}{2}$ **b** $-2, 2\frac{1}{2}$ **c** 5 **d** −2 **e** 3 **f** −7, 4

Page 75 Exercise 5

1a 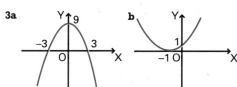 **b**

2a 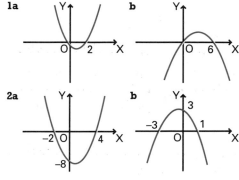 **b**

3a **b**

4a 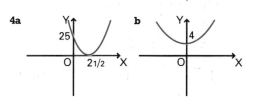 **b**

5a 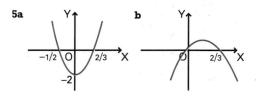 **b**

Page 76 Exercise 6

1a −4, −1 **b** −2, 4 **c** 1, 6 **d** −4, 3 **e** 0, 1 **f** −2, 2
g 6 **h** −5, −3 **i** $1\frac{1}{3}, 3$ **j** 2 **k** $\frac{1}{2}, \frac{1}{3}$ **l** $1\frac{1}{4}, 1$
2a −1, 3 **b** $\frac{1}{2}, 1$ **c** 2 **d** −4, 3
3a $(-4, 0), (10, 0)$ **b** 14 cm **4a** $(2, 0), (6, 0)$ **b** $(1, 5), (7, 5)$
5a −8, 4 **b** −3, 8 **c** $-2\frac{1}{2}, 1\frac{1}{2}$ **d** −5, 0 **e** −2, 0 **f** 0, 1
g $\frac{1}{2}, 2\frac{1}{2}$ **h** $-2, 3\frac{1}{2}$
6a −1, 6 **b** −1, 1 **c** $-2\frac{1}{2}, 3$ **d** −3, −5

Page 77 Exercise 7A

1a −1, −2 **b** −2, −4 **c** −4, 1 **d** −6, 2 **e** 1, 2 **f** 2, 3
g −1, 2 **h** −2, 4 **2a** −2.4, 0.4 **b** 0.4, 4.6 **c** −3.9, −0.1
d 2.3, 0.2 **e** −0.8, 2.1 **f** −0.4, 0.6 **g** −2.4, 0.9 **h** 1.3, 0.3

3a (i) $x = -2\frac{1}{2}, 1$ (ii) graph crosses x-axis at two points
b (i) $x = 1\frac{1}{2}$ (ii) graph touches the x-axis
c (i) no solutions (ii) graph does not meet x-axis

Page 78   Exercise 7B

1a $-9.7, 1.7$ **b** $-0.4, 12.4$ **c** $-1.6, 0.6$ **d** $-1.9, 0.9$
e $-1.3, 1.3$ **f** $-0.9, 4.0$ **g** $-2.6, 2.6$ **h** $-2.2, -0.8$
2a A$(-0.12, 0)$, B$(0.82, 0)$ **b** A$(-6.2, 0)$, B$(-1.3, 0)$
3a y: $13, 2, -5, -8, -7, -2, 7$ **c** $-2.8, 1.3$

Page 79   Exercise 8

1a, b $2\,\text{s}, 6\,\text{s}$ **2a** $1\,\text{s}, 7\,\text{s}$ **b** $3\,\text{s}, 5\,\text{s}$ **c** $4\,\text{s}$
3a (ii) $(-2, 5), (3, 0)$ **b** (ii) $(1, 2), (5, 10)$
4a $(-2, 4), (4, 16)$ **b** $(-4, -24), (0, 0)$
5 O$(0, 0)$, A$(4, 4)$, B$(3, 0)$, O$(0, 0)$ **6a** P$(5, 0)$, Q$(-6, 11)$
b $16\,\text{cm}$

Page 80   Exercise 9

1b $6\,\text{m}, 3\,\text{m}$ **2b** $10\,\text{m}, 6\,\text{m}$ **3b** $5\,\text{m}, 4\,\text{m}$
4a $5t^2 - 18t + 9 = 0; \frac{3}{5}, 3$ **b** as it rises and falls
5a 39 **b** when $t = 0$, height $= 0$ **6** $8\,\text{m}, 5\,\text{m}$ **7b** $8\,\text{m}, 6\,\text{m}$
8a $5x^2 + x - 84 = 0; x = 4$ (must be > 0) **b** $5\,\text{m}, 12\,\text{m}$
c $60\,\text{m}^3$ **9b** (ii) $\frac{1}{2}n(n+1) = 55, n = 10\ (n > 0)$ **c** $n = 20$
10a $16 - 2x\,\text{cm}$ **b** $x^2 - 8x + 16 = 0; 4\,\text{cm}, 8\,\text{cm}$

Page 83   Exercise 10

1 $f(1) = -1, f(2) = 3; 1.3$ **2a** 2.6 **b** 1.6
3a 1.5 **b** 0.3 **c** -1.9 **4a** $f(1) = 0$ **b** 2.7
5a $f(0) = 1, f(-1) = -2$ **b** -0.54
6a $x^2 - 8x + 11 = 0$ **b** 6.24 **7** 0.35 seconds **8** -1.9

Page 84   Check-up on Quadratic Equations

1a $0, 6$ **b** $1, 5$ **c** 3 **d** $2, 4$ **e** $1.6, 4.4$ **2a** $-5, 1$ **b** $-1, 0$
c $0, 3$ **d** $-5, 5$ **e** $-9, -\frac{1}{2}$ **f** $-2, 3$ **g** $\frac{1}{2}$ **h** $-\frac{1}{2}, 4$
3a $x^2 - 2x - 3 = 0; -1, 3$ **b** $y^2 - 4y - 21 = 0; -3, 7$
c $6x^2 - 13x + 6 = 0; \frac{2}{3}, 1\frac{1}{2}$ **d** $3x^2 - 2x - 1 = 0; -\frac{1}{3}, 1$
4a $x^2 + 2x - 48 = 0, x = 6$ **b** $x^2 - 6x - 27 = 0, x = 9$
c $3x^2 - 2x - 40 = 0, x = 4$
5a $(-1, 1), (3, 9)$ **b** $(-2, 2), (3, -3)$ **c** $(-2, -6), (2, 6)$
6a $-0.9, 6.9$ **b** $-2.4, 3.4$ **c** $-2.7, 0.7$ **d** $-1.1, 0.4$

7a 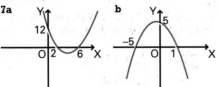 **b**

8 $-2.8, 1.3$ **9a** $d(2) = -1, d(2.2) = 1.9$ **b** (i) 2.07
(ii) $2\,\text{h}\,4\,\text{min}$

7   PROPORTION IN PRACTICE

Page 85   Looking Back

1a (i), (v) **b** (ii), (iii), (vi) **c** (iv)
2a $24, 48, 72, 96, 120$ **b** $50, 25, 10, 5, 2$
3a 4 **b** $\frac{1}{2}$ **c** 12 **d** 1 **4a** 81 **b** 4 **5a** 4 **b** 16

6a 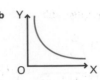 **b**

7a $2, y = 2x$ **b** $\frac{1}{2}, y = \frac{1}{2}x$ **8a** 10 **b** 6 **c** 6
9a direct **b** inverse **10b** (i) 5 (ii) $V = 5v$

Page 87   Exercise 1

1 Yes **b** (i) 7 (ii) $C = 7N$ **2** yes **b** (i) 5 (ii) $E = 5H$
3a $0, 5, 10, 15, 20$ **b** it is a straight line through the origin

c $I = \dfrac{P}{20}$ **4a** Yes. The graph is a straight line through the
origin **b** $P = 1.5H$ **c** (i) £45 (ii) $20\,\text{ft}$ **5b, d**

6a $90, 180, 270, 360$ **b** Yes, $\dfrac{A}{T} = 6$ **c** $A = 6T$

7c (i) $E = 5T$ (ii) the extension is directly proportional to the
tension **8c** (i) $F = 0.08a$ (ii) force is directly proportional to
acceleration **9c** (i) $I = 0.35V$ (ii) current is directly
proportional to voltage

Page 89   Exercise 2A

1a $W = 250I$ **b** 750 **2a** $T = \frac{1}{5}N$ **b** 52 **3a** $C = 6A$ **b** £30
4a $R = \frac{1}{10}L$ **b** 8.8 ohms **5a** $P = \frac{1}{25}D$ **b** £18
6a $N = \frac{1}{15}M$ **b** 75 minutes **7a** $T = 9N$ **b** £6480 **c** 1300

Page 90   Exercise 2B

1a $P \propto N, P = kN$ **b** $d \propto t^2, d = kt^2$ **c** $V \propto r^3, V = kr^3$
d $h \propto \sqrt{d}, h = k\sqrt{d}$ **2a** $D = 5T^2$ **b** $180\,\text{m}$ **c** $5\,\text{s}$
3a $V = 2\sqrt{R}$ **b** $18\,\text{m/s}$
4a $\sqrt{L}: 0, 3, 4, 5, 6; T: 0, 0.6, 0.8, 1.0, 1.2$ **b** graph is a straight
line through the origin **c** $T = \frac{1}{5}\sqrt{L}, 2$
5a (i) $M = 3N^2$ (ii) $12, 27, 48, 75, 108$ **b** (i) $P = \frac{1}{2}\sqrt{Q}$
(ii) $0, 0.5, 1, 1.5, 2$ **6b** (iii) $S = \frac{1}{2}L^3$ **c** 62.5
7a $A_1 = \pi r^2, A_2 = \pi(2r)^2 = 4\pi r^2$, etc
b $V_1 = kr^3, V_2 = k(2r)^3 = 8kr^3$, etc

Page 93   Exercise 3

1a $y = \dfrac{12}{x}$ **b** (i) 2 (ii) 4 **2a** $H = \dfrac{480}{N}$ **b** (i) 6 (ii) 40

3a $T = \dfrac{500}{R}$ **b** (i) 2.5 (ii) 125 **4a** $H = \dfrac{6000}{R}$ **b** 15

5a $P = \dfrac{1200}{V}$ **b** (i) 400 (ii) 1.5 **6** $R = \dfrac{0.018}{d^2}$

7a $I = \dfrac{25}{d^2}$ **b** (i) 4 (ii) 2.5 **8a** $W = \dfrac{100 \times 6400^2}{d^2}$ **b** $64\,\text{kg}$

9a (i) and (ii) **b** $P \propto \dfrac{1}{\sqrt{T}}, P = \dfrac{36}{\sqrt{T}}$

Page 94   Exercise 4A

1a $y = \dfrac{kx}{z}$ **b** $p = kqr$ **c** $a = \dfrac{kbc}{d}$ **d** $s = \dfrac{kt}{\sqrt{u}}$ **2a** $A = 3rh$

b 36 **3a** $p = 2qr$ **b** 10 **4** $V = 2xyz$ **5a** $I = 5mr^2$ **b** 360

6a $y = \dfrac{6x}{z}$ **b** 3 **7** $F = \dfrac{16m}{n}$ **8a** $A = \dfrac{75s}{t^2}$ **b** $8\frac{1}{3}$

9a $T = \dfrac{4x}{\sqrt{y}}$ **b** 20 **10a** $y = \dfrac{2xz}{t^2}$ **b** 7.5

11a C is directly proportional to D **b** P is inversely
proportional to H **c** A is directly proportional to R^2
d V varies inversely as P **e** A varies directly as L and as B
f V varies directly as T and inversely as P

Page 95   Exercise 4B

1a $E = kC^2L$ **b** $D = \dfrac{kS^2}{R}$ **c** $D = \dfrac{kC}{\sqrt{S}}$ **2a** $P = \dfrac{100H}{N}$ **b** £120

3a $T = \dfrac{NA}{60}$ **b** 6 minutes **4a** $n = \dfrac{d\sqrt{s}}{240}$ **b** 14

5a $P = \dfrac{YS}{100}$ **b** £5400 **6a** $I = \dfrac{PTR}{100}$ **b** £84

7a $V = \dfrac{600T}{P}$ **b** 210 **8a** $F = \dfrac{S^2M}{75R}$ **b** 30 newtons

9a $A = kab$ **b** (i) $A \times 2$ (ii) $A \times 2$ (iii) $A \times 4$

10a $V = 1.047r^2h$, 314.1 **b** (i) doubled (ii) $V \times 4$ (iii) $V \times 8$

Page 97   Check-up on Proportion in Practice

1b (i) $P = \dfrac{D}{40}$ (ii) P is directly proportional to D

2a $p = 5q^2$ **b** Rows: 2, 4, 10; 20, 80, 500 **3a** $M = \dfrac{72}{N}$ **b** 24

c 4.5 **4** See answer to Looking Back, question **6**

5a $B = \dfrac{P}{1250}$ **b** (i) £15 (ii) £22 500

6a $N = \dfrac{1036\,800}{A}$ **b** 288 **c** $N \times \frac{1}{2}$

7a (i) F varies directly as v^2 and inversely as r (ii) $F = \dfrac{kv^2}{r}$

b 6 **8b** 1.13 **c** 53° **9a** $C = \dfrac{40H}{N}$ **b** £4.80

10a 40, 20, 13, 10, 8 **b** $a = \dfrac{40}{M}$ **c** a straight line through O

d the acceleration is inversely proportional to the mass

8   HANDLING DATA

Page 98   Looking Back

1a 61 g **b** 60–64 g **2b** (i) 61 g (ii) about $67 - 54 \text{ g} = 13 \text{ g}$
3a (i) 0.2 (ii) 0.45 **b** 364
4a (i) 144 (ii) 36 **b** $\frac{5}{6}$ **c** about 4
5a Rows: (10, 10), ..., (10, A); (J, 10), ..., (J, A);
(Q, 10), ..., (Q, A); (K, 10), ..., (K, A); (A, 10), ..., (A, A)
b (i) $\frac{1}{25}$ (ii) $\frac{1}{5}$ (iii) $\frac{9}{25}$
6a Outcomes: (H, H, H), (H, H, T), (H, T, H), (H, T, T), (T, H, H),
(T, H, T), (T, T, H), (T, T, T,) **b** 8 **c** (i) $\frac{1}{8}$ (ii) $\frac{1}{2}$ (iii) $\frac{1}{2}$

Page 99   Exercise 1A

1c $20 \leqslant t < 30$ **d** 28 seconds **2b** 81–85 **c** 81
3b Probably Tireless Tyres—mean 30 000 km against 29 500
for Tough Tyres **4a** 200 **c** about $85 - 52 = 33$ for A,
$92 - 24 = 68$ for B **d** A is more consistent (smaller range), but
B often gives a taller crop

Page 101   Exercise 1B

1a 1.2, 1.4, 0.8, 0.5, 0.2, 0.1
2a 2, 4; 3, 6; 7, 7; 9, 9; 10, 10; 5, 10; 1, 6 **c** 26
3a 6, 15, 22, 48, 65, 52, 15, 3

4a

20–39	40–49	50–54	55–59	60–64	65–79	80–100
16	22	20	16	13	27	12

b 88

Page 102   Exercise 2

1b a (iii) should have 3 girls and 2 boys **2** Perhaps test
every 50th fuse **3** 1 manager, 3 clerical, 8 production
4 5, 4, 6, 6, 7 (round down to make 30), 2 respectively
5a Marks **b** possibly arrange in order of mark, highest first,
and select every fourth one, giving:

Mark	30	27	22	19	17	12	8
Student	08	03	11 or 20	10, 19 or 24	16	17 or 22	12

Page 104   Exercise 3

1a (i) 0.3 (ii) 0.7 **b** (i) 3600 (ii) 8400
2a 3, 4, 4, 5; 4, 5, 5, 6; 4, 5, 5, 6; 5, 6, 6, 7; 6, 7, 7, 8 **b** (i) $\frac{1}{5}$
(ii) $\frac{1}{2}$ (iii) $\frac{3}{4}$ **c** 100 **3a** (i) 0.55 (ii) 0.45 **b** 22 or 23
4b (i) $\frac{1}{4}$ (ii) $\frac{1}{8}$ (iii) $\frac{1}{4}$

Page 105   Exercise 4A

1a H, H; H, T; T, H; T, T **b** (i) $\frac{1}{2}$ (ii) $\frac{1}{2}$ (iii) $\frac{1}{4}$
2a (1, 1), ..., (1, 6); (2, 1), ..., (2, 6); (3, 1), ..., (3, 6);
(4, 1), ..., (4, 6); (5, 1), ..., (5, 6); (6, 1), ..., (6, 6) **b** (i) $\frac{1}{6}$
(ii) $\frac{1}{6}$ (iii) $\frac{1}{36}$ **3a** (H, 1), ..., (H, 6); (T, 1), ..., (T, 6) **b** (i) $\frac{1}{2}$
(ii) $\frac{1}{6}$ (iii) $\frac{1}{12}$ (iv) $P(H, 6) = P(H) \times P(6)$
4a 0.52 **b** (i) 0.23 (ii) 0.50 **5a** (i) 0.1 (ii) 0.9 **b** 0.59
6 0.512 **7a** $\frac{1}{6}$ **b** $\frac{1}{36}$ **c** $\frac{5}{36}$ **8a** 0.9 **b** 0.35
9a $\frac{1}{20}$ **b** $\frac{1}{10}$ **c** 0 **10a** $\frac{3}{8}$ **b** $\frac{3}{20}$ **c** $\frac{21}{40}$

Page 106   Exercise 4B

1a Outcomes: (H, H, H), (H, H, T), (H, T, H), (H, T, T), (T, H, H),
(T, H, T), (T, T, H), (T, T, T) **b** (i) $\frac{1}{2}$ (ii) $\frac{1}{8}$ **c** $\frac{1}{2} \times \frac{1}{2} \times \frac{1}{2} = \frac{1}{8}$
d (i) $\frac{1}{8}$ (ii) $\frac{1}{8}$ **2a** Outcomes: (W, W), (W, L), (L, W), (L, L)
b (i) $\frac{1}{9}$ (ii) $\frac{2}{9}$ (iii) $\frac{2}{9}$ (iv) $\frac{4}{9}$
3a Outcomes: (R, R), (R, B), (B, R), (B, B) **b** (i) 0.16 (ii) 0.24
(iii) 0.24 (iv) 0.36 **c** the bead was replaced **d** 0.48
4a

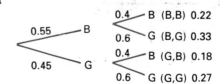

b (i) 0.27 (ii) 0.22 (iii) 0.51
5a (i) 0.08 (ii) 0.1 (iii) 0.05
b

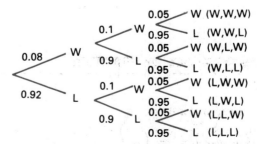

c (i) 0.0004 (ii) 0.0158 (iii) 0.1972

Page 108 Exercise 5

1a
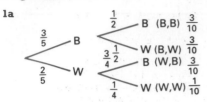

b (i) $\frac{3}{10}$ (ii) $\frac{1}{10}$ (iii) $\frac{2}{5}$ (iv) $\frac{3}{5}$
2a $\frac{1}{2}$ b (i) 9 (ii) 4 c $\frac{4}{9}$ d
e $\frac{2}{9}$

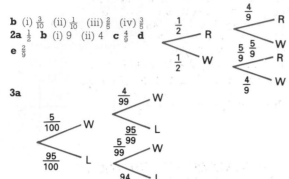

3a

b (i) $\frac{20}{9900} = 0.002$ (ii) $\frac{5 \times 95}{9900} + \frac{95 \times 5}{9900} = 0.096$

(iii) $\frac{95 \times 94}{9900} = 0.902$

4a
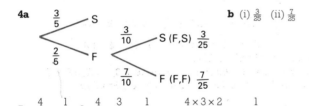
b (i) $\frac{3}{25}$ (ii) $\frac{7}{25}$

5a $\frac{4}{52} = \frac{1}{13}$ b $\frac{4}{52} \times \frac{3}{51} = \frac{1}{221}$ c $\frac{4 \times 3 \times 2}{52 \times 51 \times 50} = \frac{1}{5525}$

d $\frac{4 \times 3 \times 2 \times 1}{52 \times 51 \times 50 \times 49} = \frac{1}{270\,725}$ e 0

Page 110 Check-up on Handling Data

1a Column heights: 15, 38, 52, 37, 32, 24, 8 b 78
2 17, 10, 13, 53, 7 3b 120p
4a 0.000 000 01, or 10^{-8} b to avoid the area!

5a
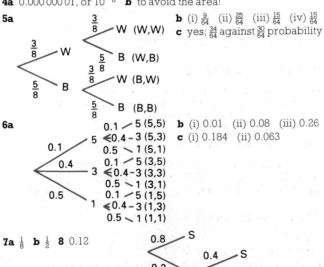
b (i) $\frac{9}{64}$ (ii) $\frac{25}{64}$ (iii) $\frac{15}{64}$ (iv) $\frac{15}{64}$
c yes; $\frac{34}{64}$ against $\frac{30}{64}$ probability

6a
b (i) 0.01 (ii) 0.08 (iii) 0.26
c (i) 0.184 (ii) 0.063

7a $\frac{1}{8}$ b $\frac{1}{2}$ 8 0.12

9 INDICES AND SURDS

Page 111 Looking Back

1a 1 b -1 c -3 d 1 e 3 f -1 2a a^2 b b^3 c $5c^4$
3 1, $\frac{1}{10}$ (or 0.1), $\frac{1}{100}$ (or 0.01) 4a 1 b 1 c $1\frac{1}{3}$ d $-\frac{1}{2}$
5a 9 b 3 6a 3×10^5 b 7×10^{-3} c 1.8×10^3
7a -10 b -3 c 6 d 0 8a 3 b -2 c $1\frac{1}{2}$
9a 32 b 1024 c 1.1×10^{15} 10a 1 b -1 c 2 d -3
11a 6 cm b 27 cm² 12a 5, $\frac{1}{3}$, 7, $\frac{3}{4}$, 10 b $-3, -\frac{1}{2}, -1, -\frac{2}{5}$
c $-\frac{1}{2}, -\frac{2}{5}$ 13a $V = e^3$ b $A = 6e^2$ 14 670; 459
15 $4 = 2^2, 9 = 3^2, 16 = 4^2, 25 = 5^2, 36 = 6^2, 49 = 7^2$
16a 8 b $\frac{1}{2}$ 17a $6x + 3$ b $x^2 - 2xy + y^2$ c $ac + ad + bc + bd$
18 $a + 3b = 5, a + b = 3; a = 2, b = 1, f(t) = 2 + t$

Page 112 Exercise 1

1a 6561 b 6561 2a (i) 1000 (ii) 1000 b (i) 243 (ii) 243
c (i) 5 764 801 (ii) 5 764 801
3a 2^4 b 5^3 c 6^5 d a^2 e b^3 f c^5 4a $3 \times 3 \times 3 \times 3$
b 9×9 c $10 \times 10 \times 10$ d $2 \times 2 \times 2 \times 2 \times 2$ e $a \times a \times a$
f $c \times c$ g $k \times k \times k \times k$ h $n \times n \times n \times n \times n$
5a $2 \times 2 \times 2 \times 2 \times 2 = 2^5$ (ii) $3 \times 3 \times 3 \times 3 \times 3 \times 3 = 3^6$
(iii) $a \times a \times a \times a \times a \times a = a^6$ (iv) $b \times b \times b \times b \times b = b^5$
b add the indices 7b 10^7
8a t^5 b y^8 c n^7 d p^6 e x^5 f y^{12} g z^6 h k^8 9a 2^5
b 3^8 c 9^7 d 10^9 e a^7 f b^{12} g c^9 h d^5 10a 10^5
b 10^8 c 10^5 d 10^{10} 11a 3×10^6 b 8×10^8 c 7.5×10^5
12a 2.1×10^9 b 9.5×10^{13} c 7.9×10^{20} d 5.2×10^{47}

Page 113 Exercise 2

1a (i) 2^2 (ii) 3^5 (iii) a^2 (iv) b b subtract indices
3a 2^4 b 2^2 c 2^2 d 2^3 4a t^2 b u^3 c v^5 d w^8 e p
f k^4 g c^2 h d 5a m^4 b n c a d c^3 e v^5
6a 3^2 b 7^3 c 9^4 d 10^3 e x^2 f y^4 g z^3 h n^6

Page 113 Exercise 3

1a (i) 2^8 (ii) 5^6 (iii) a^{12} b multiply the indices
3a 3^8 b 3^{10} c 3^9 d 3^{40} e 3^{36}
4a p^6 b q^8 c r^{10} d s^6 e t^{30} 5a 2^{12} b 7^{15} c 8^{20}
d 10^{12} e 3^{81} f u^{14} g v^{14} h w^{18} i m^{25} j n^{56}
6a T b F c T d F e T f T g T h T i T j T
7a a^2b^2 b m^3n^3 8a a^4b^4 b c^5d^5 c $x^{10}y^{10}$ d $p^{20}q^{20}$

Page 114 Exercise 4B

1a n^5 b p^8 c t^4 d u^7 e k^3 f s g v^2 h w i a^6 j b^8
k c^{10} l d^{12} 2a $2a^5$ b $3x^6$ c $6y^4$ d $4x$ e $5y$ f $2z^2$
3a 5×10^3 b 2.3×10^5 c 1.47×10^6 d 1.2×10^7
e 3.5×10^{10} 4a $x^5 + x^7$ b $y^5 - y^3$ c $z^6 - z^2$ 5a u^8v^8 b $8x^3$
c $81y^4$ d m^5n^{10} 6a 2^6 b 2^4 c 5^5 d 5^7 7a x^5 b y^6
c z^7 d t^5 8a 3 b 4 c 1 d 4 9a $x + 3 = 8, x = 5$
b $x + 4 = 7, x = 3$ c $3 + x = 6, x = 3$ 10 3.09×10^{13}
11a $100\% \to 108\% = 1.08$, so 100 bacteria $\to 100 \times 1.08$
b (i) 108 (ii) 116 (iii) 125 c 9

Page 115 Exercise 5A

2a 0.5 b 0.25 c 0.1 d 0.01
3a $10^0, 10^{-1}, 10^{-2}, 10^{-3}; \frac{1}{100}, \frac{1}{1000}$ b $1, \frac{1}{10}, \frac{1}{100}, \frac{1}{1000}$
4a 1 b 1 c 1 d 1 e 1 5a $\frac{1}{x^2}$ b $\frac{1}{y^3}$ c $\frac{1}{z^4}$ d $\frac{1}{u^6}$ e $\frac{1}{v}$
6a $\frac{1}{9}$ b $\frac{1}{3^2}$ c $\frac{1}{5^2}$ d $\frac{1}{2^3}$ e $\frac{1}{10^2}$ 7a a b t^2 c m^{-2}
d $n^0 = 1$ e x^3 f y^6 g t^{-6} h $t^0 = 1$ i u^{-6} j v^{-4} k w^4

1 $k^0 = 1$ **8a** 2^{-2} **b** 5^0 **c** 3^{-1} **9a** 1 **b** 3 **c** 8 **d** 1 **e** 5
f $\frac{1}{4}$ **g** 1 **h** 16 **10a** 8 **b** 1 **c** $\frac{1}{4}$ **d** 2 **e** $\frac{1}{2}$

Page 115 Exercise 5B

1a 2.5×10^{-3} **b** 3×10^{-2} **c** 1.9×10^{-6} **d** 3.14×10^{-3}
e 9×10^{-4} **2a** $\frac{1}{p^2}$ **b** $\frac{1}{q}$ **c** 1 **d** $\frac{1}{s^{10}}$ **e** t^6 **f** $\frac{1}{t^2}$ **g** $\frac{1}{t^6}$ **h** 1
i $\frac{1}{u^3}$ **j** $\frac{1}{v^8}$ **k** w^{25} **l** $\frac{1}{x^{10}}$ **3a** $\frac{3}{x}$ **b** $\frac{5}{y^3}$ **c** $\frac{8}{m^2}$ **d** $\frac{10}{t}$ **e** $\frac{1}{2x}$
f $\frac{1}{3t^2}$ **g** $\frac{3}{4u^3}$ **h** $\frac{2}{3v^4}$ **4a** $y^6 + y^2$ **b** $k^4 - k^2$ **c** $n + n^{-1}$
d $1 + m$ **e** $u^3 - u^{-1}$ **f** $v^{-2} - 1$ **5** $3.825 \times 10^9 \, \text{m}^2$
6a $5.5 \times 10^{-10} \text{g}$ **b** 1.2×10^{75}

Page 116 Exercise 6A

1a $\sqrt[4]{m^3}$ **b** $\sqrt[5]{n^4}$ **c** $\sqrt[3]{k^2}$ **d** $\sqrt{x}$ **e** $\sqrt[3]{y}$
2a $y^{5/3}$ **b** $z^{4/3}$ **c** $y^{2/3}$ **d** $t^{1/3}$ **e** $u^{1/2}$ **4a** 2^2 **b** 3^2 **c** 5^2
d 2^3 **e** 2^4 **f** 3^3 **g** 2^5 **h** 5^3 **i** 2^6 **j** 3^5
5a 3 **b** 2 **c** 10 **d** 5 **e** 9 **f** 2 **g** 3 **h** 4 **i** 10 **6a** 4
b 9 **c** 8 **d** 125 **7a** (i) 1000 (ii) 27 **8a** $16^{1/2}$ **b** $27^{1/3}$
9a 9 **b** 7 **10a** 3.5 cm **b** 2.7 cm **11a** 5 **b** 1 **c** 125

Page 117 Exercise 6B

1a u^2 **b** v **c** 1 **d** x **e** $y^{1/2}$ **f** y **g** t **h** p^{-1} **i** 1 **j** r
2a $x + 1$ **b** $y^2 - y$ **c** $m - m^{-1}$ **d** $n - n^{-1}$
3a 2 **b** $\frac{1}{3}$ **c** 1 **d** $\frac{1}{2}$ **4** 3 **5a** 1 **b** b^5 **c** c
6a x^{-3} **b** 1 **c** z **7a** $a^2 + a^{-2} + 2$ **b** $b^{-2} - 1$
8a $x + 2x^{1/2} + 1$ **b** $y - 1$ **c** $u^{1/2} + u^{-1/2} + 2$ **d** $v^{-1/2} - v^{1/2}$

Page 118 Exercise 7

1a 0.13, 0.25, 0.5, 1, 2, 4, 8 **2a** 8, 4, 2, 1, 0.5, 0.25, 0.13
c the y-axis **d** (i) $y = 2^x$ (ii) $y = 2^{-x}$
3a 1, 3.2, 10, 31.6, 100 **c** (i) 16 (ii) 1.6 **4b** (i) 11 (ii) 28
5a 1, 0.61, 0.37, 0.22, 0.14 **6a** $a = 320$, $b = 1.025$ **b** 410 000
7a $a = 100$, $b = 2.5$; $N(t) = 100 \times 2.5^t$
b 6 000 000 (nearest million)

Page 121 Exercise 8A

1 b, c, e, g, i, l, n **3a** 4 **b** 10 **c** 5 **d** 1 **e** 9
4a $2\sqrt{3}$ **b** $2\sqrt{5}$ **c** $3\sqrt{2}$ **d** $3\sqrt{3}$ **e** $2\sqrt{2}$ **f** $2\sqrt{6}$ **g** $2\sqrt{7}$
h $4\sqrt{2}$ **i** $3\sqrt{5}$ **j** $4\sqrt{3}$ **k** $2\sqrt{11}$ **l** $3\sqrt{7}$ **m** $5\sqrt{2}$ **n** $3\sqrt{6}$
o $10\sqrt{2}$ **5a** $2\sqrt{2}$ **b** $2\sqrt{13}$ **c** $4\sqrt{5}$ **6a** $7\sqrt{2}$ **b** $2\sqrt{2}$
c $8\sqrt{3}$ **d** $4\sqrt{3}$ **e** $2\sqrt{5}$ **f** 0 **g** $10\sqrt{2}$ **h** $\sqrt{3}$ **i** $6\sqrt{3}$
7a $8\sqrt{2}$ cm **b** $4\sqrt{10}$ cm **c** $8 + 4\sqrt{2}$ cm

Page 122 Exercise 8B

1a $10\sqrt{2}$ cm **b** $10\sqrt{3}$ cm **2a** $3\sqrt{2}$ **b** $4\sqrt{2}$ **c** 0 **d** $2\sqrt{3}$
e $\sqrt{5}$ **f** $5\sqrt{7}$ **3a** 2 **b** 6 **c** 10 **d** 6 **e** 9 **f** $2\sqrt{5}$ **g** $3\sqrt{5}$
h $5\sqrt{2}$ **i** $5\sqrt{3}$ **4a** $2\sqrt{5}, 2\sqrt{6}$ **b** (i) $2\sqrt{7}$ (ii) $2\sqrt{8}$
(iii) $2\sqrt{(n+4)}$ **5a** $8 + 5\sqrt{2}$ **b** $4 + \sqrt{2}$ **c** 2 **d** $5 - 2\sqrt{6}$
6a (i) $2\sqrt{3}$ (ii) 2 (iii) 2 **b** (i) 2 (ii) $2\sqrt{2}$ (iii) -1
c (i) $\sqrt{2}$ (ii) $2\sqrt{3} - \sqrt{2}$ (iii) $\sqrt{6} - 3$ **d** (i) $\sqrt{5}$ (ii) $\sqrt{5} - 2\sqrt{2}$
(iii) $\sqrt{10} - 2$; **a** (ii), (iii); **b** (i), (iii)
7a $PU = 2\sqrt{10}$, $QV = 2\sqrt{5}$, $PR = 2\sqrt{13}$ **b** $PV = 2\sqrt{14}$
8a $\frac{\sqrt{6}}{6}$ **b** $\frac{\sqrt{7}}{7}$ **c** $\frac{\sqrt{6}}{3}$ **d** $\sqrt{3}$ **e** $\frac{\sqrt{10}}{2}$ **f** $\frac{\sqrt{11}}{11}$ **g** $2\sqrt{2}$
h $4\sqrt{5}$ **i** $2\sqrt{3}$ **j** $2\sqrt{6}$ **9a** $2 - \sqrt{3}$ **b** $\frac{\sqrt{5}+1}{4}$ **c** $\sqrt{2} - 1$
d $\frac{2 - \sqrt{2}}{2}$ **e** $\sqrt{2} + 1$ **f** $\frac{\sqrt{3}-1}{2}$ **g** $\sqrt{5} + 1$

Page 123 Check-up on Indices and Surds

1a a^5 **b** a **c** a^6 **d** 1 **2a** b^2 **b** b^4 **c** b^{-3} **d** b^3
3a $\frac{1}{u}$ **b** $\frac{1}{v^2}$ **c** $\frac{1}{w^3}$ **d** $\frac{2}{x}$ **4a** $5^{1/2}$ **b** $x^{1/2}$ **c** $p^{1/3}$ **d** $p^{2/3}$
5a x^2 **b** $y^{1/3}$ **c** z^3 **6a** 2 **b** 3 **c** 27 **d** $\frac{1}{5}$ **e** $\frac{1}{4}$
7a x^{10} **b** x^2 **c** x^2 **d** x **8a** 5 **b** 19 **c** $\frac{5}{6}$ **d** 6
9 $2 \to \frac{1}{2} \to 2 \to \frac{1}{4} \to \frac{1}{2} \to 8 \to 2 \to 3 \to 9 \to \frac{1}{9} \to \frac{1}{3} \to 9 \to 3 \to 36 \to \frac{1}{6}$
10a 1.2×10^5 **b** 7.5×10^{-3} **c** 6×10^{12} **d** 2×10^{-4}
11a 1 **b** $\frac{1}{8}$ **c** 2 **d** 4 **12a** 3 **b** 0 **c** -1 **d** -3
13a $x^5 + x^6$ **b** $y^6 + y^{-3}$ **c** $z - 1$ **14b** (i) (0, 1) (ii) $x = 0$
15a $a = 10$, $b = 2$; $N(t) = 10 \times 2^t$ **b** 1300
16 $\sqrt{2}, \sqrt{3}, \sqrt{5}, \sqrt{6}, \sqrt{7}, \sqrt{8}, \sqrt{10}$
17a 10 **b** $10\sqrt{3}$ **c** $2\sqrt{5}$ **d** $4\sqrt{5}$ **e** $5\sqrt{6}$
18a $5\sqrt{3}$ **b** $3\sqrt{7}$ **c** $\sqrt{2}$ **19a** $3\sqrt{2}$ **b** $3\sqrt{5}$ **c** $\sqrt{65}$
20a $\frac{\sqrt{5}}{5}$ **b** $\frac{\sqrt{6}}{3}$ **c** $2\sqrt{2}$ **d** $3\sqrt{3}$ **e** $\frac{\sqrt{10}}{4}$

10 TRIGONOMETRY – TRIANGLE CALCULATIONS

Page 124 Looking Back

1a $\sin A = \frac{3}{5}$, $\cos A = \frac{4}{5}$, $\tan A = \frac{3}{4}$
b $\sin A = \frac{5}{13}$, $\cos A = \frac{12}{13}$, $\tan A = \frac{5}{12}$ **2a** 5.8 **b** 26.4
3 080°, 125°, 250° **4** 14 m **5a** 110° **b** 290° **6** 14.6°
7a 24 cm² **b** 45 cm² **c** 20 cm²
8 Rows: 50°, 134°, 30°, 60°; 0.8, 0.7, 0.5, 0.9; 0.6, -0.7, 0.9, 0.5
9a 84.3° **b** 101.5° **c** 53.1°, 126.9° **10** 1050 km, 099°
11a $x = ab$ **b** $x = \frac{ab}{c}$ **c** $x = d \sin A$
d $x = \frac{a}{b}$ **e** $x = \frac{ac}{b}$ **f** $x = \frac{d}{\sin A}$

Page 126 Exercise 1

1a $\frac{a}{\sin 60°} = \frac{5}{\sin 40°}$ **b** $\frac{a}{\sin 45°} = \frac{14}{\sin 70°}$ **c** $\frac{b}{\sin 25°} = \frac{15}{\sin 100°}$
d $\frac{c}{\sin 60°} = \frac{9}{\sin 52°}$ **2a** 8.8 **b** 26.8 **c** 8.0 **d** 12.0
3a 65° **b** 8.3 **4a** 40° **b** 10.3 **5b** (i) 315 m (ii) 406 m
6a 40 m **b** 58 m **7a** 954 m **b** 956 m

Page 127 Exercise 2

1a 46.4° **b** 77.2° **2a** $\angle Q = 50.6°$, $\angle R = 54.4°$
b $\angle X = 36.1°$, $\angle Y = 25.9°$ **3a** 47.9° **b** 23.8° **4** 65.4°
5b (i) 51.7° (ii) 46.7 cm (iii) 41.8°

Page 128 Exercise 3B

1 185.8 m **2b** $\angle C = 90.3°$ **3a** 197 m **b** 98.5 m
4a (i) 50° (ii) 62° (iii) 112° **b** 47.9° **c** 097.9°
5a 2.5 km **b** 1.6 km **6a** 34.3° **b** 37.7° **c** 8.0 m **7b** 046.2°

Page 131 Exercise 4

1 $a^2 = b^2 + c^2 - 2bc \cos A = 4^2 + 7^2 - 2 \times 4 \times 7 \times \cos 100° = 74.7$;
$a = 8.6$ **2a** 3.6 **b** 3.8 **c** 17 **d** 29.3
3a (i) $p^2 = q^2 + r^2 - 2qr \cos P$ (ii) $q^2 = r^2 + p^2 - 2rp \cos Q$
(iii) $r^2 = p^2 + q^2 - 2pq \cos R$ **b** (i) $p = 7.4$ (ii) $r = 8.3$
c $p^2 = q^2 + r^2$ **4** 146.4 m **5** 32.8 cm **6a** 8.9 **b** 7.2 **c** 6

Page 132　Exercise 5

1 $\cos A = \dfrac{b^2+c^2-a^2}{2bc}$, $\cos B = \dfrac{c^2+a^2-b^2}{2ca}$, $\cos C = \dfrac{a^2+b^2-c^2}{2ab}$

2a 41.4°　**b** 52.4°　**c** 50.7°

3a $\cos P = \dfrac{q^2+r^2-p^2}{2qr}$, $\cos Q = \dfrac{r^2+p^2-q^2}{2rp}$,

$\cos R = \dfrac{p^2+q^2-r^2}{2pq}$　**b** (i) $\angle Q = 82.8°$　(ii) $\angle P = 41.4°$

4a $\angle A = 70.6°$, $\angle B = 33.7°$, $\angle C = 75.7°$　**b** 31.3°

5a 69.5°　**b** 120°　**6** $\angle X = 24.5°$, $\angle Z = 125.9°$

7a 101.5°, 101.5°, 78.5°, 78.5°　**b** 7 m

Page 133　Exercise 6B

1 9.2 cm, 15.6 cm　**2a** 13 700 miles　**b** 19 500 miles

3b 128.6°　**4a** $\angle HLB = \angle LBN$ (alternate) $= 110°(360° - 250°)$

b 56.4 km　**5a** 295 m　**b** 211.2°

Page 135　Exercise 7

1a 12 cm²　**b** 12.7 m²　**c** 126.3 mm²　**d** 99 cm²　**2a** 51.2 m²

b 278.7 m²　**3a** 97.1 cm²　**b** 12 cm²　**4a** 5.3 cm²　**b** 4.6 m²

5 141 cm²　**6** 32.6 m²　**7a** 53.1°, 126.9°　**8a** 120°　**b** 73.2 cm²

c 219.6 cm²　**d** 311.3 cm²　**9** 4570 m²　**10** 23 471.5 cm²

Page 137　Exercise 8A

1a Cosine Rule　**b** Sine Rule　**c** Sine Rule　**d** Cosine Rule

2 7.8 cm　**3** 9.5 m　**4** 61.6°　**5a** 8.9 m　**b** 28.8 cm²

6 22.3°, 27.1°, 130.5°　**7a** 28.5 m　**b** 20.2 m　**8a** 498.2 m

b 1060.8 m　**9** 14.2　**10a** 44.4　**b** 38.2　**c** 5.6　**d** 11.3

Page 138　Exercise 8B

1a 114.3 m　**b** 7577.5 m²　**2** 684.8 km, 092.4°　**3** 27 m²

4a 13.5 m　**b** 11.3 m　**c** 22 m　**5a** 28.4 km　**b** 107.8°

6a 45 cm　**b** 36.9°

Page 139　Check-up on Trigonometry— Triangle Calculations

1a $\dfrac{a}{\sin A} = \dfrac{b}{\sin B} = \dfrac{c}{\sin C}$　**b** $a^2 = b^2 + c^2 - 2bc \cos A$

c $\cos B = \dfrac{c^2+a^2-b^2}{2ca}$　**d** area $= \frac{1}{2}ab \sin C$

2a Sine Rule　**b** Cosine Rule　**c** Sine Rule　**d** Sine Rule

e Cosine Rule　**f** Pythagoras' Theorem or the Cosine Rule

3a 7.4　**b** 6.8　**e** 81.8　**4** 92.5 m, 78.6 m

5a 101.5°　**b** 9.8 m²　**6a** 28.5°　**b** 25.8 km　**7** 263.4°, 96.4 km

8b (i) $\angle B = 44.4°$, $\angle C = 57.1°$　(ii) BI = 4.3 cm

(iii) IK = 1.6 cm

11　FRACTIONS AND EQUATIONS

Page 140　Looking Back

1a -4　**b** $4\frac{1}{2}$　**c** 6　**d** -4　**e** 2　**2a** $5x+10$　**b** $2y-1$

c $16-2z$　**3a** $3(x-4)$　**b** $y(y-2)$　**c** $(u-v)(u+v)$

d $(1-2x)(1+2x)$　**e** $(m+4)^2$　**f** $(y-7)(y+2)$

g $(2t-1)(t+3)$　**4a** (i) 3　(ii) 4　**b** $\frac{4}{3}$　**5a** 12　**b** 10　**c** xy

d $6xy$　**6a** (i) $\frac{1}{3}$　(ii) $\frac{1}{2}$　(iii) $\frac{3}{4}$　(iv) $\frac{3}{4}$　**b** (i) $\frac{1}{3}$　(ii) $\frac{1}{4}$　(iii) 3

7a 1 m², 5 m　**b** $1\frac{1}{2}$ m², 6 m　**8** $\dfrac{d}{3}$ km/h　**9a** $u = P - v - w$

b $h = \dfrac{V}{A}$　**c** $x = \dfrac{P}{4}$, $x = \sqrt{A}$　**d** $d = \dfrac{C}{\pi}$, $r = \sqrt{\dfrac{A}{\pi}}$　**e** $T = \dfrac{D}{S}$

f $C \doteqdot \dfrac{F-30}{2}$　**10a** -1　**b** 7　**c** -1　**d** 0

Page 141　Exercise 1A

1a $\dfrac{4}{5}$　**b** $\dfrac{1}{3}$　**c** $\dfrac{2}{3}$　**d** $\dfrac{2}{3}$　**e** $\dfrac{1}{2}$　**2a** $\dfrac{3}{4}$　**b** $\dfrac{2}{3}$　**c** $\dfrac{b}{c}$　**d** $\dfrac{u}{a}$

3a $\dfrac{a}{b}$　**b** $\dfrac{x}{y}$　**c** $\dfrac{1}{q}$　**d** $\dfrac{1}{y}$　**4a** $\dfrac{x}{3}$　**b** $\dfrac{2}{y}$　**c** z　**d** $\dfrac{1}{t}$　**e** $\dfrac{2a}{3}$

5a $\dfrac{x}{2y}$　**b** $3y$　**c** $\dfrac{a}{2b}$　**d** $\dfrac{c}{2}$　**e** $\dfrac{1}{k}$　**6a** b　**b** $\dfrac{3}{5}$　**c** $\dfrac{5}{2b}$　**d** $\dfrac{3u}{v}$

7a $2(x+2)$　**b** $3(y-2)$　**c** $5(p+1)$　**d** $7(t-1)$

8a $a(a+2)$　**b** $k(k-3)$　**c** $2(n^2+1)$　**d** $3(m^2-2)$　**9a** $x(x+y)$

b $v(u-v)$　**c** $y(y-3)$　**d** $z(5-z)$

10a $\dfrac{x-2}{3}$　**b** $\dfrac{u+v}{2}$　**11a** $\dfrac{m+3}{2}$　**b** $\dfrac{n+2}{3}$　**c** $p-2$　**d** $\dfrac{n-2}{3}$

12a $\dfrac{1}{x+2}$　**b** $\dfrac{1}{t-2}$　**c** $\dfrac{2}{u+3}$　**d** $\dfrac{2}{v-1}$

13a $x+y$　**b** $y-1$　**c** $m+1$　**d** $1-n$

14a $\dfrac{2}{x}$　**b** 5　**c** $x+y$　**d** $\dfrac{1}{x+y}$　**e** $\dfrac{1}{a-b}$　**f** $\dfrac{t-1}{t-3}$

15a 2　**b** 3　**c** $\dfrac{1}{2}$　**d** d　**16a** $\dfrac{2}{3}$　**b** $\dfrac{5}{2}$　**c** 2　**d** $\dfrac{m}{5}$

Page 142　Exercise 1B

1a $x(x+4)$　**b** $(y-2)(y+2)$　**c** $(n+2)(n+4)$　**d** $5(2x-5)$

e $(3-a)(3+a)$　**f** $(x-5)^2$　**g** $(y-4)(y+3)$

h $2(m-4)(m+4)$　**i** $2(p+1)^2$

2a $\dfrac{1}{x+3}$　**b** $\dfrac{1}{a+1}$　**c** $\dfrac{b-4}{b+4}$　**3a** $x+1$　**b** $x+1$　**c** $\dfrac{1}{m-3}$

4a $\dfrac{1}{3}$　**b** $\dfrac{1}{x}$　**c** $\dfrac{1}{x+1}$　**5a** $\dfrac{1}{4}$　**b** $\dfrac{1}{y-4}$　**c** $\dfrac{1}{y+2}$

6a $\dfrac{2}{b-5}$　**b** $1+x$　**c** $\dfrac{a+3}{a}$　**7a** $\dfrac{1}{3(u-2)}$　**b** $\dfrac{v+1}{v-4}$　**c** $\dfrac{2(p+q)}{p-q}$

8a $\dfrac{x+1}{2}$　**b** $\dfrac{y-2}{3}$　**c** $z+5$　**9a** $\dfrac{1}{d}$　**b** $\dfrac{1}{c+1}$　**c** 1　**10a** $\dfrac{c+3}{c-2}$

b $\dfrac{d+8}{d-1}$　**c** $\dfrac{n+k}{a}$　**11a** $1+x^2$　**b** $y-1$　**c** $\dfrac{(x+y)(x^2+y^2)}{x-y}$

Page 142　Exercise 2

1a $\dfrac{1}{4}$　**b** $\dfrac{1}{6}$　**c** $\dfrac{1}{3}$　**d** 1　**2a** $\dfrac{3}{2}$　**b** 4　**c** 2　**d** 2　**3a** $\dfrac{mp}{nq}$　**b** $\dfrac{xs}{yt}$

c $\dfrac{a^2}{b^2}$　**d** 1　**4a** $\dfrac{x^2}{6}$　**b** $\dfrac{y^2}{5}$　**c** $\dfrac{z^2}{16}$　**d** 1　**5a** $\dfrac{k}{n}$　**b** a　**c** a　**d** u^2

6a $\dfrac{x^2}{4}$ cm²　**b** $\dfrac{y^2}{5}$ cm²　**c** $\dfrac{x^2}{3}$ cm²　**d** $\dfrac{x^2}{2}$ cm²

7a $\dfrac{1}{2}$　**b** $\dfrac{1}{4}$　**c** $\dfrac{1}{4}$　**d** $\dfrac{1}{4}$　**8a** $\dfrac{3}{4}$　**b** $\dfrac{1}{2}$　**c** 2　**d** $\dfrac{1}{4}$

9a b　**b** $\dfrac{x}{2}$　**c** $\dfrac{y^2}{2}$　**d** $\dfrac{c^2}{2}$　**10a** 1　**b** ac　**c** $\dfrac{1}{2t}$　**d** $\dfrac{1}{u}$

11a $\dfrac{a}{2}$　**b** x　**c** $\dfrac{2x}{y}$　**d** $\dfrac{2}{3}$　**12a** $\dfrac{x}{2}$ cm　**b** $\dfrac{a}{b}$ cm

13 Rows: **a** $\dfrac{a^2}{b^2}, \dfrac{ac}{bd}, \dfrac{ac}{bd}, \dfrac{c^2}{d^2}$　**b** $1, \dfrac{ad}{bc}, \dfrac{bc}{ad}, 1$

Page 144   Exercise 3A

1a 6   **b** 20   **c** 8   **d** 24   **e** xy **f** mn **g** x^2 **h** $12xy$

2a $12, \frac{11}{12}$ **b** $12, \frac{5}{12}$ **c** $15, \frac{8}{15}$ **d** $10, \frac{3}{10}$ **e** $6, \frac{1}{3}$ **f** $6, \frac{1}{2}$

g $8, \frac{3}{8}$ **h** $10, \frac{1}{10}$ **3a** $\frac{3x+2y}{6}$ **b** $\frac{4u-3v}{10}$

4a $\frac{2x+5y}{10}$ **b** $\frac{2a-3b}{6}$ **c** $\frac{3c+4d}{12}$ **d** $\frac{4m-5n}{20}$ **e** $\frac{4u+3v}{6}$

f $\frac{2u-3v}{4}$ **g** $\frac{4s+5t}{10}$ **h** $\frac{4a-6b}{12}$ **5** $\frac{3y-4x}{xy}$

6a $\frac{5y+2x}{xy}$ **b** $\frac{4b-2a}{ab}$ **c** $\frac{3v+u}{uv}$ **d** $\frac{t-2s}{st}$ **e** $\frac{y+x}{xy}$ **f** $\frac{n-m}{mn}$

g $\frac{5d+c}{cd}$ **h** $\frac{q-4p}{pq}$ **7** $\frac{a^2-bc}{ab}$

8a $\frac{m^2+n^2}{mn}$ **b** $\frac{uy-vx}{vy}$ **c** $\frac{u^2+v^2}{uv}$ **d** $\frac{s^2-t^2}{ts}$

9 Rows: **a** $a+c, a+d; b+c, b+d$ **b** $\frac{c+a}{ac}, \frac{d+a}{ad}, \frac{c+b}{bc}, \frac{d+b}{bd}$

10 Rows: **a** $a-c, a-d; b-c, b-d$ **b** $\frac{c-a}{ac}, \frac{d-a}{ad}, \frac{c-b}{bc}, \frac{d-b}{bd}$

11 Rows: **a** $\frac{2a}{b}, \frac{ad+bc}{bd}, \frac{bc+ad}{bd}, \frac{2c}{d}$ **b** $0, \frac{ad-bc}{bd}, \frac{bc-ad}{bd}, 0$

Page 145   Exercise 3B

1 $\frac{6n-3-2n+2}{6} = \frac{4n-1}{6}$ **2a** $\frac{5x+1}{6}$ **b** $\frac{5a+5}{12}$ **c** $\frac{3v+5}{4}$

d $\frac{7w+11}{10}$ **e** $\frac{7x+13}{12}$ **f** $\frac{5y}{6}$

3a $\frac{x+5}{6}$ **b** $\frac{3y+7}{10}$ **c** $\frac{z-11}{12}$ **d** $\frac{4a+1}{4}$ **e** $\frac{7u-1}{20}$ **f** $\frac{3v-5}{6}$

4 $\frac{5x-15-2x-2}{(x+1)(x-3)} = \frac{3x-17}{(x+1)(x-3)}$

5a $\frac{5x+7}{(x+2)(x+1)}$ **b** $\frac{7x-11}{(x-1)(x-2)}$ **c** $\frac{3x}{(x+4)(x-2)}$

6a $\frac{2x-1}{(x+2)(x+1)}$ **b** $\frac{2x-6}{(x+1)(x-1)}$ **c** $\frac{-x+7}{(x-4)(x-1)}$

7a $\frac{5x-3}{x(x-1)}$ **b** $\frac{x-4}{x(x-2)}$ **c** $\frac{3x+3}{x(x-3)}$ **8** $\frac{1}{R} = \frac{2x+1}{(x+4)(x-3)}$

9 $\frac{1}{f} = \frac{2x-2}{x(x-2)}$ **10a** $\frac{2x-3}{x^2}$ **b** $\frac{2x-1}{x^2}$ **c** $\frac{4x-1}{x^2}$ **13** $\frac{1}{x-1}$

Page 147   Exercise 4A

1a 10   **b** 3   **c** 6   **d** 2   **2a** -6 **b** -5 **c** -1 **d** -2

3a 0   **b** $1\frac{1}{3}$ **c** -2 **4a** 3   **b** -1 **c** $1\frac{1}{3}$ **5a** $\frac{4}{5}$ **b** 3   **c** $-1\frac{1}{2}$

6a 10   **b** 1   **c** 5   **7a** 6   **b** $\frac{4}{3}$ **c** 0   **8a** -3 **b** $2\frac{1}{2}$ **c** -6

9a $a=-3$ **b** $2\frac{1}{2}$ **c** -6 **10a** 2   **b** $\frac{5}{6}$ **c** $3\frac{1}{2}$

Page 147   Exercise 4B

1a 3   **b** -12 **2a** $1\frac{2}{3}$ **b** 3   **3a** 2   **b** 8   **4a** $4\frac{1}{2}$ **b** 0

5a 8   **b** -7 **6a** 2,3   **b** $-3,2$ **c** $-5,2$ **7a** $-3,\frac{1}{2}$ **b** 2

c $-1\frac{1}{2},4$ **8a**   6,3   **b** $-1,6$ **c** $-\frac{1}{2},\frac{1}{2}$ **9** 1,4   **10a** 69°

b 195°

11a Time $= \dfrac{\text{distance}}{\text{speed}}$, so $\dfrac{d}{20}$ and $\dfrac{d}{25}$ are the times;

6 min $= \dfrac{1}{10}$ h   **b** 10 km   **12a** $\dfrac{d}{60}$ h, $\dfrac{d}{80}$ h   **b** $\dfrac{d}{60} - \dfrac{d}{80} = \dfrac{1}{2}$; 120 km

Page 149   Exercise 5A

1a $x=k+2$ **b** $x=q+p$ **c** $x=t-5$ **d** $x=n-m$

2a $x=2d$ **b** $x=cd$ **c** $x=\dfrac{b}{2}$ **d** $x=\dfrac{b}{a}$

3a $x=\dfrac{2a}{3}$ **b** $x=\dfrac{4c}{5}$ **c** $x=mn$ **d** $x=\dfrac{b}{2}$

4a $x=\dfrac{w-2}{3}$ **b** $x=\dfrac{g+h}{5}$ **c** $x=\dfrac{c-b}{a}$ **d** $x=\dfrac{q+r}{p}$

5a $x=\dfrac{2a+b}{2}$ **b** $x=\dfrac{3a+c}{a}$ **c** $x=\dfrac{c-ab}{a}$

6a $x=\dfrac{y+b}{a}$ **b** $x=\dfrac{u-q}{p}$ **c** $x=\dfrac{1-t}{c}$ **7a** $x=2(b-a)$

b $x=3(c+d)$ **c** $x=m(p+q)$ **8a** $h=\dfrac{3V}{a}$ **b** $E=IR, R=\dfrac{E}{I}$

9a $r=\dfrac{C}{2\pi}$ **b** $h=\dfrac{V}{lb}$ **10a** $x=\dfrac{P-2y}{2}$ **b** $a=P-b-c$

11a $h=\dfrac{V}{\pi r^2}, r=\sqrt{\dfrac{V}{\pi h}}$ **b** $x=\dfrac{y-c}{m}$ **12a** $S=\dfrac{D}{T}$

b $E=\sqrt{PR}, R=\dfrac{E^2}{P}$ **13a** $u=v-at, t=\dfrac{v-u}{a}$ **b** $t=\sqrt{\dfrac{2s}{g}}$

14a $x=\dfrac{4y-3}{3}$ **b** $F=\dfrac{9C+160}{5}$

Page 149   Exercise 5B

1a $x=\dfrac{a}{2}$ **b** $x=a+b$ **c** $x=q-p$ **d** $x=\dfrac{n}{m}$ **e** $x=\dfrac{n}{m+1}$

f $x=\dfrac{y}{c-d}$ **2a** $t=\dfrac{c}{a+b}$ **b** $t=\dfrac{r}{p-q}$ **c** $t=\dfrac{1}{u-v}$

d $t=\dfrac{m}{c+n}$ **e** $t=\dfrac{b}{a+1}$ **f** $t=\dfrac{d}{d-1}$

3a $y=\dfrac{c-ax}{b}$ **b** $y=\dfrac{c}{a+b}$ **c** $y=\dfrac{ax}{a-b}$ **d** $y=\dfrac{d}{a-b}$

e $y=\dfrac{m}{p+1}$ **f** $y=\dfrac{pq-r}{q}$ **4a** $x=\dfrac{ab}{a+b}$ **b** $x=\dfrac{2cd}{d-c}$

c $x=\dfrac{h}{b-a}$ **d** $x=\dfrac{m}{m+n}$ **e** $x=\dfrac{2}{a+2}$ **f** $x=\dfrac{a}{a+b}$

g $x=\dfrac{1-y}{1+y}$ **h** $x=\dfrac{b-a}{b+a}$ **i** $x=\dfrac{a}{5}$

Page 150   Check-up on Fractions and Equations

1a n **b** $\dfrac{1}{x}$ **c** $\dfrac{a}{5}$ **d** $\dfrac{3}{4}$ **2a** $y-4$ **b** $\dfrac{1}{x+1}$ **c** $\dfrac{1}{a-2}$ **d** $b+1$

e 2   **f** $\dfrac{x+2}{x-2}$ **g** $u+v$ **h** $\dfrac{m-n}{m+n}$ **3a** $2t$ **b** m **c** $\dfrac{1}{2}$ **d** a

4a $\dfrac{7x}{10}$ **b** $\dfrac{2x+5y}{10}$ **c** $\dfrac{u}{6}$ **d** $\dfrac{b+a}{ab}$ **e** $\dfrac{4a+1}{6}$ **f** $\dfrac{x+10}{6}$

g $\dfrac{x-3}{x(x-1)}$ **5a** $\dfrac{x^2}{16}$ cm², x cm   **b** y^2 cm², $\dfrac{13y}{3}$ cm

c $\dfrac{3d^2}{4}$ cm², $4d$ cm   **6a** $\dfrac{5x+1}{6}$ **b** $\dfrac{x+6}{12}$ **c** $\dfrac{3x-9}{10}$

7a 7   **b** 4   **c** 3   **8a** 6   **b** 0   **c** 5   **9a** $-2,4$ **b** -3 **c** $\frac{1}{2},1$

10a $x=\dfrac{10-b}{a}$ **b** $x=\dfrac{m}{n}$ **c** $x=\dfrac{pq-r}{p}$ **d** $x=2$

e $x=\dfrac{4}{a-1}$ **f** $x=\dfrac{b}{a-1}$ **11a** $H=\dfrac{M}{60}$ **b** $x=\dfrac{P}{4}$ **c** $h=\dfrac{2A}{b}$

d $p=\dfrac{Vc}{8}$ **e** $p=\dfrac{2000L}{w}$ **f** $r=\sqrt{\dfrac{A}{4\pi}}$ **g** $x=\dfrac{ay}{b}, y=\dfrac{bx}{a}$

h $u=R(1-v), v=\dfrac{R-u}{R}$ **12** $R=\dfrac{R_1 R_2}{R_1+R_2}$ **13** 7.2 km

12 PROBLEM SOLVING

Page 152 Exercise 1

1
Lift or stairs?

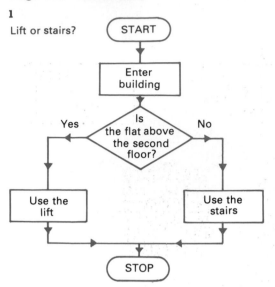

2
Transport needed

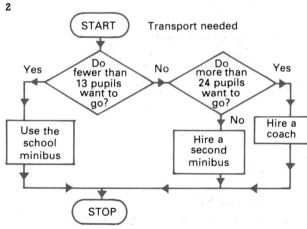

3
Student attendance

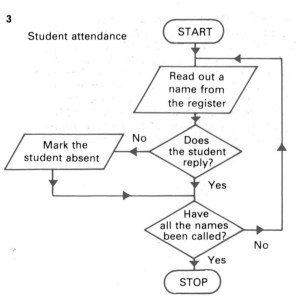

4 A game at the fair

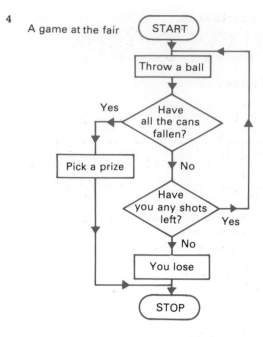

5b The number is always 1089
6a (i) 2225 (ii) 342 **b** $N = (2S+R-1) \times R \div 2$
8a Bill Adams (C); Liz Murphy (A); Ann Frazer (Fail);
Niall Jones (A); Meg O'Neill (C); Stephen Gow (B);
Ian Peters (A); Jan Smith (A) **b** grading pupils
c grading examination results **d** no-one
e no pupil will score a mark greater than 100, so a mark of
101 provides a stopping point
f

Page 156 Exercise 2

1 (i) **2** (ii) **3** (iii) **4** (ii) **5** (iii) **6** (iii)
7a (ii) **b** (i) **c** (iii)
8

9 Along North St, into East St, then South St and stopped at the traffic lights in Old Rd, leaving town by Hill St
10a (iii) **b** (iv) **c** (ii) **d** (i) **11a** (iii) **b** (iv) **c** (ii) **d** (i) **12a** (iii) **b** (i) **c** (ii) **d** (iv)

Page 158   Exercise 3

1 13 **2a** (i) 24 (ii) 17 (iii) 13 **b** $\frac{1}{24}$
3a 24 **b** (i) 2 (ii) 10 (iii) 5 (iv) 1 **c** (i) $\frac{5}{12}$ (ii) $\frac{1}{2}$
4a 0 **b** 4

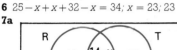

5a (i) $16-x$ (ii) $10-x$ **b** $16-x+x+10-x = 17$; $x = 9$; 9
6 $25-x+x+32-x = 34$; $x = 23$; 23
7a **b** 9

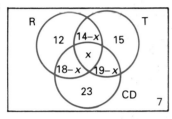

Page 159   Exercise 4

1 Corresponding angles are equal (all 90°), and corresponding sides are in the same ratio; Rows: 3, 4; 9, 16
2 The triangles are equiangular; 2, 3, 4, . . . , n; 4, 9, 16, . . . , n^2 **3** 2, 3, 4, . . . , n; 4, 9, 16, . . . ,n^2
4 Linear enlargement scale factor = 2:1 = 2; areas of triangles are $\frac{1}{2}\sqrt{3}$ and $2\sqrt{3}$, so area enlargement scale factor = 4 = 2^2 **5a** 100 **b** 10 000
6a 60 cm, 45 cm **b** 2700 cm², 10 800 cm² **c** 4 **d** yes
7a 4.5 m, 3.6 m **b** 0.9 m², 8.1 m² **c** 9 **d** 9 = 3^2
8a 1.5 **b** 2.25 **9** 1.34 **10** £54 **11** 40 824 mm²
12a $\angle ABC = \angle ADE$, $\angle ACB = \angle AED$ (corresponding angles), $\angle A$ is common; yes **b** $\frac{5}{3}$, $\frac{25}{9}$ **c** 1000 mm²
13a They are equiangular **b** $\frac{1}{4}$, $\frac{1}{16}$ **c** 50 mm²

Page 161   Exercise 5

1 Rows: 2, 3, 4, . . . , n; 8, 27, 64, . . . , n^3
2 2, 3, 4, n; 8, 27, 64, n^3 **3** 16 ml, 54 ml
4a 2 **b** 8 **c** 2000 ml **5** 5760 cm³, 19 440 cm³
6a 3.75 m **b** (i) 25 000 cm² (ii) 2.5 m² **c** 0.4 ml
7a 10 **b** 100 **c** 1000 **8a** $\frac{3}{2}$ **b** $\frac{9}{4}$ **c** $\frac{27}{8}$ **9a** 32 cm²
b 6000 cm³, 384 cm³ **c** 2200 cm², 352 cm² **10a** 12.8 cm²
b 1570 cm³, 100 cm³ **c** 785 cm², 126 cm² **11** $2\frac{1}{4}$ tonnes

Page 163   Exercise 6

1a Part of a vertical straight line **b** an arc of a circle **c** part of a sloping straight line **d** a smooth curve **e** a circle **f**

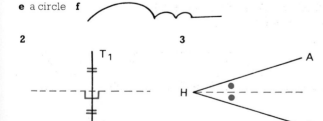

4a

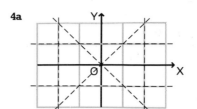

b (i) $y = \pm 1$
(ii) $x = \pm 2$
(iii) $y = \pm x$

5

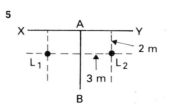

6

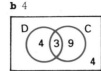

7 a

c

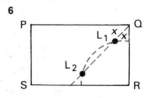

b

8

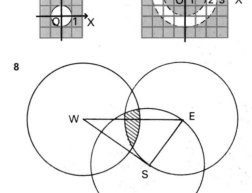

9a A line through R, parallel to PQ
b a line through D, parallel to AC

Page 165   Exercise 7

1 $\angle DEY = \angle ABE$ (corresponding) = $\angle CBX$ (vertically opposite)
2 $\angle DEB + \angle DEY = 180°$ (BEY is a straight line); but $\angle DEY = \angle ABE$ (corresponding). So $\angle DEB + \angle ABE = 180°$
3 $\angle XCA = \angle CAB$ (alternate), $\angle YCB = \angle CBA$ (alternate), $\angle CAB + \angle CBA + \angle ACB = \angle XCA + \angle YCB + \angle ACB = 180°$
4 Sum of exterior $\angle$s + interior $\angle$s = $3 \times 180° = 540°$. Subtract interior $\angle$s (sum 180°), leaving 360° for sum of exterior $\angle$s
5a $\angle ABX = \angle CBY$ (from diagram (i)) = complement of $\angle BCY$ ($\angle$s of $\triangle$ add up to 180°, and $\angle BYC = 90°$) = $\angle DCZ$ (from diagram (i)) **b** $\angle DCZ$ and DCP are complementary, so $\angle DCP = \angle ABX$, and AB∥DC (both equally inclined to parallel lines XY and PC)

6

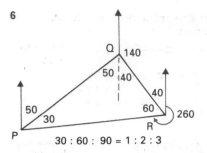

30 : 60 : 90 = 1 : 2 : 3

7 Area Q + area R = $\frac{1}{2}\pi AQ^2 + \frac{1}{2}\pi BR^2 = \frac{1}{2}\pi(AQ^2 + BR^2)$.
AQ = $\frac{1}{2}$AB, so AQ² = $\frac{1}{4}$AB². So area Q + area R =
$\frac{1}{2}\pi(\frac{1}{4}AB^2 + \frac{1}{4}BC^2) = \frac{1}{8}\pi(AB^2 + BC^2) = \frac{1}{8}\pi AC^2$ (Pythagoras'
Theorem) = area P
8 ∠EDG + ∠ADC = 180° (∠s of a square).
So ∠GDA + ∠EDC = 180° (∠s at a point total 360°).
△ADG = $\frac{1}{2}$GD.DA. sin GDA = $\frac{1}{2}$DE.DC. sin (180° − GDA) (sides
of a square are equal, sin x° = sin (180 − x)°) = △EDC
9a ∠CXZ = complement of angle ● in△CXZ = ∠CYA in
△CYA **b** ∠CYA = ∠CXZ (proved in **a**) = ∠AXY (vertically
opposite). So △AXY is isosceles
10a They are equiangular **b** congruent only if
corresponding sides are equal
11a ∠ABX = ∠CDX (alternate), ∠XAB = ∠XCD (alternate),
so △s are equiangular **b** $\dfrac{AX}{XC} = \dfrac{BX}{XD}$ **c** use △ = $\frac{1}{2}ab \sin C$,
and vertically opposite angles equal
12 ∠OQR = ∠ORQ = $67\frac{1}{2}°$ $\frac{1}{2}$ of (180° − 45°).
∠OPR = ∠ORP = $22\frac{1}{2}°$ (90° − $67\frac{1}{2}°$)
13a ∠ABO = ∠ACO = 90° (tangent − radius). By Pythagoras'
Theorem, AB² = AO² − BO² = AO² − CO² = AC², so AB = AC
b ABOC is a kite, so AO is an axis of symmetry, and BM = MC

Page 166 Exercise 8

1 −40 **2** A is higher than B for 18 < t < 20
3 (6n + 12) ÷ 3 − 4 = 2n + 4 − 4 = 2n
4 Saturn 6 g, crescent 4 g, star 5 g **5** 1.37, 9.94
6a x² + 2xy + y² **c** x⁴ + 4x³y + 6x²y² + 4xy³ + y⁴

Page 167 Exercise 9

1b 2n + (2n + 1) = 4n + 1, odd; (2n)² = 4n², even
2a n + (n + 1) + (n + 2) = 3n + 3 = 3(n + 1)
b 2n + (2n + 2) + (2n + 4) = 6n + 6 = 6(n + 1)
3a n + (n + 3) + (n + 6) + (n + 9) + (n + 12) = 5n + 30 = 5(n + 6)
b 46, 49, 52, 55, 58
4 (n + 1)² − n² = n² + 2n + 1 − n² = 2n + 1, odd

6b 10x + y − (10y + x) = 9x − 9y = 9(x − y) **7a** $\dfrac{1}{9} - \dfrac{1}{10} = \dfrac{1}{90}$

b $\dfrac{1}{n} - \dfrac{1}{n+1} = \dfrac{n+1}{n(n+1)} - \dfrac{n}{n(n+1)} = \dfrac{n+1-n}{n(n+1)} = \dfrac{1}{n(n+1)}$

Page 168 Exercise 10

1

2a 1 hour **b** 1 hour **c** 3 hours

3 2 hours

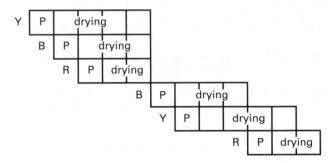

4

$$
\begin{array}{r}
37964 \\
\times 20 \\
\hline
759280 \\
\hline
\end{array}
$$

5 ■ first unit ■ second unit Time = 11 weeks

House programme – 2 units		Week											
Job	**Resource**	1	2	3	4	5	6	7	8	9	10	11	12
Site strip	Digger	■											
Foundation	Bricklayer		■	■	■	■							
Kit make	Base joiner		■										
Kit erection	Site joiner				■	■	■						
Drainage	Digger			■									
Glazing	Glazier						■		■				
Roof tiling	Slater							■		■			
Brick skin	Bricklayer								■	■	■		
Roughcast, etc.	Decorator										■	■	

CHAPTER REVISION EXERCISES

Page 173 Revision Exercise on Chapter 1: The Gradient and Equation of a Straight Line

1a (i) **b** (ii) **2a** 8 **b** 1 **c** 2
3 $m_{LM} = m_{PN} = -\frac{1}{2}$, $m_{LP} = m_{MN} = 4$, so opposite sides are parallel
4 **5** Q

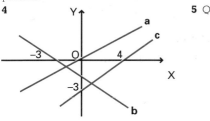

6a $y = \frac{1}{3}x$ **b** $y = -2x$ **c** $y = -x-4$ **d** $y = -\frac{3}{2}x+1$
7a,b (2, 1) **8b** (i) 2.5 m/s (ii) 17.5 m/s **c** $S = 10T$
9a (i) £22, £13 (ii) £32, £26 (iii) £42, £39 (iv) £52, £52
(v) £92, £104 **c** $C = 12+10N$, $C = 13N$
10a Mean point (0.45, 5.5) **b** $V = 13.3I-0.5$; 9.5 volts

Page 174 Revision Exercise on Chapter 2: Functions and Graphs

1a 2, 5, 7 **b** 4, 25, 64 **2a** 1 **b** $\frac{1}{2}$ **c** 2 **3a** 4 **b** 0 **c** 16
4a $2\frac{1}{2}$ **b** 1 **5a** By Pythagoras' Theorem **b** 5, 8, 13 **c** 6
6c 16 m, 8 m **7a** $y = 20-x$
b straight line through (0, 20) and (20, 0)
8b 5.75 km; after 1.5 s **c** He hit the ground
9b $y = \dfrac{a}{x}$ **c** $f(x) = \dfrac{36}{x}$ **d** 3.6 **10c** 10

Page 175 Revision Exercise on Chapter 3: Symmetry in the Circle

1

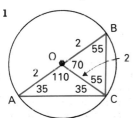

2a Angle in semi-circle; 7.8 **b** line from O to midpoint of chord; 7.5 **c** angle between tangent and radius; 5.6
d angle between tangent and radius; 36.9
3a 3 cm **b** 8 cm **c** 2 cm
4 **5** 5750 km **6** 4800 cm²

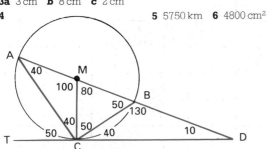

7a 183.3 mm **b** 3959.7 mm²
8a 2182 cm² **b** 349 cm² **c** 1833 cm² **9** 300°

Page 176 Revision Exercise on Chapter 4: Inequalities

1a $x \geqslant 3$ **b** $x < -1$ **c** $x > -2\frac{1}{2}$

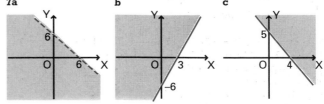

2a $u > 2$ **b** $v < 3\frac{1}{2}$ **c** $w \geqslant -2$ **d** $t \geqslant 4$ **e** $p \leqslant 3$
3 $8m > 4m+4$; $m > 1$ **4** $6x+2 \leqslant 32$; $x \leqslant 5$, 5 litres
5a 6 **b** 5 **c** 4 **6a** (i) $y = -x+3$ (ii) $y \leqslant -x+3$
b (i) $y = 2x+4$ (ii) $y > 2x+4$
7a **b** **c**

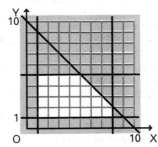

8a $50+2x < 180$ **b** 65 or more
9 $1 \leqslant x \leqslant 8$
$\quad 1 \leqslant y \leqslant 5$
$\quad x+y \leqslant 10$

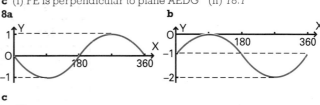

10a $x \geqslant -2$, $y \geqslant -2$, $y \leqslant x+3$, $y \geqslant \frac{3}{2}x-5$, $y \leqslant -\frac{1}{2}x+3$
b 19, -14

Page 177 Revision Exercise on Chapter 5: Trigonometry—Calculations, Graphs and Equations

1a 33.7 **b** 3.2 **c** 4.9 **2b** (i) $\dfrac{3}{5}, \dfrac{3}{4}$ (ii) $-\dfrac{4}{5}, \dfrac{3}{4}$ **3a** 20
b $\dfrac{20}{29}, \dfrac{20}{21}$ **4** Rows: $\dfrac{1}{2}, \dfrac{\sqrt{3}}{2}, \dfrac{1}{\sqrt{3}}; \dfrac{1}{\sqrt{2}}, \dfrac{1}{\sqrt{2}}, 1; \dfrac{\sqrt{3}}{2}, \dfrac{1}{2}, \sqrt{3}$
5a 13.0 km **b** 4.8°
6a $y = 4, 3.7, 3, 2, 1, 0.3, 0, 0.3, 1, 2, 3, 3.7, 4$
b max. 4 at $x = 0, 360$; min. 0 at $x = 180$
7a (i) 17 cm (ii) 61.9° **b** 3 cm
c (i) FE is perpendicular to plane AEDG (ii) 78.7°
8a **b**

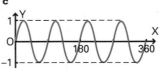

c

9 $a = -1, b = 3, c = 2$ **10a** 30, 10 **b** 11 cm **c** 12°
11a 135, 315 **b** 6, 174 **c** 134, 226 **d** 219, 321 **e** 65, 295
12a (i) 2570 m (ii) 190 m **b** 53°

Page 178 Revision Exercise on Chapter 6: Quadratic Equations

1a $0, 4$ **b** $-1, 5$ **c** $1, 3$ **d** 2
2a $x^2 - 4x = 0, x(x-4) = 0, x = 0, 4$ **b** $x^2 - 4x - 5 = 0$, etc
c $x^2 - 4x + 3 = 0$, etc **d** $x^2 - 4x + 4 = 0$, etc
3a $-2, 1$ **b** $-2, 5$ **c** $0, 4$ **d** $-1\frac{1}{2}, 1\frac{1}{2}$ **e** $-6, 2$ **f** $-9, 2$
4 $A(-\frac{1}{3}, 0), B(2, 0)$ **5a** $-2, 3$ **b** $-1, -9$ **c** $-3, 4$
d $-5, 1$ **6a** $-0.5, 1.2$ **b** $0.4, 2.6$ **c** $0.2, 2.3$ **d** $-0.9, 0.7$
7a $A(-3, 7), B(1, 3)$ **b** $A(-2, -7), B(2, 1)$
8a 12 **b** no; there would be 90 games for 10 teams, or 110 games for 11 teams **9b** 9 cm by 12 cm
10a $f(1) = 0$ **b** $f(2) = -1, f(3) = 10; 2.2$ **c** -3.19

Page 179 Revision Exercise on Chapter 7: Proportion in Practice

1a (i) **b** (v) **2a** 300 **b** 4 **3a** $y = \dfrac{108}{x^2}$ **b** (i) 12

(ii) 6.(or -6) **4a** $v = k\sqrt{d}$ **b** $v = 4\sqrt{d}$ **c** 20 m/s **d** 100 m
5b Yes; the graph is a straight line through O **c** $W = 0.3V$

6 7.8 km **7a** $n = \dfrac{512 \times 125}{v}$ **b** 125

8a $T = \dfrac{12L}{S}$ **b** 26 min 40 s **9** $P \times 2, A \times 4, V \times 8, S \div 2, d \div 4$

Page 180 Revision Exercise on Chapter 8: Handling Data

1b (i) $\frac{2}{3}$ (ii) $\frac{115}{150} = 0.77$ (2 dec. places)
3 400, 100, 900, 650, 450
4a 0.000 021 4 **b** by insuring it, or by some illegal means
5a

0–19	20–39	40–59	60–119	120–239
20	36	30	42	72

b 0.6 **c** 98
6a $(1,1), \ldots, (1, 6); (2,1), \ldots, (2, 6); (3,1), \ldots, (3, 6)$
b (i) $\frac{1}{6}$ (ii) $\frac{17}{18}$ (iii) $\frac{4}{9}$ **c** false; each can score 3 **d** 50
7a $\frac{1}{8}$ **b** $\frac{1}{4}$

Page 181 Revision Exercise on Chapter 9: Indices and Surds

1a 3.52×10^{13} **b** 7.74×10^{-9}
2a x **b** 6 **c** $2z^3$ **d** p^2 **e** $x-1$ **f** t^5
3a 8 **b** $\frac{1}{8}$ **c** 1 **d** 3 **e** 27 **f** 2 **g** $\frac{1}{3}$ **h** 10 **i** $\frac{1}{10}$
4a 16 **b** $\frac{1}{16}$ **c** 4 **d** 2 **e** $\frac{1}{2}$ **5a** $\frac{3}{2}$ **b** $\frac{1}{9}$ **c** $8\frac{1}{2}$
6a $a-1$ **b** $b^{-2}+1$ **7a** 9 **b** 1 **8a** $x-1$ **b** $y^3 + 2y^{3/2} + 1$
9a $A^{1/2}$ **b** $V^{1/3}$ **10a** 0.7 **b** 1.4 **c** 2.8 **d** 5.7
11 $x = 1$ and 2 **12a** 47 300 approximately **b** 38 years
13a $2\sqrt{2}$ **b** $3\sqrt{2}$ **c** $4\sqrt{2}$ **d** $7\sqrt{2}$ **e** $10\sqrt{7}$ **f** $2\sqrt{3}$ **g** $4\sqrt{2}$
h $\sqrt{2}$ **i** 0 **j** 5 **k** 12 **14a** $\sqrt{10}$ cm **b** $\sqrt{14}$ cm **c** 3 cm
15a $\sqrt{2}$ **b** $2\sqrt{3}$ **c** $2\sqrt{5}$ **d** $2(\sqrt{3} - \sqrt{2})$

Page 182 Revision Exercise on Chapter 10: Trigonometry—Triangle Calculations

1a 34.3 **b** 7.0 **c** 101.5 **d** 17.8 **2a** 21.5 cm **b** 17°
c 56.6 cm² **3a** 48.7 cm **b** 305.1 cm²
4 $\angle BDC = \angle DBC = 60°, \angle ABD = 80°, BD = 4$ m, AB = 7.5 m,
AD = 7.9 m **5a** 908.1 m **b** 520.9 m **6** 4988.3 cm²
7a 28.8°, 151.2° **b** 6 m, 20.4 m **8** Right-hand triangle:
51.8 m, 75°, 75°; other triangle: 71.8°, 58.8°, 49.4(5)°
9a 69.3 m **b** 18.4° **c** 86.3 m **10** 786.4 km, 137.9°

Page 183 Revision Exercise on Chapter 11: Fractions and Equations

1a b **b** $\dfrac{1}{x}$ **c** $\dfrac{1}{a}$ **d** $\dfrac{1}{2y}$ **e** $\dfrac{2n}{m}$ **f** $\dfrac{x-y}{x+y}$ **2a** $\dfrac{2}{3}$ **b** $\dfrac{3}{x+1}$ **c** $\dfrac{3}{2}$

d $x-1$ **e** $\dfrac{a+b}{2}$ **f** $\dfrac{2x+y}{a}$ **g** $\dfrac{x}{2(x-7)}$ **h** $\dfrac{m-3}{m+1}$ **i** $\dfrac{3x+2}{2x+1}$

3a (i) $\dfrac{a^2}{8}$ cm² (ii) $\dfrac{3a}{2}$ cm **b** (i) 1 cm² (ii) $\dfrac{2a^2 + 2b^2}{ab}$ cm

4a (i) $\dfrac{x}{4}$ cm (ii) 2 cm (iii) $\dfrac{x}{n}$ cm (iv) $\dfrac{2}{x}$ cm **b** $\dfrac{3x}{2}$ cm

5a $\dfrac{9+y}{3y}$ **b** $\dfrac{2x-15}{5x}$ **c** $\dfrac{5b+2a}{ab}$ **d** $\dfrac{1-5x}{x^2}$ **e** $\dfrac{6a+b}{14}$ **f** $\dfrac{a}{2x}$

g $-\dfrac{7}{6n}$ **h** $\dfrac{2+5m}{m^2}$ **i** $\dfrac{a+b}{2}$ **j** $\dfrac{x+3}{4}$ **k** $\dfrac{y-1}{10}$ **l** $\dfrac{5a-6}{6}$

m $\dfrac{6k-1}{k^2}$ **n** $\dfrac{2x+1}{(x-2)(x+3)}$ **o** $\dfrac{5m+n}{(m-n)(m+n)}$

p $\dfrac{-2}{(3y+1)(3y-1)}$ **6a** 15 **b** 17 **c** 5 **d** 17 **e** 18

7 120 km **8a** 1, 4 **b** $-2, 3$ **c** 1 **d** $-1\frac{1}{2}, \frac{2}{3}$

9a $R = \dfrac{I}{V}$ **b** $t = T - DR$ **c** $x = \dfrac{A - 2\pi}{2\pi}$ or $\dfrac{A}{2\pi} - 1$

d $Z = \dfrac{ACW}{VX}$ **e** $t = \dfrac{V}{A+d}$ **f** $b = \dfrac{E - a - 1}{E}$ **g** $a = \dfrac{b-c}{b+c}$

h $A = \dfrac{3t+8}{t-2}$ **i** $T = \dfrac{1000r}{1000 - r}$

GENERAL REVISION EXERCISES

Page 184 General Revision Exercise 1A

1a 25, 36; next square number **b** 16, -32; multiply by -2
c 15, 21; add 1 more than the previous difference
2a $5p$ **b** $6p^2$ **c** 0 **d** $6a$ **e** $6a^4$
3a $x + y = 90$ **b** $y = 55$ **c** $y < 60$ **d** both x and $y = 45$
4 £30 **5a** -3 **b** 8 **c** 1 **d** 32 **e** 8 **6a** 1.5 m **b** 110 m
7a $x = 3$ **b** $t = -1, 4$ **8** $a = 70, b = 70, c = 110$
9a **b** **c**

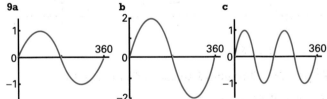

10a $6x, 10 - 4x, 10 + 2x$ **b** $6x + 10 - 4x + 10 + 2x = 28, x = 2$
c 12 m, 2 m, 14 m **11b** 10.6 km, 086° **12a** $\frac{9}{40}$ **b** 13°
13b Angles of sectors are 120°, 160° and 80°

Page 185 General Revision Exercise 1B

1a $x = -3$ **b** $x = -1$ **c** $y = -2$ **d** $a = 1$ **e** $t \geqslant 1$
f $n < 5$ **2c** By means of a half-turn about O
3a (i) 26 (ii) 7.5 **b** 22.6° **4a** 0 **b** 2 **5** 4500 **6** 24 min
7a $a^2 + 2ab + b^2$ **b** $a^2 - 2ab + b^2$ **c** $3x^2 - 2x - 1$

d $4t^2 + 12t + 9$ **e** $x^2 - 2 + \dfrac{1}{x^2}$ **f** $a^2 + a - b^2 + b$

8a $8n-7$ **b** $(n+1)^2$ **9a** Each is perpendicular to AE
b $x=100, y=52$ **10** £429.54 **11a** 5 **b** $(2,0),(0,-10)$
c 10 square units **12a** 80 cm² **b** 500 cm²
13b (i) 52 (ii) 57 **14b** (i) 50, 10 (ii) 52, 20 (approximately)

Page 186 General Revision Exercise 2A

1 24 exposures **2a** $\frac{2}{5}$ **b** 0.4 **c** 40%
3a $x=9$ **b** $y=-1$ **c** $x=40$ **d** $n=7$
4a

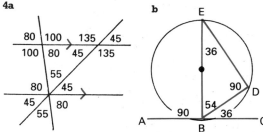

b

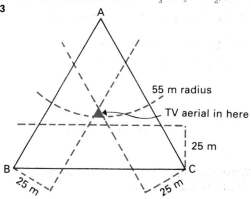

5 $4.5\times10^9, 8.55\times10^{-3}$ **6** Rows: 3, -2, 4, -3, -2, -1;
2, -1, -2, 5, 5, -1; 5, -3, 2, 2, 3, -2; 1, -1, 6, -8, -7, 0
7a 50 cm **b** 73.7° **8** 540 cm, 12 600 cm²
9c $(1,1),(6,1),(6,3)$ **10** $3(2x-1)=8x-7, x=2;$ 3 cm, 9 cm
11 £71.65 **12a** $m(m-n)$ **b** $(m-n)(m+n)$
c $(m-2)(m+3)$ **13a** £15, £14, £13 **b** 8 cm, 8 cm, 9 cm

Page 187 General Revision Exercise 2B

1a 3 **b** 1 **c** $\frac{1}{25}$ **d** $\frac{1}{2}$ **e** $\frac{1}{9}$ **2a** (1) $4x+1<3x+5, x<4$
(ii) $3x+4>x+6, x>1$ **b** 2, 3 **3a** £13 200 **b** £7916
4a 6 cm **b** 10.4 cm **c** 31 cm² **5a** $t=6$ **b** $=-4$

c $t=\frac{1}{2}(3b-a)$ **d** $t=(p-q)^2$ **6a** $y\propto x$ **b** $y\propto\frac{1}{x}$

7a $5, x=0, 360; -5, x=180$ **b** $3, x=180; 1, x=0, 360$

8 3.2×10^7 m/s **9a** $\frac{x+3}{5}$ **b** $\frac{x+4}{2x+1}$ **c** $\frac{a+b}{c+d}$ **10a** $30x^3$ m³

b $55x^2$ m² **11a** $\cos A=\frac{b^2+c^2-a^2}{2bc}$ **b** 92.6°

12a They are equiangular **b** $\frac{3}{5}$ **c** $\frac{3}{5}, \frac{x}{x+4}=\frac{3}{5}$ **d** $x=6$
13a   **b**   **c**

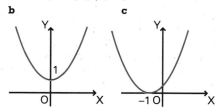

14b 15 **c** 2% **d** $\frac{7}{30}$

Page 188 General Revision Exercise 3A

1a $x\geqslant2$ **b** $x=2, y=-1$
2a (i) $\angle$GFE (ii) $\angle$FEB (iii) $\angle$ABE
b

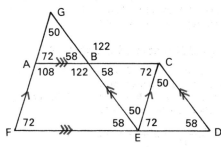

3a 7 **b** 4 **c** $7\frac{3}{4}$ **d** 0.143 **4a** $10t-5n$ **b** a^3+a **c** d^3-d^2
d $-2x+2y$ **e** $-p-q$ **f** $3-3u+6v$ **g** $7-2x$ **h** $1+2x$
5 150 **6** £90, £84 **7** 20 **8a** £31 **b** £34 **c** £52 **d** £70
9 $(x+1)^2=x^2+4^2, x=7.5; 7.5$ m **10a** 157 cm **b** 578 cm²
11b 8 square units

Page 189 General Revision Exercise 3B

1a $x=-3$ **b** $x=-1$ **2** £12 **3** $8\sqrt{2}$ cm **4a** 48 km
b 64 km/h **5a** $2\sqrt{2}$ cm **b** $2\sqrt{3}$ cm **6a** 128 m **b** 116 m
7 Jam £1.50, roll 30p **8a** O (iii), A (i), (ii), (iii), B (i), (ii)
b

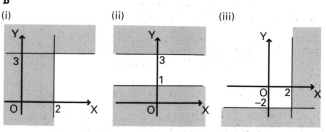

9a x^8 **b** $y+1$ **c** t^{-2} **d** $x-2+x^{-1}$ **e** $x^{1/4}-x^{-1/4}$
10a $\frac{4}{3}$ **b** 8 cm **c** 48 cm² **d** 128 cm³ **11a** (i) 1 (ii) 25
(iii) 0 **b** (i) 0.5 (ii) 0.84 **12b** $c=25+15t$ **c** 4

13a (i) 15 (ii) -15 (iii) -20 **b** $F=\frac{9C+160}{5}$

14a $-1.62, 0.618$ **b** $-1.35, 1.85$ **c** $-2.16, 4.16$

Page 190 General Revision Exercise 4A

1a 404 **b** 8 h 10 min **2a** $x=-\frac{2}{3}$ **b** $y=-\frac{1}{2}, 3$
3

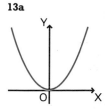

55 m radius
TV aerial in here
25 m

4a 32.1% **b** (i) £3.06 (ii) £38.59 **5a** 9 cm **b** 106°
6 106.25 m², 86.25 m²; 42 m, 38 m **7a** $x=0, y=6$
b $x=-11, y=-11$ **c** $x=-2, y=7$
8a 30 min, 24 min **b** 67 mph, 50 mph, 67 mph **c** (i) 48 mph
(ii) 61 mph **9** The region is the interior of a triangle with
vertices O (0, 0), (0, 6) and (3, 0) (boundaries dotted)
10 The second one; 4.7 cm³ **11** 3
12a (H, H), (H, T); (T, H), (T, T)
b (i) $\frac{1}{4}$ (ii) $\frac{1}{2}$ (iii) $\frac{1}{4}$ (iv) 0

Page 191 General Revision Exercise 4B

1a (i) $4\frac{1}{2}$ (ii) $1\frac{4}{5}$ (iii) $4\frac{1}{2}$ (iv) $1\frac{1}{2}$ **b** 80 **c** $\frac{17}{20}$
2a (i) 12 cm (ii) 150 cm² **b** (i) $25^2=20^2+15^2$, and use
converse of Pythagoras' Theorem (ii) they are equiangular
3a h: 0, 9, 16, 24, 24, 16, 9, 0 **c** 5 s **d** (i) $t=0, 5$
(ii) $t=1.5, 3.5$ **e** after 0.7 s and 4.3 s **4** 2800 cm²

5a $x=-\frac{2}{3}$ **b** $x=\frac{c-b}{a}$ **c** $x=\frac{y-c}{m}$ **d** $x=5$

e $x=pd+c$ **f** $x=\frac{t-n}{t}$ **6a** 30°, 150° **b** 132°, 228°

7a 44 m **b** 73° **c** 147°   **8a** $t \leqslant 1\frac{3}{4}$ **b** $x < 2$
9a
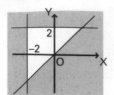
b 8 square units

10a h: 3, 5, 7, 9; t: 13, 19, 25, 31
b (i) $h = 2n + 1$ (ii) $t = 6n + 7$ (iii) $t = 3h + 4$
11 15 newtons   **12a** 1.3   **b** 2.3

Page 192   General Revision Exercise 5A

1a 2880 **b** £73.30   **2a** 900 cm² **b** 40 500 cm³
3a
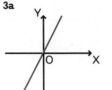
b
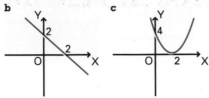
c

4a (i) 2340°   (ii) 156°   **b** $n = \dfrac{S + 360}{180}$, 7
5a Rows: (1, 1), (1, 2), (1, 3); (2, 1), (2, 2), (2, 3); (3, 1), (3, 2), (3, 3)   **b** (i) $\frac{1}{3}$ (ii) $\frac{1}{9}$ (iii) $\frac{1}{3}$ (iv) $\frac{2}{3}$
6a $\dfrac{2y + 3x}{xy}$ **b** $\dfrac{5x + 1}{(x + 2)(x - 1)}$ **c** $\dfrac{-y - 1}{(y - 1)(y - 2)}$

7a (i) 15 cm   (ii) 25 cm   **b** 36
8 $(2x + 3)^2 = x^2 + (x + 7)^2$, $x = 5$; 5 cm, 12 cm, 13 cm
9a 4.5   **b** 2   **c** $y = 2x - 4$ **10b** (i) Speedy
(ii) Speedy and Rentacar are equal
(iii) Rentacar and Costacar are equal   (iv) Costacar
11 3.4 cm²   **12** £25, £45
13a 2, 3, 5, 7, 11, 13, 17, 19, 23, 29, 31, 37, 41, 43, 47
b (i) 6   (ii) 7   (iii) 2   **c** (i) 40%   (ii) 47%   (iii) 13%

Page 193   General Revision Exercise 5B

1a $x = -2$ **b** $y < -2\frac{1}{2}$ **c** $x = 5$ **d** $x = 2$
2a (i) $30^2 = 18^2 + 24^2$, and use the converse of Pythagoras' Theorem   (ii) $\angle ACB = 90°$, so ACB is a semi-circle
b (i) 9 cm   (ii) 12 cm
3a (1, 24), (2, 12), (3, 8), (4, 6), (6, 4), (8, 3), (12, 2), (24, 1), and the same with negative signs   **c** $xy = 24$ **d** a hyperbola

4a $2\sqrt{5}$ **b** $2\sqrt{3}$ **c** $2\sqrt{3} + 3\sqrt{2}$ **d** $5 - 2\sqrt{6}$ **e** $\sqrt{2}$ **f** $\dfrac{\sqrt{6}}{4}$

5b 5   **6b** 120°   **7** 21%
8a $\dfrac{5}{3}$ **b** $\dfrac{2}{x - 1}$ **c** $\dfrac{a + b}{3}$ **d** $\dfrac{u - v}{u + v}$ **e** $\dfrac{3(y - 2)}{2y - 1}$
9a (i) $d_1{}^2 = 2n^2 + 2$, $d_2{}^2 = 2n^2 + 8$, $d_3{}^2 = 2n^2 + 18$ (ii) 6, 10
b 14, $4n + 2$ **10a** $-1, 2$ **b** $-1\frac{1}{2}, \frac{1}{2}$ **c** $-2.35, 0.85$
11 5.846 m³   **12a** 1.33×10^{-1} **b** 4.5×10^3
13a Mid-prices: 1.57, 1.72, 1.87, . . . , 2.62; Frequencies: 3, 3, 6, 4, 3, 2, 3, 3   **b** £2.06
c Cumulative frequencies: 3, 6, 12, 16, 19, 21, 24, 27
d £1.98, £0.51 (LQ £1.84, median £1.98, UQ £2.35)
14 $1^2 + 2^2 + 3^2 + \ldots + n^2$

MATHS
IN ACTION

BOOK 4B STATISTICS APPENDIX

The statistics material in this appendix updates the material in *Maths in Action Book 4B* in line with the SCE Standard Grade requirements at Credit level for the first examination in 2001.

CONTENTS	PAGE

STANDARD DEVIATION

The **range** measures spread.
Unfortunately any big change in either the largest or smallest score will mean a big change in the range even though only one piece of data may have changed.

The semi-interquartile range is less sensitive to a single number changing but is only really based on two of the scores.

A measure of spread which uses all the data is the **standard deviation**.

The **deviation** of a score is how much the score differs from the mean.

Example 1   Find the standard deviation of these five scores: 9, 12, 15, 19, 20.

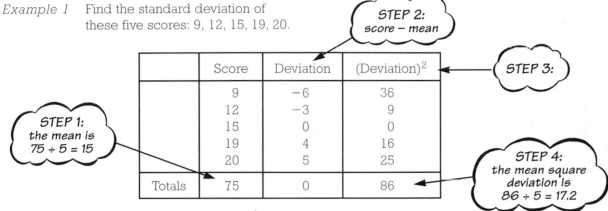

STEP 2: *score − mean*

STEP 3:

STEP 1: *the mean is 75 ÷ 5 = 15*

STEP 4: *the mean square deviation is 86 ÷ 5 = 17.2*

	Score	Deviation	(Deviation)^2
	9	−6	36
	12	−3	9
	15	0	0
	19	4	16
	20	5	25
Totals	75	0	86

The standard deviation is $\sqrt{17.2} = 4.1$ to 1 d.p.

Notes	Step 1	Calculate the mean.
	Step 2	Calculate the deviation of each score. Note that the negative sign signifies *below the mean*. *If we tried to average these deviations we would end up with zero.*
	Step 3	Square each deviation. *This removes the negative signs.*
	Step 4	Add the squared deviations and divide by the number of scores to find *the mean square deviation.*
	Step 5	Take the square root of this value. The standard deviation = 4.1.

Having squared and then taken the root we know that
the standard deviation is in the same units as the scores.

Example 2   The heights of six Christmas trees at a garden centre are:
1.1 m, 1.7 m, 1.9 m, 2.1 m, 2.3 m, 2.9 m.
Find the mean and standard deviation of these six heights.

	Height	Deviation	(Deviation)^2
	1.1	−0.9	0.81
	1.7	−0.3	0.09
	1.9	−0.1	0.01
	2.1	0.1	0.01
	2.3	0.3	0.09
	2.9	0.9	0.81
Totals	12.0	0.0	1.82

Mean score: $12.0 \div 6 = 2.0$
Mean square deviation:
$$1.82 \div 6 = 0.303$$
Standard deviation:
$$\sqrt{0.303} = 0.55 \text{ (2 d.p.)}$$
The mean height is 2.0 m with a standard deviation of 0.55 m.

When the standard deviation is low it means the scores are close to the mean.

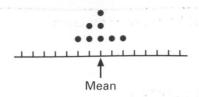

Mean

When the standard deviation is high it means the scores are spread out from the mean.

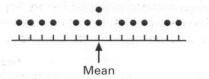

Mean

EXERCISE CCS1

1 Five radishes are weighed. The weights are: 100 g, 115 g, 118 g, 120 g, 122 g.

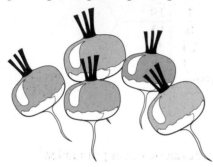

a Check that the mean weight is 115 g.

b Copy and complete the table.

	Weight (g)	Deviation	(Deviation)^2
	100	−15	225
	115		
	118		
	120		
	122		
Totals			

c Find the mean square deviation (the mean of the last column).

d Find the standard deviation.

2 a Blueboy is a greyhound. He completed his last five races in the following times: 8.2 s, 9.1 s, 9.2 s, 9.3 s, 9.7 s.

(i) Calculate the mean time.
(ii) Copy and complete the table.

	Time (s)	Deviation	(Deviation)^2
	8.2		
	9.1		
	9.2		
	9.3		
	9.7		
Totals			

(iii) Calculate the standard deviation of Blueboy's times.

b Nipper, a rival, has times of 7.9 s, 8.0 s, 9.0 s, 9.7 s, 9.9 s.

	Time (s)	Deviation	(Deviation)^2
	7.9		
	8.0		
	9.0		
	9.7		
	9.9		
Totals			

(i) Calculate the mean.
(ii) Calculate the standard deviation correct to 1 d.p.
(iii) Who, on average, is faster – Blueboy or Nipper?
(iv) Do the times of Nipper vary more than those of Blueboy?

FINDING THE STANDARD DEVIATION FROM A SAMPLE

The 100 employees of Sound Savers Supermarket all live within a 20 km radius of the store.
The table below gives the actual distances to the nearest kilometre.
The standard deviation of the distribution has been calculated as 6.05 km.

Second random number

	0	1	2	3	4	5	6	7	8	9
0	16	7	18	5	15	5	7	4	8	18
1	7	15	4	19	16	3	8	17	19	11
2	13	14	4	11	16	15	16	4	12	4
3	19	0	3	19	6	18	12	5	5	12
4	7	19	18	9	8	14	15	8	6	11
5	19	1	4	10	15	5	6	1	1	12
6	10	8	17	1	2	11	19	3	1	19
7	0	17	6	7	11	15	5	13	5	13
8	1	4	16	9	19	16	1	9	15	9
9	7	17	1	9	19	16	2	20	14	3

First random number (vertical label on left axis)

Standard deviation 6.05

It costs time and money to collect this complete set of data.
It would be cheaper to just take a **sample**.

How is the standard deviation of the sample related to the standard deviation of the population?

CLASS ACTIVITY

> Set your calculator to Fix mode with 0 decimal places.
>
> Rand × 10 = will generate a random number between 0 and 9.

Generate random number pairs which you can then use as coordinates to pick out a sample of six numbers from the table. (Using the constant facility of your calculator may be labour saving here.)

Calculate the standard deviation of the six numbers using the formula:
$$\sqrt{(\text{sum of squared deviations})/n}$$
where n is the size of the sample.
Now use the formula:
$$\sqrt{(\text{sum of squared deviations})/(n-1)}$$

Try this several times.
Average the results of your attempts.
Over many trials you should find that, on average, the second formula provides a better estimate for the standard deviation of the whole set of numbers.

For the rest of the chapter we will assume we are always working with a sample and therefore will always work with the second formula.

$$\text{Mean} = \frac{\text{sum of scores}}{n}$$

$$\text{Standard deviation} = \sqrt{\left(\frac{\text{sum of squared deviations}}{n-1}\right)}$$

When you calculate the mean and standard deviation of the sample in this manner, you are also finding an estimate for the mean and standard deviation of the underlying population.

NOTATION

When dealing with samples, the following symbols are fairly standard:

n ... the number of pieces of data in the sample.
x ... this is used to represent a typical piece of data in the sample.
$\bar{x}$ ... read as 'x bar', the mean of the sample.
s ... the standard deviation of the sample.
Σ ... pronounced *sigma*, this stands for the phrase 'the sum of',
    e.g. Σx represents the sum of the x values, i.e. the sum of the data.

This notation is used in these formulae for:

(i) the mean: $$\bar{x} = \frac{\Sigma x}{n}$$

(ii) the standard deviation: $$s = \sqrt{\left(\frac{\Sigma(x - \bar{x})^2}{n - 1}\right)}$$

Note that $\Sigma(x - \bar{x})^2$ means the sum of the squared deviations.

When working with real data, and rounding as you calculate, this formula can lead to the build-up of relatively large rounding errors. The formula can be rearranged, though it is beyond the needs of the course to prove it, to a form which is:

- more convenient for calculation
- doesn't need the mean to be calculated first
- cuts down on the rounding error.

Alternative formula for the standard deviation:
In this form it is often referred to as the **one-pass** formula.

$$s = \sqrt{\left(\frac{\Sigma x^2 - \frac{(\Sigma x)^2}{n}}{n - 1}\right)}$$

Example   Find the standard deviation of the following data:
    1, 3, 3, 4, 5, 5, 6, 7, 7, 7.

Method 1

x	$x - \bar{x}$	$(x - \bar{x})^2$
1	−3.8	14.44
3	−1.8	3.24
3	−1.8	3.24
4	−0.8	0.64
5	0.2	0.04
5	0.2	0.04
6	1.2	1.44
7	2.2	4.84
7	2.2	4.84
7	2.2	4.84
$\Sigma x = 48$	$\Sigma(x - \bar{x})^2 = 37.6$	

$$\bar{x} = \frac{\Sigma x}{n} = \frac{48}{10} = 4.8$$

$$s = \sqrt{\left(\frac{\Sigma(x - \bar{x})^2}{n - 1}\right)}$$

$$s = \sqrt{\left(\frac{37.6}{9}\right)}$$

$s = 2.04$ to 2 d.p.

Method 2

x	x^2
1	1
3	9
3	9
4	16
5	25
5	25
6	36
7	49
7	49
7	49
$\Sigma x = 48$	$\Sigma x^2 = 268$

$$s = \sqrt{\left(\frac{\Sigma x^2 - \frac{(\Sigma x)^2}{n}}{n - 1}\right)}$$

$$s = \sqrt{\left(\frac{268 - \frac{48^2}{10}}{9}\right)}$$

$s = 2.04$ to 2 d.p.

EXERCISE CCS2

Use this formula for questions **1** and **2**.

$$s = \sqrt{\left(\frac{\Sigma(x - \overline{x})^2}{n - 1}\right)}$$

1 The contents in a sample of ten tubes of toothpaste are measured. The results are:
60 ml, 62 ml, 64 ml, 64 ml, 65 ml,
65 ml, 66 ml, 66 ml, 67 ml, 67 ml.
Calculate the mean volume and standard deviation correct to 1 d.p.

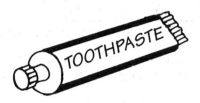

2 A machine in a factory is stamping out components.
The quality controller counts the number of rejects per minute made by the machine.
1 2 3 3 4 6 8 9
a (i) Calculate the mean number of rejects per minute.
(ii) Calculate the sample standard deviation.
b The machine is stopped and adjusted.
Again a record is kept of the number of rejects per minute.
3 4 4 4 5 5 5 6
(i) Calculate the new mean and standard deviation.
(ii) Has the mean improved?
(iii) Has the machine's consistency improved?

3 Use this alternative formula to repeat question **1**:

$$s = \sqrt{\left(\frac{\Sigma x^2 - \dfrac{(\Sigma x)^2}{n}}{n - 1}\right)}$$

4 On 21 June the Arctic circle enjoys 24 hours of daylight. At 49°N there are 16 hours of daylight; at the equator 12 hours; at 49°S 8 hours; and at the Antarctic Circle 0 hours.
Use this sample to estimate the mean and standard deviation number of hours of daylight. (Use the one-pass formula.)

5 The numbers of feral cats in various city centres were counted in a survey.
8 12 18 23 26 34 65

a Calculate:
(i) the range
(ii) the semi-interquartile range
(iii) the sample standard deviation using the alternative formula.
b A year later a second survey was done.
7 14 17 24 28 40 70
Calculate the new:
(i) range
(ii) semi-interquartile range
(iii) standard deviation.
c Which measure of spread was affected most by the small changes in the data?

6 The number of pond skater insects at various sites on a loch is counted.
12 22 56 58 60 60 68 70
a Calculate:
(i) the mean
(ii) the sample standard deviation.
b These insects are fairly sensitive to pollution. To examine the effects of a chemical spillage a second survey is done.
8 20 42 48 52 56 58 60
Calculate the new:
(i) mean (ii) standard deviation.
c (i) By how much is the mean altered?
(ii) Comment on the effect of the spillage.

USING A CALCULATOR

You need to be in STAT mode.　| MODE | | • | or | MODE | | 1 |

It is good practice to clear all the memories.　| AC |

Example　You want to enter the list of numbers: 3, 4, 5, 6, 6, 7, 7, 8, 8, 9.

3 | M+ | 4 | M+ | 5 | M+ | 6 | M+ | 6 | M+ | 7 | M+ | 7 | M+ | 8 | M+ | 8 | M+ | 9 | M+ |

If you wish to know how many numbers have been entered, press

| n |　In this example, the calculator will tell you 10.

If you wish to know the sum of the list, press

| Σx |　In this case the answer is 63.

> Not all calculators behave in the same way. Check your manual. If in doubt, ask!

If you wish to know the sum of the squared data, press

| Σx^2 |　The answer here is 429.

If you wish to know the mean of the list, press　| $\bar{x}$ |　The calculator will give you 6.3.

If you wish to know the standard deviation of the list, assuming you are working

with a sample, press　| s |　The answer in this example is 1.89 (to 2 d.p.) ———▶

> On some calculators you will need to use
> | σ_{n-1} | or | s_x |

EXERCISE CCS3

1 Figurite make pocket calculators.
They test sample batches, picking 100 at a time and counting faulty machines.
The results are:

3, 4, 2, 5, 1, 5, 2, 1, 3, 6, 3, 3, 1, 2, 2.

  a Calculate:
    (i) the mean
    (ii) the standard deviation correct to 1 d.p.
  b They expect the process to run at 97% efficiency, i.e. no more than 3 out of 100 faulty. Should they be pleased with this sample? Explain.

c If the standard deviation is greater than 2 the manufacturing process has to be improved. What do the results of this sample suggest about the process?

2 The fuse in a plug is set to blow at 13 amps. When tested, a batch of fuses blew at the following readings:

12.7, 12.8, 12.8, 12.8, 12.9,
12.9, 13.0. 13.1, 13.2, 13.2.

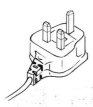

a Calculate:
   (i) the mean
   (ii) the standard deviation correct to 2 d.p.
b The quality control department say the mean should be 13 ± 0.05 amp and the standard deviation should be less than 0.2 amp.
What do the results show?

3 A company makes light bulbs.

Samples of the bulbs are tested to destruction. The number of hours of continuous use is noted. The times, in hours, are:

101, 107, 93, 102, 97, 93, 96, 106, 103, 95,
101, 94, 100, 103, 94, 93, 105, 109, 104, 91.

a Calculate:
   (i) the mean life of a bulb
   (ii) the standard deviation correct to 1 d.p.
b If the mean life is within 2 hours of the advertised life of 100 hours and the standard deviation is less than 5 hours, the batch of bulbs from which the sample is taken passes; if not, another sample from the batch is tested to destruction.
What action should be taken?

4 Two seaside resorts record their daily rainfall (in millimetres) one fortnight in autumn.

Riverdale:
2, 11, 12, 13, 13, 15, 15, 15, 16, 16, 17, 18, 18, 19.
Sandaybay:
3, 4, 4, 5, 9, 9, 10, 13, 13 15, 15, 20, 22, 25.
a Calculate:
   (i) the mean
   (ii) the standard deviation for each resort.
b Which of the two would you recommend for an autumn break? Give reasons.

5 What is value for money in the music business? The CDs of two groups were examined. The lengths (in seconds) of the tracks were compared.

Group	Bugs	Katz
Mean length	180 s	150 s
Standard deviation	20 s	45 s

Compare the two groups to find which gives:
a the longest tracks
b the more consistent length of track.

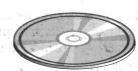

ANSWERS

Page CC4 Exercise CCS1

1a/b deviations: −15, 0, 3, 5, 7; deviation^2: 225, 0, 9, 25, 49
c 61.6 **d** 7.85 g
2a (i) 9.1 s (ii) deviations: −0.9, 0, 0.1, 0.2, 0.6;
deviation^2: 0.81, 0, 0.01, 0.04, 0.36 (iii) 0.49 s
b (i) 8.9 s (ii) 0.83 s (iii) Blueboy (iv) Yes, they are more variable; a higher standard deviation

Page CC7 Exercise CCS2

1 Mean = 64.6 ml; s = 2.2 ml
2a (i) 4.5 rejects/min (ii) 2.9 rejects/min
b (i) 4.5 rejects/min, 0.9 reject/min (ii) no (iii) yes
3 Answers are the same as Q1.
4 Mean = 12 hours; s = 8.9 hours
5a (i) 57 cats (ii) 11 cats (iii) 19.0 cats
b (i) 63 cats (ii) 13 cats (iii) 21.1 cats **c** range
6a (i) 50.8 skaters (ii) 21.5 skaters
b (i) 43 skaters (ii) 19.1 skaters **c** (i) It has dropped by 8
(ii) If skaters are typical of pond life, the effect is measurable.

Page CC8 Exercise CCS3

1a (i) 2.9 machines (ii) 1.6 machines
b Mean is running below 3%, so yes **c** Process satisfactory
2a (i) 12.9 amps (ii) 0.18 amp
b Mean is too low; standard deviation is fine.
3a (i) 99.4 hours (ii) 5.5 hours **b** Another batch is needed.
4a Riverdale: 14.3 mm, 4.3 mm; Sandaybay: 11.9 mm, 7.0 mm
b Sandaybay has better mean (lower) and varies more so more of a chance of getting a dry day.
5a Bugs **b** Bugs